Politecnico di Milano

D1449936

Concrete Structures
"Fratelli Pesenti"

Costruzioni in Calcestruzzo
"Fratelli Pesenti"

# Studies and Researches
## *Annual Review of Structural Concrete*
## Volume 29

**Editorial Board**

Antonio Migliacci,
Pietro G. Gambarova, Paola Ronca

*Editors*: Antonio Migliacci, Pietro G. Gambarova, Paola Ronca

*Title:* Studies and Researches
Annual Review of Structural Concrete
Volume 29

© 2009 **Starrylink Editrice** Brescia
Contrada S. Urbano, 14 - 25121 Brescia, Italy
*Thesis and Research*
www.starrylink.it

ISBN 978-88-96225-28-8

Printed by *Color Art* - Italy - Rodengo Saiano (BS), December 2009

# STUDIES AND RESEARCHES

## Annual Review of Structural Concrete

Volume 29 – December 2009

# Foreword

The end of 2009, marked by the highly-controversial conference of Copenhagen about climate changes, recalls everybody that stopping and reversing the trend of global warming is still a top - albeit rather elusive - priority for Mankind. It is true that this priority has been recognized since Kyoto in the nineties of the past century, but the limited results so far achieved have been mostly wiped out by the burgeoning economies of a few large developing countries, as well as by the reluctance of the most industrialized countries to be involved in the risks – and opportunities - of Green Economy and Green Industry. As a matter of fact, Green Industry requires a lot of investments in new technologies, a thrifty use of natural riches, and a change in the mind-set of both most-developed and least-developed nations (both should limit their expectations!).

Within the highly-demanding framework of Green Economy/Green Industry, however, the World of the Constructions is ready to give a number of badly-needed answers, that are based on the enormous and valuable experience accumulated in the reconstruction of entire cities (since World War 2), in the construction of new facilities, industries and infrastructures (in both developed and emerging countries), in the extension of informatics to design and planning, and in the development of new efficient materials.

As a matter of fact, in the last decades the focus has shifted from straight structural resistance to structural safety and durability, and – more recently – to sustainability, something not easily accepted in rather traditional countries like Italy, where concrete - to quote one of the most-extensively used structural materials – was considered for many decades as an everlasting and rather nature-friendly material. Even stones, however, are prone to weathering, and so concrete and reinforced concrete! Furthermore, aggregates are extracted from land-scarring quarries and energy-hungry klinker production releases an awful amount of carbon dioxide in the atmosphere, something that is forcing the Industry to look for less energy-demanding materials (either cementitious or not).

Durability and sustainability have brought in new pass-words, like "life-cycle", "cost-benefit ratio", "eco-compatibility", "green design", "reuse", "recycling", "footprint reduction", "staging-area minimization", "Albedo level" (= level of solar-light reflection), "energy reduction", "thermal-mass principles", "regional priority", "pervious materials",..... The underlying concepts are having a sizable impact on both building materials and structural design, even though to-day's research activity is mostly focused on materials.

As a matter of fact, structural materials – either innovative or not – take the lion's share with reference to (a) existing structures ($\Rightarrow$ repair, strengthening, rehabilitation); (b) future structures ($\Rightarrow$ functional flexibility, durability, footprint reduction, energy saving); and (c) production and transportation technologies ($\Rightarrow$ from the quarry to the building site, in the case of concrete, which implies "regional priorities"). More specifically:

- <u>Existing structures:</u> since demolition and reconstruction are expensive and often critical in terms of environmental impact (especially in congested or historical areas), new materials (like fiber-reinforced polymers and high/ultra high-performance cementitious composites) are increasingly used for structural strengthening/rehabilitation/protection, as well as for improving structural resistance to severe environmental conditions ($\Rightarrow$ seismic loads, impact, vibrations, high temperature).

- Future structures: since durability is one of the keywords, the conception and production of "engineered materials" (i.e. artificial materials "tailored" according to specific needs) are in progress, to guarantee an appropriate useful life without major maintenance requirements, often in constructions subjected to extreme environmental conditions ($\Rightarrow$ fire, cryogenic temperatures, radiations, earthquakes).

- Production and transportation technologies: future structures should be "sustainable", or – in other terms – should be designed and built in such a way that not only their performance be adequate ($\Rightarrow$ safety and durability), but their impact on the environment – and on the Society as a whole – be minimal ($\Rightarrow$ reduction of carbon-dioxide emissions during materials production; reuse of in-situ waste materials; recycling of industrial by-products; minimization of the staging areas; respect of the time schedule of the various activities in the building site; choice of the materials and of the structural members on the basis of their availability close to the building site; .....). The many factors that make a structure "sustainable" are taken care of in the recently-proposed LEED system (Leadership in Energy and Environmental Design) aimed at the rating of the constructions according to their evironmental/societal impact.

Many of the above-mentioned topics are addressed in the twelve technical papers and three technical notes published in this volume, as a further demonstration of the continuous involvement of Structural and Materials Engineering in the safety, durability and sustainability of our R/C constructions.

Three papers (1, 2 and 6) are devoted to concrete constitutive behavior under multi-axial compression, after tensile cracking and at high temperature.

Three papers and one note (4, 5, 9 and 14) are about some highly-debated structural problems (slab punching, stability of un-notched/notched columns and slabs in bending).

Three papers (3, 10 and 12) are focused on the seismic behavior of coupling beams, columns and post-installed metal anchors.

Three papers and one note (7, 8, 11 and 13) deal with the effects of severe environmental conditions (post-fire repair, corrosion in P/C beams, cover delamination in R/C beams and concrete protection by means of special chemical products).

Last but not least, one note (15) treats a very general problem, i.e. how to optimize the procedure to assess the damage in architecturally-valuable weathered high-rise buildings.

As usual, the news of the School "Fratelli Pesenti" end this volume.

Milan, December 2009

Pietro G. Gambarova and Antonio Migliacci

# Premessa

La conclusione del 2009, segnata dalla tanto discussa conferenza di Copenhagen sui cambiamenti climatici, è un monito per tutti sul dovere prioritario – anche se di non facile attuazione - di fermare (o almeno ridurre) la tendenza al riscaldamento globale. E' pur vero che questa priorità è stata riconosciuta fin dalla convenzione di Kyoto negli anni novanta del secolo passato, ma i limitati risultati raggiunti da allora sono stati pressoché totalmente spazzati via dall'impetuoso sviluppo economico di alcuni grandi paesi, così come dalla riluttanza dei paesi più industrializzati a lasciarsi coinvolgere nei rischi – e nelle opportunità - dell'Economia e dell'Industria eco-compatibili. In effetti, l'Industria "verde" richiede grandi investimenti in nuove tecnologie, l'uso parsimonioso delle ricchezze naturali e la conversione nel modo di pensare dei paesi sia più sviluppati, che meno sviluppati, con l'obiettivo comune di porre limiti alle proprie aspettative di sviluppo.

In risposta alle esigenze dell'Economia e dell'Industria eco-compatibili, il Mondo delle Costruzioni si sta attrezzando su vari fronti, forte dell'enorme esperienza maturata nella ricostruzione di intere città (nel secondo dopoguerra), nella costruzione di nuove industrie ed infrastrutture (in pressoché tutti i paesi), nell'impiego generalizzato dell'informatica a fini di pianificazione e progettazione, e nello sviluppo di materiali sempre più efficienti.

In tale contesto, gli ultimi decenni hanno visto il centro degli interessi spostarsi dalla pura resistenza meccanica alla sicurezza ed alla durabilità strutturale, e – più recentemente - alla sostenibilità, con qualche problema di adattamento in paesi piuttosto tradizionali come l'Italia, dove il calcestruzzo – ad esempio - è stato considerato da sempre come "eterno" e compatibile con l'ambiente naturale. Così non è! Senza nulla togliere ai pregi del calcestruzzo, è ormai riconosciuto come tale materiale si deteriori né più né meno delle pietre naturali. Inoltre, l'impatto delle cave sul territorio ed il consumo energetico nella produzione del cemento, unito all'emissione di anidride carbonica, spingono sempre più verso lo sviluppo di conglomerati cementizi ultraperformanti e di materiali alternativi.

La durabilità e la sostenibilità hanno portato all'introduzione di nuove parole-chiave, come "ciclo di vita", "rapporto costo-benefici", "compatibilità ambientale", "progettazione ecologica", "riutilizzo", "riciclo", "riduzione dell'impatto locale", "minimizzazione delle zone di cantiere", "riflettanza", "risparmio energetico", "inerzia termica", "priorità locali", "materiali permeabili", .....). Questi concetti stanno avendo un notevole impatto sullo sviluppo dei materiali da costruzione ed anche sulla progettazione strutturale, sebbene l'orientamento attuale della ricerca sia sopratutto focalizzato sui materiali.

In effetti, i materiali strutturali continuano a giocare un ruolo predominante in riferimento a: (a) costruzioni esistenti ($\Rightarrow$ ripristino, rinforzo ed adeguamento); (b) costruzioni future ($\Rightarrow$ flessibilità funzionale, durabilità, riduzione dell'impatto locale, risparmio energetico); e (c) tecnologie di produzione e movimentazione ($\Rightarrow$ dalla cava al cantiere, nel caso del calcestruzzo). In dettaglio:

- Costruzioni esistenti: il costo e la criticità (specialmente in aree urbanizzate o di interesse storico) della demolizione e ricostruzione di edifici esistenti propongono sempre più spesso il ricupero di tali edifici, richiedendo a tal fine l'uso di materiali innovativi (quali polimeri fibrorinforzati e conglomerati cementizi ad alte/altissime prestazioni) per rafforzare/adeguare/proteggere, anche a fronte di condizioni ambientali gravose ($\Rightarrow$ carichi sismici, impatto, vibrazioni, alta temperatura).

- <u>Costruzioni future</u>: la durabilità richiede sempre più di progettare, produrre ed impiegare materiali "ingegnerizzati" (cioè materiali artificiali "ritagliati" su specifiche esigenze), al fine di garantire un'adeguata vita strutturale utile, senza necessità di gravosi interventi manutentivi, pur in presenza spesso di condizioni ambientali estreme ($\Rightarrow$ incendio, bassissime temperature, radiazioni, sismicità).

- <u>Tecnologie di produzione e movimentazione</u>: le costruzioni future dovranno essere "sostenibili", cioè progettate e costruite in modo tale da garantire non solo prestazioni adeguate ($\Rightarrow$ sicurezza e durabilità), ma anche ridotto impatto sull'ambiente – e sulla Società nel suo complesso ($\Rightarrow$ riduzione delle emissioni di anidride carbonica durante la produzione dei materiali; riutilizzo dei materiali risultanti dalle demolizioni; riciclo di sottoprodotti industriali; riduzione delle aree di cantiere; controllo dei tempi di costruzione; scelta dei materiali e delle tecniche costruttive sulla base della loro disponibilità vicino al cantiere; .....). I molti fattori che rendono una costruzione "sostenibile" sono stati introdotti nel sistema di valutazione LEED (Leadership in Energy and Environmental Design), recentemente proposto negli USA per valutare le costruzioni sulla base del loro impatto socio/ambientale.

Molti degli argomenti appena menzionati sono trattati nelle dodici note scientifiche e nelle tre note tecniche pubblicate in questo volume, il che è un'ulteriore dimostrazione del continuo coinvolgimento dell'Ingegneria Strutturale e delle Scienze dei Materiali nella sicurezza, durabilità e sostenibilità delle costruzioni in calcestruzzo armato. In particolare:
- tre note (1, 2 e 6) sono dedicate al comportamento costitutivo del calcestruzzo (compressione pluriassiale e monoassiale, ed alta temperatura);
- quattro note (4, 5, 9 e 14) trattano aspetti strutturali di grande interesse (punzonamento, stabilità di colonne integre ed intagliate, collasso a flessione delle piastre);
- tre note (3, 10 e 12) riguardano il comportamento sismico delle travi di accoppiamento, delle colonne e degli ancoraggi metallici post-installati;
- quattro note (7, 8, 11 e 13) considerano gli effetti su materiali e strutture di condizioni ambientali gravose (ripristino dopo incendio, corrosione negli elementi precompressi, perdita del copriferro e protezione del calcestruzzo con speciali prodotti chimici);
- una nota (15) affronta il problema molto generale dell'ottimizzazione delle procedure di valutazione del danno in edifici alti di notevole pregio architettonico, a seguito di esposizione agli agenti atmosferici.

Come d'uso, le notizie sulla Scuola "Fratelli Pesenti" terminano il volume.

Milano, Dicembre 2009

Pietro G. Gambarova and Antonio Migliacci

(Questa premessa è ripresa ed ampliata nell'editoriale a pagina 367)

Technical Papers

STUDIES AND RESEARCHES – V29, 2009
Graduate School in Concrete Structures – Fratelli Pesenti
Politecnico di Milano, Italy

# STRESS-STRAIN RELATIONSHIP FOR STEEL FIBER-REINFORCED SELF-CONSOLIDATING CONCRETE UNDER MULTIAXIAL COMPRESSION

Bernardino Chiaia[1], Alessandro P. Fantilli[2], Paolo Vallini[3]

## ABSTRACT

The results of a number of multiaxial compression tests performed on cylinders made of self-consolidating concrete (SCC), with and without steel fibers, are presented in this paper. In the experimental campaign, four "reference" confining pressures (0, 1, 3 and 10 MPa) were applied on the lateral surface of the specimens. After the first stage of loading, when a hydraulic stress was applied to the cylinders, and progressively increased up to a pre-established confining pressure, a longitudinal compressive load was applied as well, up to concrete failure by crushing. The stress-strain relationships of different SCCs, measured with the aid of local transducers, show the increase of concrete strength, and of the corresponding strain, with the confining pressure. However, compared to the values measured in ordinary (vibrated) concrete, the strains at the peak stress are higher in self-consolidating concrete. In addition, the test results give indications on how to modify the stress-strain relationships formulated so far for ordinary concrete, in the case of SCC subjected to multiaxial compression. To this end, by using the Colonnetti's theory of "elastic coactions", a new formulation of the well-known Sargin's relationship is proposed in the paper.

[1] Professor, [2] Assistant Professor, [3] Associate Professor
  Department of Structural and Geotechnical Engineering
  Politecnico di Torino, Torino (Italy).

# 1. INTRODUCTION

The stress-strain relationships of concrete and other quasi-brittle materials under uniaxial compression can be divided into two parts (Fig.1a). In the first part, when the nominal stress of concrete $\sigma_c$ is lower than the strength $f_{c,0}$ (and the strain $\varepsilon_c$ is lower than $\varepsilon_{c1,0}$), the specimen can be considered undamaged. In the case of plain concrete, the ascending branch of the $\sigma_c$-$\varepsilon_c$ curve can be defined by the Sargin's relationship, already proposed by CEB-FIP Model Code (CEB, 1993). As soon as $\varepsilon_c > \varepsilon_{c,0}$, localized damage develops and strain softening begins (van Mier, 1984). In this phase, there is the formation of either a system of longitudinal cracks (parallel to the applied load) or an inclined cracked band, which subdivides the specimen into two progressively-sliding blocks. In the latter case (Fig.1b), the angle between the vertical axis of the specimen and the sliding surfaces $\alpha$ is close to 18° (van Mier, 1984; Jansen and Shah, 1997), as confirmed by the Mohr-Coulomb failure criterion, if the ratio between the tensile strength and the compression strength is assumed to be 1/10 ($f_{ct} = 0.1\, f_{c,0}$).

The inelastic displacements of the specimen, and the ensuing sliding of the blocks along the sliding surface (Fig.1b), are the parameters governing the mean post-peak compressive strain $\varepsilon_c$ of the specimen. They have to be considered as the kinematical variables of a fictitious crack model, similar to that already introduced by Hillerborg et al. (1976) for describing strain localization in tension. For instance, Fantilli et al. (2007) proposed different stress-inelastic displacement relationships for the post-peak branch of ordinary and high performance concrete under uniaxial compression.

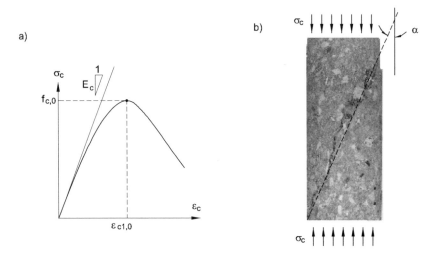

Figure 1 – Concrete cylinders subjected to uniaxial compression: (a) stress-strain relationship $\sigma_c$-$\varepsilon_c$; and (b) onset of strain localization.

In the literature, several models have been proposed for the mechanical response of ordinary confined concrete. In accordance with Lokuge et al. (2005), the existing stress-strain relationships can be divided into three groups: some models use the relationship proposed by Sargin, other models are based on the equations introduced by Kent and Park, and, finally, the third group includes the formulations suggested by Popovics.

The effectiveness of such relationships is not always well-founded, because the results obtained for ordinary concrete cannot be directly extended to self-consolidating concrete (SCC) and to fiber-reinforced concrete (FRC). For instance, in several experimental campaigns (Paultre et al., 2005; Ganesan and Ramana Murthy, 1990), the mechanical response of confined columns appeared strongly dependent on the type of concrete.

Moreover, laboratory conditions, and in particular the types of confinement (active or passive), also affect the shape of the stress-strain curve of concrete in compression.

Passive confinement, provided by lateral reinforcement (e.g., stirrups, pipes and spirals, made of steel or carbon composites), is only activated by the lateral dilation of concrete. Thus, to obtain the stress-strain relationship under multiaxial compression, the axial stress-lateral strain relationship of concrete must be defined in advance.

Conversely, in the case of active confinement, it is not necessary to know concrete dilations. In fact, the confining pressure, applied to cubes (in one or two directions) or cylinders (in triaxial tests), is directly controlled by the operator (see the state-of-art study by van Mier, 1996). Nevertheless, such tests are rarely found in the domain of cement-based composites. Only the complete stress-strain curves of a micro-concrete (triaxial tests by Jamet et al., 1984) are reported in the literature. No tests of this type have been so far carried out on self-consolidating concrete, with or without steel fibers.


## 2. TRIAXIAL TESTS

The mechanical behavior of SCC under multiaxial compressions is here investigated through a series of triaxial tests performed in the Department of Structural and Geotechnical Engineering (DIsaster Planning LABoratory - DIPLAB) of Politecnico di Torino (Italy).

### 2.1 Experimental set-up

The experimental equipment, named HTPA (High Pressure Triaxial Apparatus), is generally used to test cylindrical specimens made of soft rocks, or normal-strength concrete, under confined compression. HPTA is composed by the following parts (Fig. 2, Barla et al., 2007):

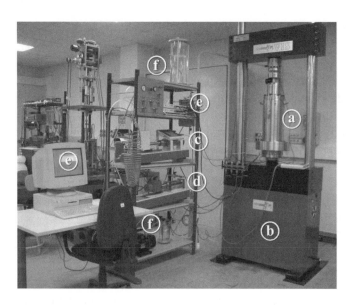

Figure 2 – The High Triaxial Test Apparatus (HPTA) used to test SCC under multiaxial compression.

(a)     Triaxial cell, where the specimen, jacketed in a rubber membrane (to separate the concrete from silicone oil at pressure $\sigma_3$), is placed.

(b)     Loading machine, connected to a load cell of 250 kN ($\pm$ 60 N), which applies the longitudinal load $P$ on the cylinder (Fig.3a). Each test is conducted by controlling the axial displacement of specimen end sections.

(c)(d)     Hydraulic actuators, which control the cell pressure (i.e., the pressure of the silicone oil within the triaxial cell) and the back pressure $\sigma_b$ (i.e., the pressure of the water contained into the specimen). The maximum value of the cell pressure is $\sigma_3 = 64$ MPa ($\pm$ 16 kPa), whereas the maximum back pressure is $\sigma_b = 32$ MPa ($\pm 8$ kPa). In the case of geo-materials, the triaxial tests can be performed on drained or saturated specimens. In the first case (that is also the case of concrete), the back pressures (i.e., the pressure of the water contained inside the specimen) is kept equal to $\sigma_b = 0$ MPa, whereas in all the other cases $\sigma_b > 0$ MPa.

(e)     Digital-measurement system, which records the values of the load $P$, of the confinement stresses $\sigma_3$, and of the external and local displacements. The external displacements are those measured between of the press (maximum relative displacement 100 mm $\pm 1$ μm). The local displacements of the gauges $l_{B1}$ and $l_{B2}$ are measured by means of two linear variable differential transducers

(LVDTs; maximum displacement $5 \text{ mm} \pm 0.5$ µm), set on the cylinder surface along its vertical axis (Fig.3a). The LVDTs are designed on purpose to work in an environment filled with silicon oil, and are attached either to concrete surface (in the case of no pressure = unconfined tests), or to the rubber jacket (in the case of confined tests with confining pressure). In the latter case, the presence of $\sigma_3 > 0$MPa guarantees a relatively high friction on the membrane-to-concrete interface; hence, no slip occurs between the rubber jacket and the concrete. In other words, the displacements measured by the LVDTs on the rubber membrane coincide with concrete displacements. Another LVDT (not used in this project, and provided with a circular belt) can be placed around the mid-span section, to measure the hoop displacement, which in turn is related to the radial displacement.

(f) Hydraulic tanks, which contain water (to control the back pressure) and silicon oil (to control the confining pressure).

## 2.2 Specimens and experimental procedure

Two self-consolidating concretes (named SC-mix 1 and SC-mix 2, respectively) have been investigated. Their constituents and strengths are reported in Table 1. The two self-consolidating concretes have the same mass per unit volume, but different amounts of aggregates.

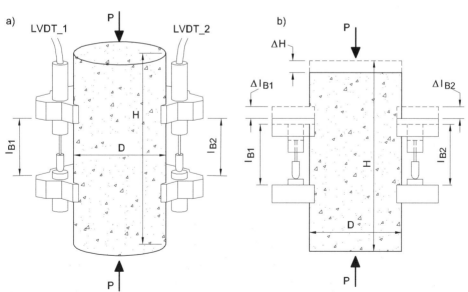

Figure 3 – The application of the load $P$: (a) positions of the LVDTs; and (b) local and global displacements.

Compared to SC-mix 1, in a cube meter of SC-mix 2 the content of carbonate filler is increased by 9 kg and at the same time the mass of coarse aggregate is reduced by the same quantity, in order to keep the mass constant.

Dramix RC 65/35 BN steel fibers (length $L = 35$ mm; diameter $\Phi = 0.55$ mm), having hooked ends and indicated with the acronym SF, were added to the self-consolidating concrete in the proportion of 35 kg/m$^3$ (volume fraction $V_f = 0.45\%$, Reinforced index $RI = 28.8\%$) or 70 kg/m$^3$ ($V_f = 0.9\%$, $RI = 57.6\%$).

Five series of specimens, each composed by four cylinders (height $H = 140$ mm and diameter $D = 70$ mm), were cast using the concretes reported in Table 1. Eight cylinders were made of SC-mix 1 and twelve cylinders were made of SC-mix 2. The specimens of each series were cast simultaneously in polystyrene form, then cured for one week under identical laboratory conditions, and finally tested one month later.

The characteristics of the specimens – that are indicated with an alphanumeric acronym - are reported in Table 2. In the acronym (second column), the first digits (one or two) refer to the fiber content (0, 35 or 70 kg/m$^3$), while the last digits (one or two) refer to confining pressure (0, 1, 3 or 10 MPa). The last letter "b" identifies the specimens made with SC-mix 2 (there is no letter for those made of SC-mix 1).

It should be observed that a series of cylinders made of SC-mix 1 with 70kg/m$^3$ of steel fibers has not been considered in the present work. This composite showed a reduced workability, and did not guarantee the smoothness of the lateral surface of the cylinders. The absence of micro-holes and cavities on the surfaces is a necessary condition to avoid leakages in the rubber membrane, when the confining pressure is applied.

| Constituents | SC-mix 1 kg/m$^3$ | SC-mix 2 kg/m$^3$ |
|---|---|---|
| Water | 180 | 180 |
| Superplasticizer (Addiment Compactcrete 39/T100) | 4.49 | 4.49 |
| Cement (Buzzi Unicem II/A-LL 42.5 R) | 250 | 250 |
| Carbonate filler (Nicem Carb VG1-2) | 330 | 380 |
| Fine aggregate (0÷4 mm) | 910 | 910 |
| Coarse aggregate (6.3÷12 mm)) | 650 | 600 |

| | SC-mix 1 | SC-mix 2 |
|---|---|---|
| Cubic strength -MPa- | 31.1 | 30.4 |

Table 1 – Composition and strength of SC-mix 1 and SC-mix 2.

| Series | Specimen | $H$ (mm) | $D$ (mm) | Type of concrete | $\sigma_3$ (MPa) | SF (kg/m$^3$) |
|---|---|---|---|---|---|---|
| 1 | 0SC0 | 140 | 70 | SC-mix 1 | 0 | 0 |
| | 0SC1 | 140 | 70 | SC-mix 1 | 1 | 0 |
| | 0SC3 | 140 | 70 | SC-mix 1 | 3 | 0 |
| | 0SC10 | 140 | 70 | SC-mix 1 | 10 | 0 |
| 2 | 0SC0b | 140 | 70 | SC-mix 2 | 0 | 0 |
| | 0SC1b | 140 | 70 | SC-mix 2 | 1 | 0 |
| | 0SC3b | 140 | 70 | SC-mix 2 | 3 | 0 |
| | 0SC10b | 140 | 70 | SC-mix 2 | 10 | 0 |
| 3 | 35SC0 | 140 | 70 | SC-mix 1 | 0 | 35 |
| | 35SC1 | 140 | 70 | SC-mix 1 | 1 | 35 |
| | 35SC3 | 140 | 70 | SC-mix 1 | 3 | 35 |
| | 35SC10 | 140 | 70 | SC-mix 1 | 10 | 35 |
| 4 | 35SC0b | 140 | 70 | SC-mix 2 | 0 | 35 |
| | 35SC1b | 140 | 70 | SC-mix 2 | 1 | 35 |
| | 35SC3b | 140 | 70 | SC-mix 2 | 3 | 35 |
| | 35SC10b | 140 | 70 | SC-mix 2 | 10 | 35 |
| 5 | 70SC0b | 140 | 70 | SC-mix 2 | 0 | 70 |
| | 70SC1b | 140 | 70 | SC-mix 2 | 1 | 70 |
| | 70SC3b | 140 | 70 | SC-mix 2 | 3 | 70 |
| | 70SC10b | 140 | 70 | SC-mix 2 | 10 | 70 |

Table 2 – The cylindrical specimens tested in triaxial compression.

Each triaxial test is carried out in drained conditions ($\sigma_b = 0$) and consists of two stages. In the first stage the specimen is simply loaded by a hydrostatic stress (which coincides with the pre-established pressure $\sigma_3$) generated by the silicone oil contained in the triaxial cell (Fig.4a). Four were the values of the oil pressure ($\sigma_3 = 0$ MPa; $\sigma_3 = 1$ MPa, reached in about 10 minutes; $\sigma_3 = 3$ MPa, reached in about 30 minutes; and $\sigma_3 = 10$ MPa, reached in about 60 minutes). Afterwards, a longitudinal compressive load $P$ was applied, according to a displacement-controlled procedure (displacement rate = 37 $\mu$m per minute). In this second stage (Fig.4b), the lateral surface is under a constant pressure $\sigma_3$ and the longitudinal stress $\sigma_c$ consists of two contributions:

$$\sigma_c = \sigma_3 + \frac{4P}{\pi D^2} \qquad (1)$$

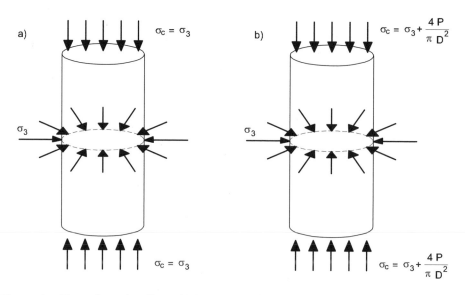

Figure 4 – Two-phase loading: (a) lateral pressure; and (b) axial load.

During the first stage of loading (Fig.4a), the values of $\sigma_3$ have been recorded every ten seconds. With the same time interval, the loads and the local/global displacements ($\Delta l_{B1}$, $\Delta l_{B2}$ / $\Delta H$, respectively) have been recorded during the second loading stage (Fig.3b). The maximum admissible contraction of the specimen was fixed to $\Delta H = 14$ mm ($\varepsilon_c = 10\%$).

## 3. EXPERIMENTAL RESULTS

Under triaxial compression, the diagram $\sigma_c$-$\varepsilon_c$ consists of three parts (Fig.5). In the first part, corresponding to the first stage of loading (Fig.4a), the hydrostatic stresses are applied to the specimen. During this stage, the local displacements of the gauges $l_{B1}$ and $l_{B2}$ are very small and cannot be accurately measured by the LVDTs glued to the external surface (Fig.3b).

The nominal strain $\varepsilon_c$ can be obtained from the volume variation $\Delta V$ of the specimen (which should be equal to the volume variation of the silicone oil inside the triaxial cell) by applying the formula (Corradi Dell'Acqua, 1992):

$$\varepsilon_c = 1 - \sqrt[3]{1 - \frac{\Delta V}{V}} \tag{2}$$

where $V$ and $\Delta V$ are the initial volume and the volume variation of the specimen, respectively.

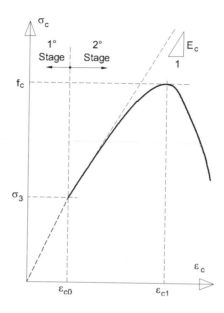

Figure 5 – The typical shape of the stress-strain relationship.

Similarly to $\Delta l_{B1}$ and $\Delta l_{B2}$, the measured values of $\Delta V$ are not reliable, because of the unavoidable presence of air inside the cell. As a matter of fact, during the hydrostatic loading of a specimen (for instance that of the Specimen 35SC3b reported in Fig.6), the confining pressure $\sigma_3$ does not increase proportionally with time (al least in the first part of the $\sigma_3$-time plot). Although the air inside the cell does not alter the results of the triaxial tests, this air makes Eq.(2) useless for evaluating $\varepsilon_c$.

For the above-mentioned reasons, only with the following formula, which comes from the theory of elasticity (Corradi Dell'Acqua, 1992), the concrete strain can be evaluated:

$$\varepsilon_c = \frac{\sigma_3}{E_c}(1 - 2v) = 0.7 \frac{\sigma_3}{E_c} \tag{3}$$

where the Poisson's ratio is assumed to be $v = 0.15$. As shown in Fig.5, $\varepsilon_{c0}$ is the maximum strain reached at the end of the first loading stage.

In the ascending branch of the second loading stage ($\varepsilon_{c0} < \varepsilon_c < \varepsilon_{c1}$), the nominal stresses are always computed by means of Eq.(1), whereas the nominal strains are evaluated from the local displacements $\Delta l_{B1}$ and $\Delta l_{B2}$ (Fig.3):

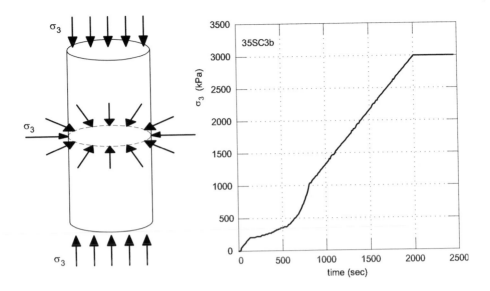

Figure 6 – The hydrostatic pressure in Specimen 35SC3b.

$$\varepsilon_c = \frac{1}{2}\left(\frac{\Delta l_{B1}}{l_{B1}} + \frac{\Delta l_{B2}}{l_{B2}}\right) \tag{4}$$

In the ascending branch of the $\sigma_c$-$\varepsilon_c$ curve, the global displacements of specimen end sections are not taken into consideration. For small values of $P$, the surface conditions of the cylinders, as well as the axial clearance of the load machine, markedly affect the values of $\Delta H$. Conversely, in the descending branch, when $\varepsilon_c$ is higher than the value $\varepsilon_{c1}$ (reached at the peak stress $f_c$), the nominal strain can be computed by means of the following equation (Fig.3):

$$\varepsilon_c = \varepsilon_{c1} + \frac{\Delta H - \Delta H_p}{H} \tag{5}$$

where, $\Delta H_p$= displacement of specimen end sections measured at the peak stress.

On the other hand, when $\varepsilon_c > \varepsilon_{c1}$, the LVDTs shown in Fig.3 cease to work properly. (These instruments become often partially or completely detached from the lateral surface of the cylinder at the onset of the sliding along the slanted crack, Fig.1b). During the whole second loading stage, Eq.(1) is used to evaluate the nominal stress $\sigma_c$.

All the experimental stress-strain relationships are reported in Fig.7, where they are grouped together by series (Series 1 in Fig.7a, Series 2 in Fig.7b, Series 3 in Fig.7c, Series 4 in Fig.7d, and Series 5 in Fig.7e). In these Figures, all the stress-strain relationships show a remarkable softening after the peak stress.

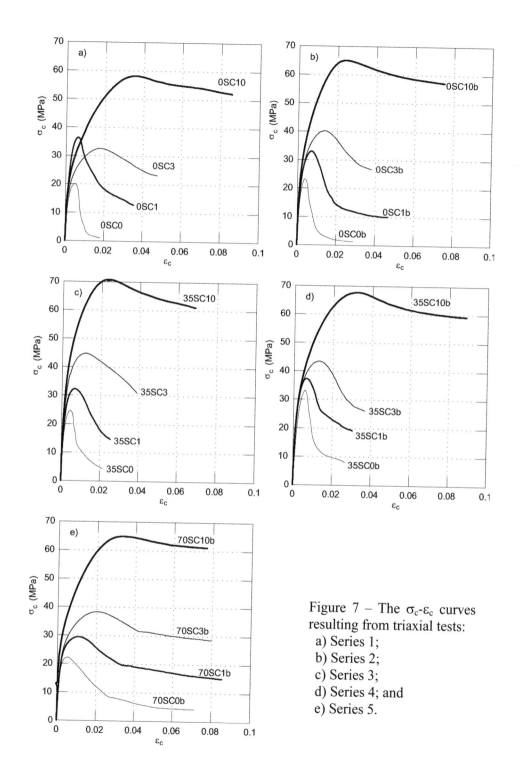

Figure 7 – The $\sigma_c$-$\varepsilon_c$ curves resulting from triaxial tests:
a) Series 1;
b) Series 2;
c) Series 3;
d) Series 4; and
e) Series 5.

| Series | Specimen | $f_c$ (MPa) | $\varepsilon_{c1}$ | $E_c$ (MPa) |
|--------|----------|-------------|--------------------|-------------|
| 1 | 0SC0 | 20.1 | 0.00479 | 17000 |
| | 0SC1 | 36.4 | 0.00604 | 19000 |
| | 0SC3 | 32.6 | 0.0177 | 26000 |
| | 0SC10 | 58.2 | 0.0356 | 27000 |
| 2 | 0SC0b | 26.3 | 0.00513 | 25000 |
| | 0SC1b | 32.0 | 0.00696 | 27000 |
| | 0SC3b | 40.3 | 0.0135 | 27000 |
| | 0SC10b | 65.1 | 0.0245 | 35000 |
| 3 | 35SC0 | 24.6 | 0.00429 | 20000 |
| | 35SC1 | 32.3 | 0.00642 | 27000 |
| | 35SC3 | 44.8 | 0.0120 | 28000 |
| | 35SC10 | 70.8 | 0.0245 | 42000 |
| 4 | 35SC0b | 34.5 | 0.00611 | 25000 |
| | 35SC1b | 37.3 | 0.00629 | 27000 |
| | 35SC3b | 42.5 | 0.0125 | 28000 |
| | 35SC10b | 67.8 | 0.0326 | 30000 |
| 5 | 70SC0b | 22.2 | 0.00534 | 19000 |
| | 70SC1b | 29.5 | 0.0109 | 20000 |
| | 70SC3b | 38.3 | 0.0207 | 26000 |
| | 70SC10b | 64.9 | 0.0339 | 42000 |

Table 3 - Main mechanical properties of the SCCs investigated in this project.

Nevertheless, the slope of the post-peak branch diminishes at high confining pressures. For $\sigma_3 = 10$ MPa, past the initial ascending branch, the mechanical response of SCC is practically plastic. In addition, both the concrete strength and the corresponding strain increase with $\sigma_3$. The measured values of $f_c$, $\varepsilon_{c1}$ and $E_c$ are reported in Table 3.

## 4. STRESS-STRAIN RELATIONSHIPS FOR CONFINED SCC

As stated in the Introduction, the behavior of cement-based composite under multiaxial compression depends on the confining pressure $\sigma_3$ and on the type of concrete. In many cases, the mechanical response, in terms of nominal stress versus nominal strain, appears to be very different from that predicted by commonly-used relationships.

According to Shah et al. (1995), as strain localization occurs, the post-peak stage can be described (for any specimen length), either by a discrete model (i.e., stress-sliding displacement relationship) or by a crack-band model (i.e., stress-strain relationships smeared within a band). In the present tests, no measurements were taken on the width of the band where strains localize. Hence, the results of the previously-described triaxial tests are here only used to formulate a new and more reliable <u>pre-peak</u> relationship for SCC, with and without steel fibers. Further efforts will be made in future to formulate a stress-sliding displacement relationship for the softening branch of such cement-based composites.

## 4.1. The pre-peak branch of the stress-strain curve

Existing stress-strain relationships for cementitious composites are based on the definition of few parameters (Lokuge et al., 2005). More precisely, to model the pre-peak branch of the $\sigma_c$-$\varepsilon_c$ curve, the strength and the corresponding strain of concrete, as well as the elastic modulus, are required. These mechanical properties have to be defined as a function of the confining pressure $\sigma_3$ (Fig.8), on the basis of the experimental evidence.

Under uniaxial compression, Sargins' stress-strain relationship suggested by CEB-FIP Model Code (CEB, 2003) can be adopted:

$$\sigma_c = f_{c,0} \frac{\dfrac{E_c}{E_{c1}} \dfrac{\varepsilon_c}{\varepsilon_{c1,0}} - \left(\dfrac{\varepsilon_c}{\varepsilon_{c1,0}}\right)^2}{1 + \left(\dfrac{E_c}{E_{c1,0}} - 2\right)\dfrac{\varepsilon_c}{\varepsilon_{c1,0}}} \tag{6}$$

where, $E_c$ = tangent modulus; $E_{c1} = f_{c,0}/\varepsilon_{c1,0}$ = secant modulus from the origin to the peak of stress (Fig.8a). In this case, it is sufficient to measure experimentally the values of $f_{c,0}$ and $\varepsilon_{c1,0}$, and to compute $E_c$ as a function of concrete strength, coarse aggregates and mineral admixtures (Noguchi et al., 2009).

When $\sigma_3 > 0$, the values of $f_{c,0}$ and $\varepsilon_{c1,0}$ should be replaced respectively by concrete strength, $f_c$, and by the corresponding strain $\varepsilon_{c1}$ (Fig.8b). Both parameters should be evaluated analytically, in case they are not available from tests. For instance, starting from $f_{c,0}$ and $\sigma_3$, the strength $f_c$ can be estimated by means of Binici's formula (Binici, 2005):

$$f_c = f_{c,0}\left[ k\sqrt{c + m\frac{\sigma_3}{f_{c,0}}} - (1-k)\left(\frac{\sigma_3}{f_{c,0}}\right)^2 + \frac{\sigma_3}{f_{c,0}} \right] \tag{7}$$

If the coefficients $c = 1$, $m = 9.9$, and $k = 1$, already introduced for ordinary concrete (Binici, 2005), are adopted, the strength $f_c$ is correctly evaluated also in the case of SCC. This is confirmed by the diagram $f_c/f_{c,0}$ versus $\sigma_3/f_{c,0}$ of Fig. 9a,

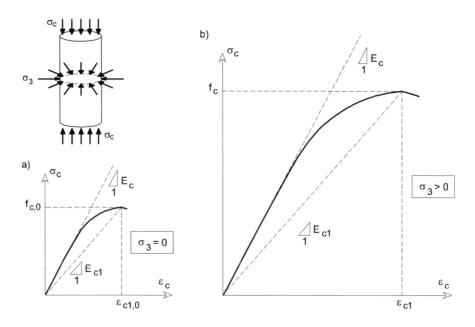

Figure 8 – Effect of the confining pressure on the stress-strain curve: (a) uniaxial compression; and (b) multiaxial compression.

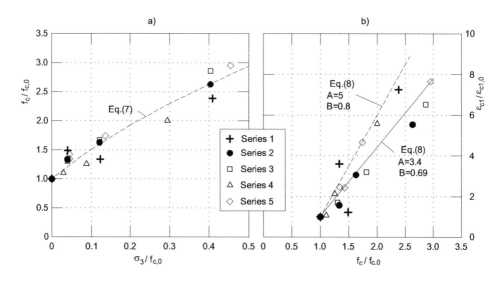

Figure 9 – The parameters of the stress-strain relationship under multiaxial compression: (a) the stress peak as a function of the confining pressure; and (b) the strain at the stress peak.

where the strength values predicted by Eq.(7) are in good agreement with those experimentally measured in the current tests on SCC (with/without steel fibers).

In the same way, to estimate $\varepsilon_{c1}$, the following equation proposed by Richart et al. (Binici, 2005), can be adopted:

$$\frac{\varepsilon_{c1}}{\varepsilon_{c1,0}} = A\left(\frac{f_c}{f_{c,0}} - B\right) \tag{8}$$

As shown in Fig.9b, the values of $\varepsilon_{c1}$ are underestimated by Eq.(8), if the coefficients $A$ and $B$ are assumed to be those of ordinary concrete (i.e., $A = 5$ and $B = 0.8$). In other words, the coefficients calibrated for ordinary concrete are not appropriate for self-consolidating concrete. In particular, under uniaxial compression, the value $\varepsilon_{c1,0} = 0.0022$ suggested by CEB-FIP Model Code (CEB, 1993) for ordinary concrete, is markedly lower than those measured by testing (see Table 3). In the case of SCC, Eq.(8) provides a better approximation of $\varepsilon_{c1}$, when $A = 3.4$ and $B = 0.69$. These values derive from the least-square approximation of the experimental results reported in Table 3. With respect to ordinary concrete, the best fit line of self-consolidating concrete shows a higher slope (Fig.9b).

Under multiaxial compression, the whole ascending branch of $\sigma_c$-$\varepsilon_c$ may be computed by Sargin's model as well, if in Eq.(6) the parameters $f_{c,0}$ and $\varepsilon_{c1,0}$ are replaced with $f_c$ and $\varepsilon_{c1}$. In the present case, instead of computing these values through Eqs.(7)-(8), $f_c$, $\varepsilon_{c1}$ and $E_c$ are those experimentally measured in triaxial tests (Table 3). Both the analytical and experimental stress-strain relationships are reported in Fig.10 (uniaxial compression, i.e. $\sigma_3 = 0$ MPa) and in Figs.11-12-13 ($\sigma_3 = 1$, 3 and 10 MPa, respectively). For any fiber amount, Eq.(6) gives a reasonable approximation of the experimental data only for low confining pressures ($\sigma_3 = 0$ in Fig.10, and $\sigma_3 = 1$ MPa in Fig.11). By increasing $\sigma_3$, Sargin's formula is no longer effective in predicting the behavior of SCC ($\sigma_3 = 3$ in Fig.12, and $\sigma_3 = 10$ MPa in Fig.13). Generally, for any given strain, the corresponding stress is systematically overestimated by Eq.(6).

In the case of passive confinements, a stress-strain relationship, similar to Eq.(6), was proposed by Sargin et al. (1971), on the basis of an experimental campaign concerning laterally-reinforced concrete prisms. According to Sargin's procedure, the previously-described triaxial tests can be used to formulate a new relationship for compressed concrete under active confinement. Referring to Colonnetti's theory of coactions, the general form of the $\sigma_c$-$\varepsilon_c$ curve should not differ from a linear elastic law, as in the following:

$$\sigma_n = \frac{E_c}{E_{c1}}\left(\varepsilon_n - \bar{\varepsilon}_n\right) \tag{9}$$

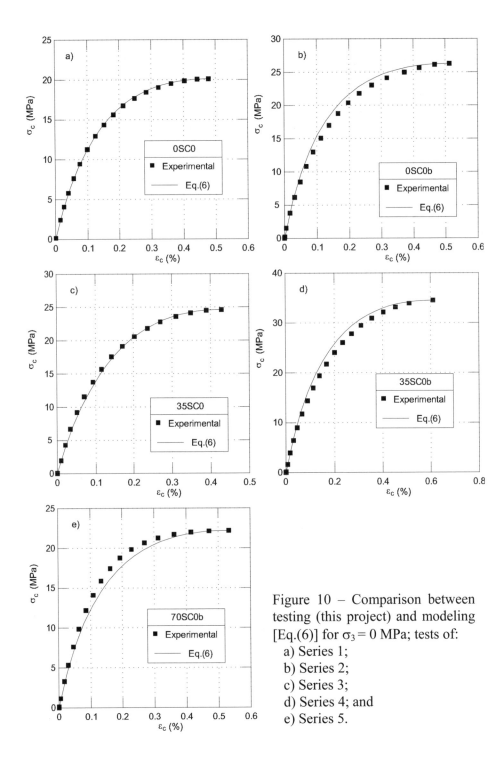

Figure 10 – Comparison between testing (this project) and modeling [Eq.(6)] for $\sigma_3 = 0$ MPa; tests of:
a) Series 1;
b) Series 2;
c) Series 3;
d) Series 4; and
e) Series 5.

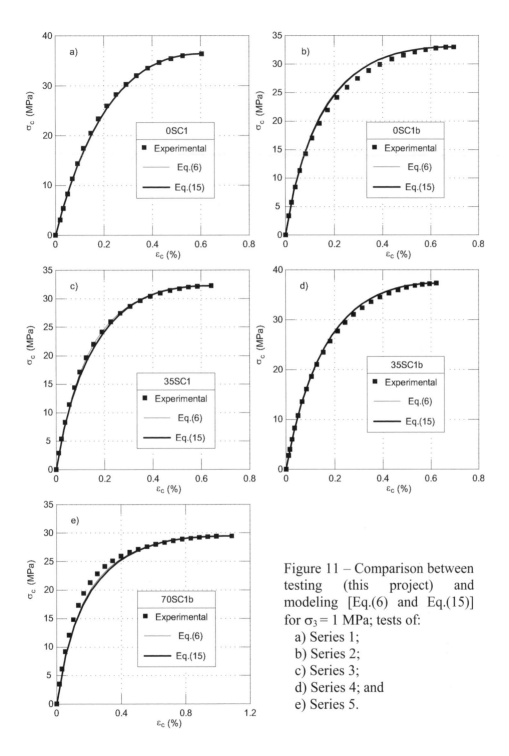

Figure 11 – Comparison between testing (this project) and modeling [Eq.(6) and Eq.(15)] for $\sigma_3 = 1$ MPa; tests of:
a) Series 1;
b) Series 2;
c) Series 3;
d) Series 4; and
e) Series 5.

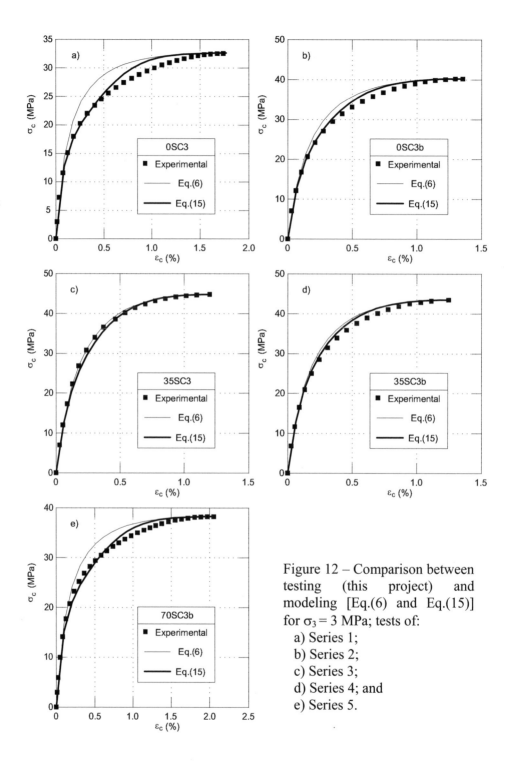

Figure 12 – Comparison between testing (this project) and modeling [Eq.(6) and Eq.(15)] for $\sigma_3 = 3$ MPa; tests of:
a) Series 1;
b) Series 2;
c) Series 3;
d) Series 4; and
e) Series 5.

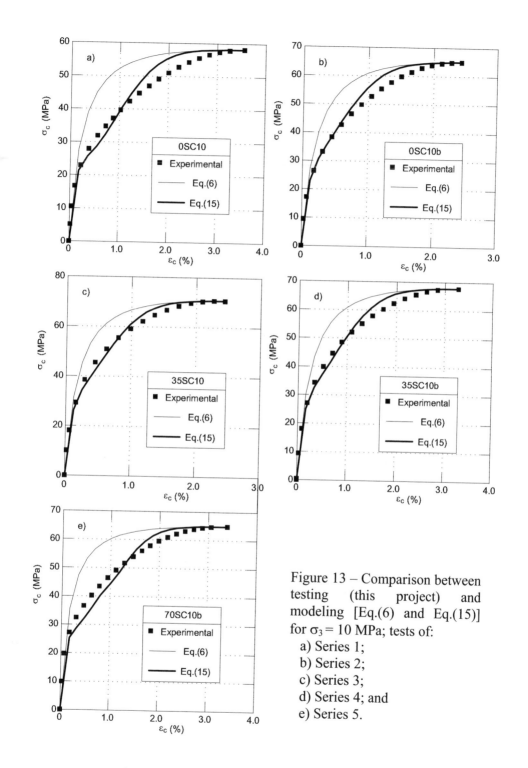

Figure 13 – Comparison between testing (this project) and modeling [Eq.(6) and Eq.(15)] for $\sigma_3 = 10$ MPa; tests of:
 a) Series 1;
 b) Series 2;
 c) Series 3;
 d) Series 4; and
 e) Series 5.

where, $\sigma_n = \sigma_c / f_c$ = normalized stress; $\varepsilon_n = \varepsilon_c / \varepsilon_{c1}$ = normalized total strain; and $\bar{\varepsilon}_n$ = normalized imposed strain (the difference between the total and imposed strains are the elastic strains). The use of Eq.(9) within the frame of the classical theory of elasticity is ensured by the theorem of elastic coactions (Appendix 1).

For zero confinement, Sargin's model - Eq.(6) - is still valid, and the normalized imposed strain, $\bar{\varepsilon}_{n,S}$, becomes:

$$\bar{\varepsilon}_{n,S} = \frac{\left(\dfrac{E_c}{E_{c1}} - 2 + \dfrac{E_{c1}}{E_c}\right)\varepsilon_n^2}{1 + \left(\dfrac{E_c}{E_{c1}} - 2\right)\varepsilon_n} \tag{10}$$

On the contrary, when $\sigma_3 > 0$, the imposed strains should be calibrated according to the results of the triaxial tests. More specifically, the normalized imposed strains are assumed to be linearly related to $\bar{\varepsilon}_{n,S}$ [Eq.(10)]:

$$\bar{\varepsilon}_n = \omega\,\bar{\varepsilon}_{n,S} \tag{11}$$

The coefficient $\omega$, which is a function of $\sigma_3$ and $\varepsilon_n$, is defined below.

As shown in Fig.14a, the maximum value of the coefficient of proportionality, $\omega_{max}$, increases with the confining pressure (whereas, $\omega_{max}=1$ when $\sigma_3 = 0$). If the results of the triaxial tests performed at higher confining pressure ($\sigma_3 = 3$ -10 MPa) are taken into account, the maximum value of the coefficient of proportionality is a linear function of the ratio $\sigma_3 / f_c$ (Fig.14a):

$$\omega_{max} = 1 + 2\frac{\sigma_3}{f_c} \tag{12}$$

Since $\omega_{max}$ is reached for small $\varepsilon_n$ (lower than 4%), the general form of $\omega$ is obtained by inserting the coefficient $\beta$ (a function of $\varepsilon_n$) into Eq.(12):

$$\omega = 1 + 2\frac{\sigma_3}{f_c}\beta \tag{13}$$

where $\beta=0$ when $\varepsilon_n < 0.04$.

The values of $\beta$, obtained from the results of triaxial tests, are included in the range depicted in Fig.14b. In the same Figure, such values are also compared with those given by the following best-fit curve:

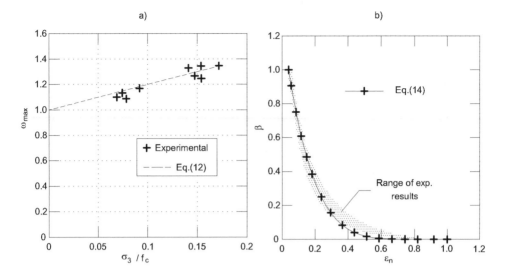

Figure 14 – The coefficients of the proposed stress-strain relationship: (a) $\omega_{\max}$ as a function of confining pressure; and (b) $\beta$ as a function of normalized strain.

$$\beta = \left(\frac{1-\varepsilon_n}{0.96}\right)^6 \tag{14}$$

Finally, under active confinement, Eq.(6) can be given a more general formulation, as follows:

$$\sigma_c = f_c \frac{E_c}{E_{c1}}\left(\varepsilon_n - \overline{\varepsilon}_{n,S}\right) \qquad \text{if} \quad \varepsilon_n \le 0.04 \tag{15a}$$

$$\sigma_c = f_c \frac{E_c}{E_{c1}}\left\{\varepsilon_n - \left[1 + 2\frac{\sigma_3}{f_c}\left(\frac{1-\varepsilon_n}{0.96}\right)^6\right]\overline{\varepsilon}_{n,S}\right\} \qquad \text{if} \quad \varepsilon_n > 0.04 \tag{15b}$$

With respect to the Sargin's formula [Eq.(6)], Eqs.(15) give a more reliable stress-strain relationship for confined SCC. This is particularly true in the case of high confining pressures ($\sigma_3 = 3$ MPa in Fig.12, and $\sigma_3 = 10$ MPa in Fig.13). Conversely, Eq.(6) - which coincides with Eqs.(15) when $\sigma_3 = 0$ – is reliable in the case of low confinement ($\sigma_3 = 0$ MPa in Fig.10, and $\sigma_3 = 1$ MPa in Fig.11).

Finally, if fiber volume fraction is lower than 1%, as in this experimental campaign, Eqs.(15) are valid for all the SCCs, regardless of the fiber content. The same results can be also obtained for ordinary concrete in tension (Balaguru and Shah, 1992).


## 5. CONCLUSIONS

The experimental campaign carried out by the authors has been used to propose a new stress-strain relationship capable of modeling the pre-peak stage of concrete under active confinement. In accordance with the experimental evidence, the following conclusions can be drawn:

- The compressive strength $f_c$ increases with confining pressures $\sigma_3$. If the strength under uniaxial compression ($f_{c,0}$) is known, $f_c$ can be correctly estimated by the Binici's formula [Eq.(7)]. This is true both for ordinary and self-consolidating concrete, with and without steel fibers.

- Strains at peak of stress increase with confining pressure $\sigma_3$. The equation proposed by Richart et al. [Eq.(8)] can be used to compute $\varepsilon_{c1}$, if the corresponding value $\varepsilon_{c1,0}$, obtained in absence of confinement, is known. However, the coefficients $A$, $B$ of Eq.(8) adopted for ordinary concrete are different from those used for SCC, regardless the fiber-reinforcement. This is due to the higher strains developed by self-consolidating concrete, with respect to ordinary concrete, at the same level of stress.

- The Sargin's stress-strain relationship [Eq.(6)] cannot be used in the case of high confining pressures ($\sigma_3 > 3MPa$). A more reliable relationship, developed by the authors, is given by Eqs.(15) and can be applied to self-consolidating concrete, with and without steel fibers.

To complete the present research project on the mechanical behavior of SCC under multiaxial compression, further analyses have to be developed in order to introduce stress-sliding displacement relationships for the softening branch of such cement-based composites.

## ACKNOWLEDGEMENTS

The authors wish to express their gratitude to Fondazione Cassa di Risparmio di Alessandria for financing this research project.

Buzzi Unicem S.p.A. should be thanked for providing the technical support throughout the whole project.

# REFERENCES

Balaguru P. N. and Shah S. P. (1992). *Fiber Reinforced Cement Composites.* McGraw Hill, New York.

Barla G., Barla M., Camusso M., Debernardi D. and Martinotti M.E. (2007). "Innovative Laboratory Equipment for Rock Characterization". *Memorie in ricordo di Renato Ribacchi*, pub. by Patron, Bologna (Italy), pp. 55-66.

Binici B. (2005). "An Analytical Model for Stress–Strain Behavior of Confined Concrete". *Engineering Structures*, Vol.27, No.7, pp. 1040-1051

CEB (1993) - Comité Euro-International du Béton - *CEB-FIP Model Code 1990.* Bulletin d'information, No. 203-205, pub. by Thomas Telford, London (UK).

Colonnetti G. (1948). *Scienza delle Costruzioni (Structural Mechanics, in Italian).* Giulio Einaudi Editore, Torino (Italy).

Corradi Dell'Acqua L. (1992). *Meccanica delle strutture – Il comportamento dei mezzi continui (Structural Mechanics – Continuum Mechanics, in Italian).* McGraw-Hill Italia, Milan (Italy).

Fantilli A. P., Mihashi H. and Vallini P. (2007). "Post-Peak Behavior of Cement-Based Materials in Compression". *ACI Mat. J.*, Vol.104, No.5, pp. 501-510.

Ganesan N. and Ramana Murthy J. V. (1990). "Strength and Behavior of Confined Steel Fiber Reinforced Concrete Columns". *ACI Materials Journal*, Vol.87, No.3, pp. 221-227.

Jamet P., Millard A. and Nahas G. (1984). "Triaxial Behaviour of a Micro-Concrete Complete Stress-Strain Curves for Confining Pressures Ranging from 0 to 100 MPa". *Proc. Int. Conf. on Concrete under Multiaxial Conditions*, pub. by RILEM, Toulouse (France), pp. 133-140.

Jansen D. C. and Shah S. P. (1997). "Effect of Length on Compressive Strain Softening of Concrete". *ASCE Journal of Engineering Mechanics*, Vol.123, No.1, pp.25-35.

Hillerborg A., Modeer M. and Peterson P. (1976). "Analysis of Crack Formation and Crack Growth in Concrete by means of Fracture Mechanics and Finite Elements". *Cement and Concrete Research*, Vol.6, No.6, pp. 773–782.

Lokuge W. P., Sanjayan J. G. and Setunge S. (2005). "Stress – Strain Model for Laterally Confined Concrete". *ASCE Journal of Materials in Civil Engineering*, Vol.17, No.6, pp. 607-616.

Noguchi T., Tomosawa F., Nemati K. M., Chiaia B. M, and Fantilli A. P. (2009). "A Practical Equation for Elastic Modulus of Concrete". *ACI Structural Journal*, Vol. 106, No.5.

Paultre P., Khayat K. H., Cusson D. and Tremblay S. (2005). "Structural Performance of Self-Consolidating Concrete Used in Confined Concrete Columns". *ACI Structural Journal*, Vol.102, No.4, pp. 560-568.

Sargin M., Ghosh S.K. and Handa V.K. (1971). "Effects of Lateral Reinforcement upon the Strength and Deformation Properties of Concrete". *Magazine of Concrete Research*, Vol.23, No.75–76, pp. 99-110.

Shah S. P., Swartz S. E. and Ouyang C. (1995). *Fracture Mechanics of Concrete: Applications of Fracture Mechanics to Concrete, Rock and Other Quasi-Brittle Materials*. John Wiley, New York.

van Mier J. G. M. (1984). *Strain Softening of Concrete under Multiaxial Loading Conditions*. Doctoral Thesis, Delft University of Technology, Delft (The Netherlands).

van Mier J. G. M. (1996). *Fracture Processes of Concrete: Assessment of Material Parameters for Fracture Models*. CRC Press, Boca Raton (Florida, USA).

## APPENDIX 1: THE THEOREM OF ELASTIC COACTIONS

The theory of elastic coactions is based on the theorem firstly enounced by Gustavo Colonnetti in a series of papers published by the Accademia Nazionale dei Lincei during the years 1918-1921. This theorem is valid for all types of imposed strains, including the nonlinear strains considered in the present paper. By means of Colonnetti's theorem, the equilibrium equations of a body, subjected to a set of external loads and imposed strains, can be written independently of the types of strain (elastic, inelastic, or plastic).

Let us introduce the six unknown components of the stress tensor that characterizes the equilibrium of a body:

$$\sigma_x, \sigma_y, \ldots\ldots, \tau_{yz} \tag{A1}$$

Suppose a small variation of such components:

$$\delta\sigma_x, \delta\sigma_y, \ldots\ldots, \delta\tau_{yz} \tag{A2}$$

which forms a self-equilibrated system of stresses. From the principle of Virtual Works, it follows that the work done by the stress components of Eq.(A2) and a system of compatible strains must be equal to zero:

$$\int_V \left[ \left(\varepsilon_x + \overline{\varepsilon}_x\right)\delta\sigma_x + \left(\varepsilon_y + \overline{\varepsilon}_y\right)\delta\sigma_y + \ldots\ldots + \left(\gamma_{yz} + \overline{\gamma}_{yz}\right)\delta\tau_{yz} \right] dV = 0 \tag{A3}$$

The following six components of the strain tensor:

$$\varepsilon_x + \bar{\varepsilon}_x, \varepsilon_y + \bar{\varepsilon}_y, \ldots\ldots, \gamma_{yz} + \bar{\gamma}_{yz} \tag{A4}$$

originated in the body by passing from the unstrained natural state to actual equilibrated state, are here assumed to be the compatible system of strains.

If $\varphi$ is the elastic-strain energy density, the elastic-strain components of Eq.(A4) can be written as a function of the stress components :

$$\varepsilon_x = \frac{\partial \varphi}{\partial \sigma_x}, \varepsilon_y = \frac{\partial \varphi}{\partial \sigma_y}, \ldots\ldots, \gamma_{yz} = \frac{\partial \varphi}{\partial \tau_{yz}} \tag{A5}$$

By substituting Eq(A5) and Eq.(A4) into Eq.(A3), the following equation can be written:

$$\int_V \left[ \frac{\partial \varphi}{\partial \sigma_x} \delta\sigma_x + \frac{\partial \varphi}{\partial \sigma_y} \delta\sigma_y + \ldots\ldots + \frac{\partial \varphi}{\partial \tau_{yz}} \delta\tau_{yz} \right] dV +$$

$$\int_V \left[ \bar{\varepsilon}_x \delta\sigma_x + \bar{\varepsilon}_y \delta\sigma_y + \ldots\ldots + \bar{\gamma}_{yz} \delta\tau_{yz} \right] dV = 0 \tag{A6}$$

The first member of Eq.(A6) is the first variation of the functional:

$$\psi = \int_V \varphi\left(\sigma_x, \sigma_y, \ldots, \tau_{yz}\right) dV + \int_V \left[ \bar{\varepsilon}_x \delta\sigma_x + \bar{\varepsilon}_y \delta\sigma_y + \ldots\ldots + \bar{\gamma}_{yz} \delta\tau_{yz} \right] dV \tag{A7}$$

whose second variation

$$\int_V \varphi\left(\delta\sigma_x, \delta\sigma_y, \ldots, \delta\tau_{yz}\right) dV \tag{A8}$$

is always positive. Thus, the following theorem can be stated:

*For each system of loads and inelastic strains, the state of stress characterizing the equilibrium of the body minimizes the functional $\psi$ [Eq.(A7)].*

Should the inelastic strains be zero, this theorem would lead to the minimum of the elastic strain energy (i.e., Menabrea's theorem).

Conversely, the mechanical nonlinearities can be analyzed within the frame of the classical theory of elasticity, by replacing the six components of the elastic strain with those of the total strain [Eq.(A4)].

STUDIES AND RESEARCHES – V. 29, 2009
Graduate School in Concrete Structures – Fratelli Pesenti
Politecnico di Milano, Italy

# ON THE COMPRESSIVE STRENGTH OF CONCRETE DAMAGED BY PREVIOUS TRANSVERSE TENSION AND CRACKING

Elisseos S. Katsaragakis[1]

## ABSTRACT

The behaviour of plain concrete under sequentially-applied loads in two directions is experimentally investigated in this paper. Concrete compressive strength is measured on cylindrical specimens previously fractured by splitting, to make comparisons and correlations with concrete conventional compressive strength measured in virgin cylinders.

The compressive strength measured by testing pre-split specimens turns out to be from 5% to 15% lower than that measured on standard cylinders, depending on the number of splitting planes (one or two).

This investigation may provide some useful information on concrete behaviour in compression, whenever previous cracks exist in the direction of the subsequent compressive load, as it occurs in anchorage zones and in the shear span of R/C beams.

The results may also benefit Nonlinear Finite-Element Analysis of concrete structures.

Last but not least, the numerical coefficients and the diagrams worked out in this paper may be used in the evaluation of concrete tensile and compressive strength, on the basis of two sequential tests performed on a single specimen.

[1] PhD Civ. Eng., Lecturer, Dept of Civil Engineering, National Technical University of Athens, Athens, Greece.

# 1. INTRODUCTION

The fracture of a plain-concrete specimens is the final stage of a process in which a microcrack (or a number of microcracks), being critical under the specific applied stress, develops into a pattern of major cracks, leading to the fracture of the specimen. According to the type of the applied stresses, and to the stress level, large parts of the specimen, beyond the path of the developing fracture, undergo some damage varying in type and severity, or they even remain virtually unaffected by the fracture process. Thus, a specimen fractured under a certain stress state contains areas - or parts (if it is split) - which may resist a new load; in other words the specimen may exhibit a certain strength under a new stress state.

An axially-loaded specimen may be considered as subjected to a sequence of "n" individual loads, applied to the specimen in sequential steps. Among the multiaxial stress-states, those including tension arouse a particular interest, since in such cases concrete behaviour is still not fully understood.

In the following, the behaviour of concrete under compression is examined in specimens already fractured under tension. A limited decrease of the compressive strength has been measured, compared to standard "solid" specimens, this result being a possible indication of the extent of concrete damage in tension.

# 2. THEORETICAL CONSIDERATIONS

Let $S(s_1,...,s_n)$ be a multiaxial n-dimensional load consisting of n components, which vary in direction and/or type (i.e., tension, compression, lateral compression, etc.). This load is applied on a given specimen, through "n" steps of a sequential load-path, as follows:

  1st step: $S_1(s_1)$
  2nd  "  : $S_2(s_1, s_2)$
  . . . . . . . . . . . . . . . . .
  n-th  "  : $S_n(s_1, s_2,..., s_n)$

Should any one of the above uniaxial loads $s_i$ be applied alone, the specimen would exhibit the strength $f_i$,:

  load: $s_1$ , strength: $f_1$
    $s_2$,    "    $f_2$
    . . . .      . . . .
    $s_n$,    "    $f_n$

If the multiaxial loads $S_i$ are applied sequentially, the strengths at each step shall be:

  1st step: $(f_1)$

. . . . . . . . . . . . . . . .

i-th  "  : $(f_j = 0, f_i^*,$ with $1 \leq j \leq i - 1)$

. . . . . . . . . . . . . . . .

n-th  "  : $(f_j = 0, f_n^*,$ with $1 \leq j \leq n - 1),$

where the asterisk (*) denotes the strength of the specimen after being loaded up to failure in the last step. Obviously, in each consecutive step, the strength that has been encountered in the previous step becomes zero.

If, for a specific specimen and for a specific set of actions, a correlation is established between $f_i$ and $f_i^*$, this correlation and the same specimen may be used for the evaluation of concrete strength under both the different loads $S_j$ ($1 \leq j \leq i - 1$) and $S_i$.

For the specific case of two loads, namely an axial tension and an axial compression, applied to the same specimen, the above loading procedure is modified as follows:

- independent application of the loads:

  tensile stress:           $\sigma_t$ , strength : $f_t$

  compressive stress:    $\sigma_c$ , strength : $f_c$

- sequential application of the loads:

  1st step   : tensile stress          $\sigma_t$, strength : $f_t$

  2nd  step : compressive stress   $\sigma_c$ , strength : $f_{tc}$

The correlation between $f_{tc}$ and $f_c$, in the specific case of a concrete specimen, will be investigated in the following.


## 3. LOADING IN COMPRESSION A SPECIMEN PRE-FRACTURED IN TENSION

The above procedure is applied to concrete specimens pre-fractured in tension and subsequently subjected to a compressive loading, according to the following procedure.

A cylindrical specimen is subjected to a splitting test. Subsequently, the two parts of the diametrically-fractured specimen are brought together, forming again a cylinder to be subjected to a conventional test in compression.

During the splitting test, a part of the specimen around the fracture surface develops high biaxial stresses, causing local damage at the micro-level, in the form of microcracks. Such areas should be unable to resist the stresses developed during the subsequent compressive test; in other words, the effective area of the compressive specimen would be equal to the nominal area minus the damaged area.

The total fractured area of the specimen past the splitting test, as a percentage of the cross-section of the specimen, is an indicator of the reduced strength that the "new" specimen will exhibit under compression. This fractured area is assessed in the following by applying a criterion of fracture at each point of the cross-section of the diametrically-loaded specimen.

A cylindrical specimen of radius R and unit length, under a unit load, is considered (Fig. 1). In a system of cartesian co-ordinates having its origin in the centroid of the circular section, the stresses at a point $(x = \alpha R, y = \beta R)$ have the following expressions (Peltier, 1954):

$$\sigma_x = \frac{2}{\pi R} \left[ \frac{\alpha^2(1+\beta)}{[\alpha^2+(1+\beta)^2]^2} + \frac{\alpha^2(1-\beta)}{[\alpha^2+(1-\beta)^2]^2} - \frac{1}{2} \right] \tag{1}$$

$$\sigma_y = \frac{2}{\pi R} \left[ \frac{(1+\beta)^3}{[\alpha^2+(1+\beta)^2]^2} + \frac{(1-\beta)^3}{[\alpha^2+(1-\beta)^2]^2} - \frac{1}{2} \right] \tag{2}$$

$$\tau_{xy} = \frac{2}{\pi R} \left[ \frac{\alpha(1+\beta)^2}{[\alpha^2+(1+\beta)^2]^2} - \frac{\alpha(1-\beta)^2}{[\alpha^2+(1-\beta)^2]^2} \right] \tag{3}$$

The failure criterion adopted for the biaxial stress-state developed inside the specimen is presented in Fig. 2, in the form of a polygonal strength-envelope, approximating the actual strength envelope in the combined tension and compression domain (Kupfer et al,, 1969; Nelissen, 1972; Katsaragakis, 1988).

On the basis of the previous failure criterion, the comparison of the stresses evaluated in the points of a dense grid, yields the picture of the damaged cross-section presented in Fig. 3. The damaged area amounts to about 15% of the cross-section, this being a figure indicative of the expected strength loss under the axial compressive load. This loss depends also on a number of parameters, in some way related to the fracture process:

• Scale effect

   The specimen loaded in compression consists of two parts, that are the two halves of the split cylinder; since each part has half the size of the original cylinder, the scale effect increases the strength of the two smaller specimens.

• Slenderness of the specimen

   The two separate halves of the fractured specimen are more slender than the original specimen (which implies a strength decrease).

- Confinement of the fractured area

    The fractured area occupies the central part of the specimen and is confined by the surrounding undamaged material; hence, the fractured area can still resist a certain (small) part of the applied load (which implies a strength increase).

- Inclination of the critical microcrack

    As justified by Fracture Mechanics, the orientation of the critical microcracks to be developed inside the specimen loaded in compression is at an angle to the direction of the applied load, whilst the major cracks developed under the previous splitting process are parallel to the direction of the compressive load. Consequently, this misalignment favours a strength increase.

    Though some of the above influences are self balancing, their individual effect can be assessed only in probabilistic terms, at the microlevel of the material.

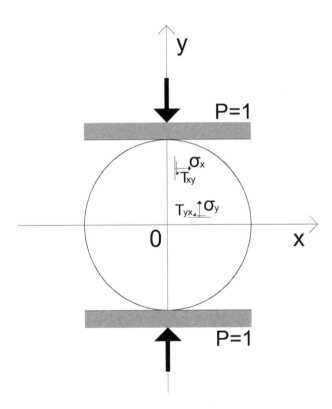

Figure 1 - Stresses in a unit-length cylinder subjected to a splitting load.

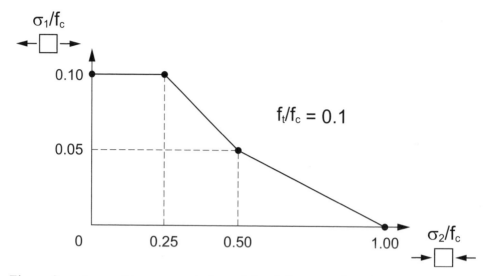

Figure 2 - A possible representation of the failure envelope in the plane of the normalized principal stresses.

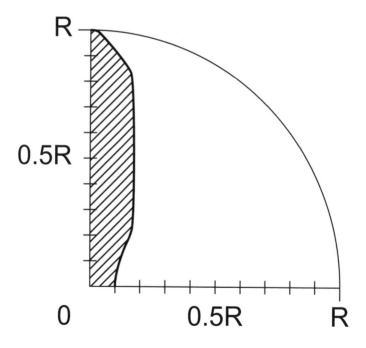

Figure 3 – Assessment of the fractured area as a part of the full section of a specimen subjected to splitting.

# 4. EXPERIMENTAL INVESTIGATION

An experimental project based on 162 concrete specimens was developed, in order to investigate concrete behaviour in compression, after the formation of splitting cracks parallel to the applied compressive load.

The cylindrical specimens (diameter/height = 150/300 mm) were cast in batches of 18 specimens each. Crushed limestone aggregates, with a maximum size of 30 mm, and Portland-type cement were used.

The curing conditions were the same for all specimens. After casting, the specimens were covered with a burlap fabric kept wet for 20 days; later - and until testing - the cylinders were stored in controlled higro-thermal conditions.

The four concrete mixes had a mean compressive strength comprised between 22 and 37 MPa (Table 1).

Table 1. Mixes and number of specimens

| Mix, $f_c$ (MPa) | $f_c$ 22 | $f_c$ 25* | $f_c$ 31 | $f_c$ 37 |
|---|---|---|---|---|
| Number of specimens | 36 | 36 | 54 | 36 |

(*)  $f_c = 24.5$ MPa

The specimens of each batch were tested as follows:

- 3 specimens were tested in compression, in order to obtain the nominal compressive strength of the batch.

- 12 specimens were loaded along two opposite generators to cause a splitting failure, and the fractured cylinders were later tested in axial compression (Fig. 4a).

- 3 specimens were loaded along two opposite generators to cause a splitting failure; then each fractured cylinder was subjected to a second splitting process by applying a load at right angles to the previous one; finally, the twice-fractured cylinder was tested in axial compression (Fig. 4b).

Concrete stress-strain curve in compression and the modulus of elasticity were obtained from each test.

(a)                                                        (b)

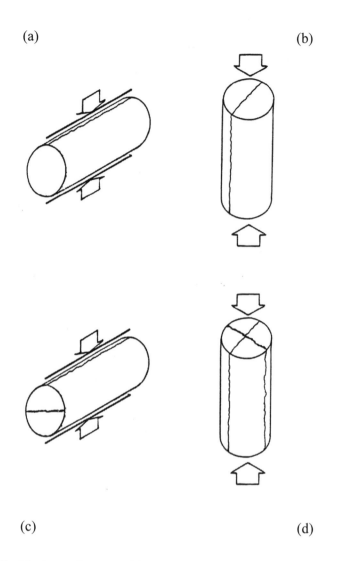

(c)                                                        (d)

Figure 4 – Cylindrical specimens subjected to single splitting (a); compression past single splitting (b); double splitting (c); and compression past double splitting (d).

## 5.  TEST RESULTS

### 5.1 Compressive strength

The test results (Table 2) include the mean compressive strength, its coefficient of variation (COV), and the percent  strength loss after the first and the second splitting processes.

Table 2. Mean strengths $f_c$ (MPa) and coefficients of variation v (%).

| Mix | $f_c$ 22 | | $f_c$ 25 | | $f_c$ 31 | | $f_c$ 37 | |
|---|---|---|---|---|---|---|---|---|
| Mean strength, COV | $f_c$ | v(%) | $f_c$ | v | $f_c$ | v | $f_c$ | v |
| Compression | 22.12 | 2.16 | 24.44 | 2.81 | 31.14 | 2.32 | 36.95 | 1.22 |
| Splitting | 1.97 | 13.20 | 1.86 | 12.80 | 2.39 | 12.64 | 2.70 | 12.85 |
| Compression past single splitting | 20.97 -5.2% | 3.54 | 23.09 -5.5% | 2.53 | 28.84 -7.4% | 3.29 | 33.77 -8.6% | 4.82 |
| Compression past double splitting | 18.83 -15% | 3.45 | 22.02 -10% | 4.11 | 28.20 -9% | 2.35 | - | - |

The reduction of the compressive strength $f_{tc}$ of the fractured specimens was about 5%, for $f_c$ 22, but increased gradually with concrete strength, to reach about 9%, for $f_c$ 37 (Table 2). These reductions are small indeed compared to the damaged area of the sections, that was evaluated as about 15% in Chapter 3. These results are plotted in Fig. 5, where the linear regression is plotted as well ($r^2$=0.995):

$$f_{tc} / f_c = 1 - 0.0023 f_c \text{ (MPa)}$$

with $f_{tc}$ = compressive strength of the fractured specimen (single splitting), and $f_c$ = compressive strength of the virgin specimen.

The twice-fractured specimens exhibit a greater decrease of their compressive strength $f_{ttc}$ (Table 3). However, due to the small number of the specimens, these results should be considered as a mere indication.

Table 3. Compressive strength $f_{tc}$ of the fractured specimens.

| Mix | $f_c$ 22 | $f_c$ 25 | $f_c$ 31 | $f_c$ 37 |
|---|---|---|---|---|
| $f_{tc} / f_c$ | 0.948 | 0.945 | 0.926 | 0.914 |
| $f_{ttc} / f_c$ | 0.851 | 0.901 | 0,905 | - |

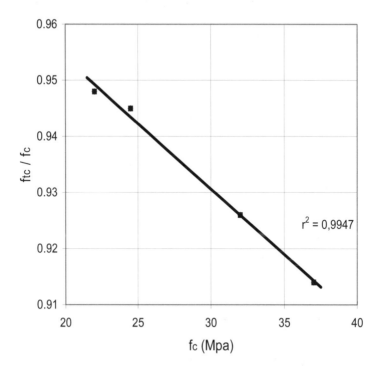

Figure 5 – Reduction of the compression strength in pre-fractured specimens (past single splitting).

## 5.2 Deformation at the peak-load

The deformation $\varepsilon_{cu}$ at the peak-load was about 2.3‰ for all concretes and generally decreased (by 7% to 19%,) in the strongest concretes (Table 4).

These results are plotted in Fig. 6. The linear regression ($r^2$=0,930) yields the following relation between the strains at the peak-load of the fractured and unfractured specimens:

$$\varepsilon_{tcu} / \varepsilon_{cu} = 1,12 - 0,008 \ f_c \ (MPa)$$

Table 4. Deformation $\varepsilon_{tcu}$ at the peak-load of the fractured specimens.

| Mix | $f_c$ 22 | $f_c$ 25 | $f_c$ 32 | $f_c$ 37 |
|---|---|---|---|---|
| $\varepsilon_{tcu}/\varepsilon_{cu}$ | 0.93 | 0.93 | 0.88 | 0.81 |

The above results allow to estimate the displacement of the peak point ($\varepsilon_{cu}$, $f_c$) of the stress-strain curve, from its initial position in the virgin specimens, to its new position ($\varepsilon_{tcu}$, $f_{tc}$) in the fractured specimens, see Figures 7 and 8. The fitting curves are polynomials of degree 2; the related $r^2$ are indicated in the figures.

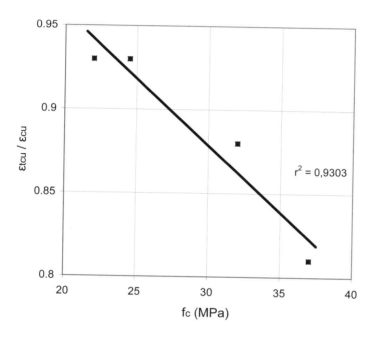

Figure 6 – Strain at the peak load in fractured and virgin specimens (single splitting).

## 5.3 Stress-strain curves and modulus of elasticity

The σ-ε curves of the fractured specimens are regular, with no sign of local abrupt changes. The tangent modulus of elasticity is the same for both virgin and fractured specimens at the origin, and keeps constant up to about 30% (15%) of the peak load in virgin (pre-fractured) cylinders.

At 15% of the peak load, the modulus of elasticity of the fractured specimens is close to 70% of the elastic modulus of the virgin specimens at 70% of their peak load.

Hence, in the case of fractured specimens, the σ-ε curve up to the peak load may be obtained by means of a transformation of the σ-ε curve of the virgin specimens, as shown in Fig. 9.

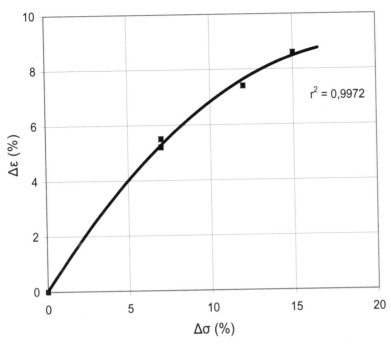

Figure 7 - Shift of the stress-strain curve at the peak stress.

## 6. DISCUSSION AND CONCLUSIONS

The following conclusions can be drawn from this investigation:

- The cylindrical strength in compression decreases slightly after either a single or double splitting process; in the former case the strength loss is roughly comprised between 5% and 9% ($f_c$ = 22-37 MPa), and in the latter case between 9% and 15% ($f_c$ = 22-31 MPa). Since a single splitting-process, with the formation of a single fractured plane, may represent a fractured 2-D situation, in such a case – (7-8%) looks like a reasonable guess. Furthermore, since a double splitting-process, with the formation of more fractured planes, may represent a 3-D situation, in such a case – (14-16%) is again a reasonable guess.

- The decrease of the residual strength (past a single splitting-process) accompanying the increase of concrete strength may be attributed to the fact that the stronger the concrete, the greater its brittleness.

- The same cylindrical specimen may be used twice for the evaluation of both concrete tensile and compressive strengths, by applying the correlation factors proposed in this study.

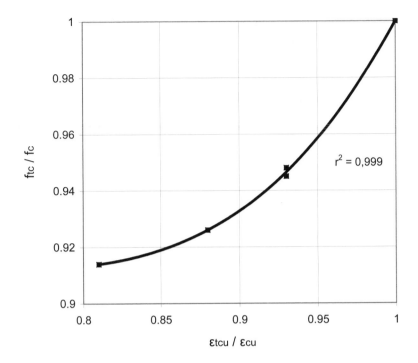

Figure 8 – Reduction of the strain at the peak load in fractured specimens (single splitting).

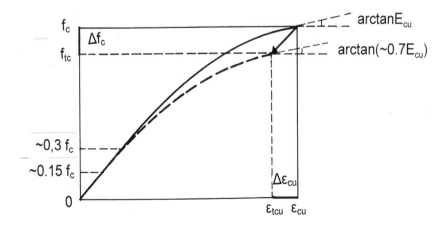

Figure 9 – Possible reduced stress-strain curves for fractured concrete.

- The proposed test procedure suggests a new way to measure concrete mechanical decay in tension-compression, in order to work out modified 2-D strength envelopes, to be compared with those published by previous authors (for instance, Kupfer et al., 1969). Concrete cylinders may be first loaded along two opposite generators (at different load levels or up to cracking) and subsequently tested in compression (Fig.10). Alternatively, concrete cylinders may be first loaded in compression (at different load levels) and subsequently tested by splitting. In both cases, envelopes different from those published by Kupfer et al. (1969) could be obtained for sequentially-applied tensile/compressive loads.

- The mechanical decay measured in this study, where the tests in compression were performed past either a single or double splitting-process, is smaller than that measured by Delibes Liniers (1987), where the tests in tension were performed after loading in compression up to concrete failure. The more severe damage accumulated in the latter case may be due to the fact that in compression microcracking is dispersed inside the whole volume of the specimen and the subsequent tensile load is applied to an extensively-weakened material. On the contrary, the damage accumulated in the former case (i.e. in this study) is mostly localised close to a single or double crack (past concrete splitting) and the subsequent compressive load is applied to a mostly-intact material. (As a matter of fact, Gopalaratman and Shah, 1985, observed no further microcracks prior to the attainment of the peak load in compression, when loading in compression a split specimen).

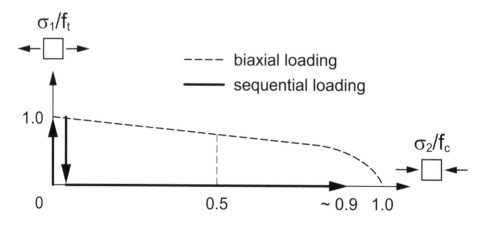

Figure 10 – Biaxial strength envelope and stress path in case of sequential loading (first, splitting-type loading stopped after concrete fracture - as in the figure – or at various levels before concrete fracture; then, loading in compression until concrete crushing.

## ACKNOWLEDGEMENTS

The author gratefully thanks Professor Giorgio Macchi for his encouragement and remarks in the preparation of this paper.

## REFERENCES

Delibes Liniers A. (1987). "Microcracking of Concrete under Compression and its Influence on Tensile Strength". *Materials and Structures*, V. 20, No. 116, pp. 111-116.

Gopalaratnam V. S. and Surendra P. Shah (1985). "Softening Response of Plain Concrete in Direct Tension". *ACI Journal*, V. 8, No 3, pp. 310-320.

Katsaragakis E.S. (1988). "Concrete Strength under Biaxial Opposite Stresses" (in Greek), *PhD Thesis, NTUA- Nat. Tech. University of Athens*, Athens (Greece).

Kupfer H, Hilsdorf H.K. and Rusch H. (1969). "Behaviour of Concrete under Biaxial Stresses". *ACI Journal*, Proc. Vol. 66, No 8, pp. 656-666.

Nelissen L.J. (1972). "Biaxial Testing of Normal Concrete". *Heron*, Vol. 18, No. 1, Stevin Lab., Delft University of Technology, Delft (The Netherlands).

Peltier M.R. (1954). *Étude Théorique de l'Essai Brésilien (Theoretical Investigation on the Brazilian Test, in French)*. Laboratoire Central des Ponts et Chausses, Paris (France).

## NOTATIONS

**Main symbols**

$\alpha, \beta$ = x/R, y/R
$\varepsilon$     deformation
$\sigma, \tau$     normal, shear stress
f     strength
R     radius of cylindrical specimen
r     correlation coefficient
S, s     load, load component
v     coefficient of variation
x,y     Cartesian co-ordinates

**Subscripts**

c, t     compression, tension
u     ultimate
tc     compression past single splitting
ttc     compression past double splitting
(tc, ttc = tensional fracture)

STUDIES AND RESEARCHES – V. 29, 2009
Graduate School in Concrete Structures – Fratelli Pesenti
Politecnico di Milano, Italy

# MODELLING TECHNIQUES TO DESCRIBE THE BACKBONE CURVES OF R/C COUPLING BEAMS SUBJECTED TO SEISMIC LOADING

Sergio Breña[1], Miguel Fernández Ruiz[2], Neven Kostic[3] and Aurelio Muttoni[4]

## ABSTRACT

Structural R/C cores are a popular and efficient solution for resisting lateral loads in medium-to-tall buildings. The walls of the cores typically exhibit large openings providing access to elevators. Consequently, the shear induced by the lateral forces is transmitted by limited portions of the core (the walls between two contiguous openings), which are commonly indicated as *coupling beams*. Such beams are subjected to large deformation demands, as the system undergoes lateral displacements associated with wind or earthquake forces, and govern the response of the structural system. Performance-based assessment and design of these members have been gaining popularity within the structural engineering community in the last 15 years. These techniques rely on an accurate definition of the structural behavior of each member (shear force – chord rotation), in order to successfully describe the global system performance. In current seismic design and assessment documents, the role of certain structural parameters (such as slenderness, reinforcement layout or even failure mode) is not always properly addressed. In this paper, the influence of these parameters is investigated on the basis of the results of an experimental campaign. Several approaches to generate the force-deformation envelopes (*backbone curves*) of coupling beams are discussed and compared. Specific reference is made to the *stress fields*, as a promising approach aimed to rationally describe the hysteretic behaviour of R/C members subjected to cyclic loading.

---

[1] Associate Professor, University of Massachusetts, Amherst, USA (on sabbatical leave at the Ecole Polytechnique Fédérale de Lausanne, Switzerland, Spring 2009).
[2] Lecturer, Ecole Polytechnique Fédérale de Lausanne, Switzerland.
[3] Researcher, Ecole Polytechnique Fédérale de Lausanne, Switzerland.
[4] Professor, Ecole Polytechnique Fédérale de Lausanne, Switzerland.

# 1. INTRODUCTION

Most medium-to-tall buildings resist horizontal loading (earthquake or wind) by means of internal reinforced-concrete cores (Figs. 1a,b). Consequently, such horizontal actions usually govern the structural design of the cores, which in turn control the deformability of the building (Fig. 1c).

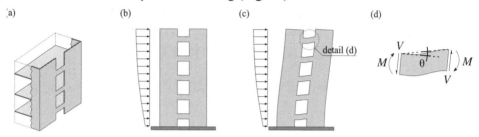

Figure 1– Coupling beams in reinforced-concrete cores: (a) view of a core with openings; (b) core subjected to horizontal loading; (c) deformation of the core; and (d) internal forces in a coupling beam.

In order to provide access to elevators or other facilities, cores usually have a number of aligned openings (Fig. 1a), that require shear forces to be carried by limited portions (the *coupling beams* between the openings). Being subjected to relatively large internal forces (bending and shear, Fig. 1d), coupling beams become the controlling members of the global response of the wall system (the shear failure of coupling beams causes the loss of the wall stiffness).

## 1.1 Summary of existing studies on coupling beams

Initial experimental research on reinforced-concrete coupling beams focused on the development of rebar details to improve the structural ductility under cyclic actions. Prior to mid-1970s, the most commonly-used reinforcement pattern in coupling beams consisted of an orthogonal arrangement of longitudinal and transverse bars (conventional reinforcement, Fig. 2a). The failure of the Mt. McKinley apartment building during the Alaska earthquake in 1964 demonstrated that beams with conventional reinforcement patterns and small amounts of transverse reinforcement could fail in a brittle manner under strong ground shaking, and prompted researchers to develop alternative reinforcement configurations, that would enhance the ductile behavior of coupling beams.

In the early 1970s, Paulay and coworkers at the University of Canterbury (New Zealand) carried out monotonic and cyclic tests on coupling beams with different reinforcement patterns (Paulay 1971a,b). These studies were instrumental in identifying the two predominant shear-failure modes, that occur in conventionally-reinforced coupling beams: diagonal-tension failure and sliding-shear failure. The tests indicated that diagonal-tension failure may occur at low-to-moderate ductility demands, even if the beam yields initially in bending. Additionally, for beams with low clear span-to-depth ratios and high amounts of transverse reinforcement (designed to prevent any diagonal tension failure), sliding-shear failure occurred at higher deformation demands, due to plastic-strain accumulation in the longitudinal reinforcement and to damage accumulation in the concrete close to beam ends. To enhance the ductility of the coupling beams, Paulay proposed a reinforcement pattern consisting of a set of corner-to-corner diagonally-placed bars (Fig. 2b), as suggested by the crack patterns observed in laboratory tests: Such a bar arrangement could also avoid any premature failures associated with low ductility, because of crack widening at beam ends (Paulay 1971b; Paulay and Binney 1974).

As a rule, to avoid buckling phenomena under large inelastic load reversals, the diagonal bars are laterally confined by means of closely-spaced hoops.

(a)     (b)     (c)     (d)

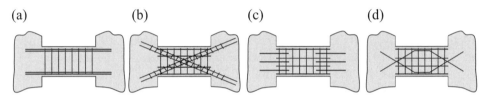

Figure 2 – Reinforcement patterns in coupling beams: (a) conventionally-reinforced beams; (b) diagonally-reinforced beams; (c) beams with dowel bars at each end; and (d) rhombic reinforcement pattern.

Paulay and Santhakumar (1976) compared the effects that different reinforcement patterns in coupling beams have on the lateral-load response of coupled-wall systems, by testing one-quarter scale coupled-wall specimens with conventionally-reinforced or diagonally-reinforced beams. Their results indicated that sliding-shear failures may occur at the ends of conventionally-reinforced coupling beams after several shear reversals. In contrast, beams with diagonal reinforcing bars exhibited a stable response without any sizable strength or stiffness degradation under large displacements. Current and past codes (*UBC 1997*; *IBC 2009*; *ACI 318-08*) promote the use of diagonal bars in coupling beams with low aspect ratios subjected to high shear loads.

Diagonally-reinforced beams, however, brings in a number of constructive problems, because of reinforcement congestion, interference between horizontal and vertical bars, and further reinforcement required to increase the confinement. To simplify the construction without sacrificing the ductile response of the coupling beams, several investigators have proposed alternate reinforcement patterns that would improve the performance of coupling beams under large load reversals (Barney et al. 1980; Tassios *et al.*, 1996; Galano and Vignoli, 2000). Some of the proposed patterns are shown in Figures 2c,d. Other investigators have developed *hybrid* (or *composite*) coupling beams, by embedding structural steel elements in the concrete (Harries *et al.*, 1997). Recent studies have also suggested the use of high-performance fiber-reinforced cementitious composites characterized by a high tensile strength in order to simplify the reinforcement in the coupling beams of future buildings (Canbolat *et al.*, 2005). These techniques are extremely promising, but little has been done so far concerning the systematic development of rehabilitation techniques to be used in existing coupling beams exhibiting obsolete reinforcement patterns.

Many research studies based on linear elasticity were carried out in the 1960s to investigate the role of the parameters affecting the elastic response of coupled-wall systems (e.g. Beck 1962; Coull and Choudhury, 1967; Coull and Puri, 1968; Coull *et al.*, 1973). Among the parameters that control the lateral behavior of a structural system, the *degree of coupling* was recognized as one of the most effective. It was later found that the earthquake response of coupled-wall systems cannot be accurately described by using elastic analysis. Hence, most of the efforts were concentrated on the application of nonlinear analysis to coupled-wall structures (Paulay, 1970; Glueck, 1973; Elkholy and Robinson, 1974; Takayanagi and Schnobrich, 1979). Mahin and Bertero (1976) carried out the nonlinear 2-D dynamic analysis of the shear walls of the "Banco de America" Building (Managua, Guatemala), which was moderately damaged during the 1972 earthquake. Three different force-deformation curves representing the behavior of the coupling beams were introduced to take care of their possible brittle shear-failure or ductile flexural-failure (with/without strength and stiffness degradation). Two different ground-motion records were used in the analysis. The numerical results showed that in coupling beams the number of the cycles exhibiting inelastic displacements could significantly exceed the number of the cycles undergone by the roof, because of higher-mode effects in the coupling beams. It was found also that elastic analysis cannot provide realistic estimates of the deformation and internal forces generated in coupled-wall systems.

Not only these analytical studies are the backbone of current practice in the analysis of coupled-wall structures, but they paved the way to the use of nonlinear analysis, that is instrumental in obtaining a more realistic description of the expected seismic response in coupled-wall systems.

## 1.2 Nonlinear static methods for the seismic performance-based evaluation of coupling beams

Since its publication, *Standard ASCE/SEI 41-06 – Seismic Rehabilitation for Existing Buildings* (2006) has become a common tool for any structural engineer involved in the assessment and rehabilitation of existing buildings. This standard evolved from *FEMA 356 – Prestandard and Commentary for the Seismic Rehabilitation of Buildings* (2000), which had been used for several years in the rehabilitation projects throughout the United States. The above-mentioned documents were aimed to guide designers in the performance-based rehabilitation process required by seismically-vulnerable buildings.

One of the first steps in the performance-based rehabilitation process is to evaluate the force and displacement capacity of a given existing structure. *ASCE/SEI 41-06* provides details for various nonlinear-analysis techniques to be used by engineers in the evaluation process, including dynamic time-history or static (pushover) techniques. To date, the static nonlinear analysis based on imposed forces (*pushover*) has been extensively used by structural engineers in the evaluation process, because of its relative simplicity and of the availability of dedicated commercial softwares. According to this numerical technique, the response of the structure is calculated by introducing the nonlinear response of each individual member of the system (*force-deformation* relationship). The individual force-deformation relationships in combination with a model of the whole structural system are believed to provide an acceptable estimate of the entire structural response. It is assumed that the nonlinear behavior is restricted to specific zones of the structural system, this simplification being often very realistic. In the case of coupled-wall structures, the nonlinear zones are concentrated either within the coupling beams or close the base of the shear walls, where the bending moment due to the lateral forces is the largest. The system is then subjected to a set of lateral forces that is increased until a mechanism is formed. The monotonic nonlinear force-displacement response of the structural system is computed, in order to check whether the lateral displacements (represented by the *drift* of each storey) respect certain given acceptable values, that depend on the required level of performance (e.g. actual occupancy, life safety, collapse prevention, .....).

In coupled-wall systems, the force-deformation envelopes of each structural member (*backbone curves*) are generally used instead of modeling the complete hysteretic behavior of each member (the coupling beams in the case in question). The force-deformation curves of the coupling beams are worked out by making reference to the shear force-chord rotation curves. These curves provide the rotation experienced by the coupling beam ($\theta$, see Figure 1d) for a given value of the applied shear force. The accuracy of nonlinear static analysis obviously depends (a) on the quality of the backbone curve of each member, and (b) on the technique used to derive the curves. It is believed that the guidance provided by *ASCE/SEI 41-06* to construct the backbone curves for coupling beams is inadequate. Therefore, a critical review of the techniques contained in this document is presented in the following.

### 1.2.1 Calculation of the capacity of coupling beams according to ASCE/SEI 41-06

According to *ASCE/SEI 41-06*, to work out the shear force-chord rotation envelope of any given coupling beam, its shear strength should be evaluated according to *ACI Building Code* (*ACI 318-08*), by introducing the actual (or expected) materials strengths and by adopting a strength reduction factor (or partial safety factors) equal to 1.0 in all equations. The expected bending strength is calculated taking into account the multiple layers (should it be the case) of the longitudinal reinforcement. The shear forces are derived from the bending

57

moments through equilibrium considerations, by assuming for the beam an effective length between the plastic hinges. The shear force in the beams will then depend on the plasticized length at beam ends. If the plasticized length at the ends of the the longitudinal reinforcement is small (as in the case of brittle shear failures), assuming the end moments to be applied at the beam-wall connections is reasonable. On the contrary, if the plasticized length is sizable (as in the case of stable plastic hinges), assuming the end moments to be applied at the extremities of the plasticized zones is a must. Thus, the shear forces corresponding to these two conditions can be calculated by using Eqs. (1a) and (1b), respectively:

$$V_{end} = \frac{2M_n}{l_n} \qquad\qquad V_{hinge} = \frac{2M_n}{l_n - l_p} \qquad\qquad (1a,b)$$

where $M$ is the moment at the ends of the beam, $l_n$ is the clear span of the beam, and $l_p$ is the (assumed) length of the plastic-hinge. The recommended length of the plastic-hinge in *ASCE/SEI 41-06* is equal to the section flexural depth divided by 2. In deep members (such as coupling beams, that are generally short) the shear force required to generate a hinge may be quite large, because the difference between the clear span and the length of the plastic hinge can be very small (it approaches zero when $l_n = h$).

The shear strength of a coupling beam (diagonal tension) is calculated according to *ACI 318-08* (Eq. 21-7, normal-weight concrete), see Eq.(2):

$$V_n = A_{cv}\left(\alpha_c \sqrt{f_c'} + \rho_v f_{yt}\right) \qquad\qquad (2)$$

where $\alpha_c = 3$ for a clear span-to-depth ratio $l_n/h < 1.5$, or 2 for $l_n/h > 2$ (linear interpolation should be used for intermediate values); $\rho_v = A_v/(b_w s)$ = transverse reinforcement ratio; $A_{cv}$ = cross-sectional area of the beam parallel to the applied shear force; $b_w$ = width of the web of the beam; $s$ = spacing of transverse reinforcement and $f_{yt}$ = expected yield strength of the transverse reinforcement. One of the limitations of Eq. (2) is that it considers neither the shear-strength degradation due to beam cycling, nor the other shear-failure modes documented in coupling beams (e.g. sliding shear). Other available documents provide more detailed procedures to evaluate the shear strength as a function of displacement capacity (*FEMA 306*, for example).

## 1.2.2 Chord rotation as deformation parameter

The most extensively-used deformation parameter to work out the backbone curves of coupling beams is chord rotation (see the "Notation" for its definition; see also Figure 1d). Coupling-beam chord rotations are evaluated by using the tabulated values (modeling parameters) listed in Table 1 (from *ASCE/SEI 41-06*). These values depend on the mechanism controlling the behaviour of coupling beams (bending or shear), but criteria to make a distinction are not specified in the document. For example, a member may be identified as "bending-governed", if flexural hinges form at its ends prior to reaching the shear strength. For low amounts of longitudinal reinforcement, flexural hinges may form when the acting moment is close to the expected yield moment. Because of shear strength degradation at high displacements, the given coupling beam may subsequently fail in shear, though failure may have been initially classified as bending-controlled.

Table 1 – Modeling parameters for coupling beams in *ASCE/SEI 41-06* (see Fig. 3 for the definition of the parameters).

| Reinforcement Configuration | $\dfrac{V}{b_w h \sqrt{f_c'}}$ [b] | Controlled by Bending | | | Controlled by Shear | | |
|---|---|---|---|---|---|---|---|
| | | a | b | c | d | e | c |
| With conforming transverse reinforcement[a] | $\leq 3$ | 0.025 | 0.050 | 0.75 | 0.020 | 0.030 | 0.60 |
| | $\geq 6$ | 0.020 | 0.040 | 0.50 | 0.016 | 0.024 | 0.30 |
| With nonconforming transverse reinforcement[a] | $\leq 3$ | 0.020 | 0.035 | 0.50 | 0.012 | 0.025 | 0.40 |
| | $\geq 6$ | 0.010 | 0.025 | 0.25 | 0.008 | 0.014 | 0.20 |
| Diagonal reinforcement | n.a. | 0.030 | 0.050 | 0.80 | — | — | — |

[a]Conforming transverse reinforcement consists of : (a) closed stirrups along the entire beam length at a spacing $\leq d/3$, and (b) shear capacity guaranteed by the closed stirrups $V_s \geq 3/4$ of the required shear strength of the coupling beam; [b] $f_c'$ in [lb/in$^2$]

Chord rotations in shear-controlled beams are estimated by using rotations $d$ and $e$ (see Table 1 and Fig. 3a). In bending-controlled beams, however, all post-yield chord rotation values (rotations $a$ and $b$) are referred to the chord rotation at yielding. A "shear-force retention" coefficient is given in Table 1 (parameter $c$), which is the fraction of the shear at yielding retained under large displacements.

*ASCE/SEI 41-06* defines the chord rotation at yield as:

$$\theta_y = \frac{M_y}{E_c I_{cr}} l_p \tag{3}$$

where $M_y$ represents the yield moment; $E_c$ is concrete secant modulus of elasticity ($E_c = 57000 \sqrt{f_c'}$ [psi]; $= 4730 \sqrt{f_c'}$ [MPa]); $I_{cr}$ is the moment of inertia of the cracked cross section; and $l_p$ is the length of the plastic hinge. According to *ASCE/SEI 41-06*, the cracked (effective) bending and shear stiffnesses of a coupling beam is $0.3 \, E_c I_g$ and $0.4 \, E_c A_{cv}$, respectively, where $A_{cv}$ is the shear-resistant gross sectional area ($= b_w h$). It should be noted that the value of the shear stiffness adopted in *ASCE/SEI 41-06* can be obtained by using the relationship between the elastic modulus $E_c$ and the shear modulus $G_c=E_c/[2(1+\nu)]$, with $\nu$ (Poisson's ratio) taken equal to 0.25 ($G_c$ close to *0.4E_c*). This observation implies that any shear stiffness degradation due to concrete cracking is neglected.

A reassessment of existing test results of coupling beams conducted by Ihtiyar and Breña (2006) shows that the shear stiffness in coupling beams can decrease substantially even under small deformations. This is a confirmation of what had been previously observed by Paulay (1971), who highlighted the necessity of introducing appropriately the shear stiffness in the analysis of short coupling beams, including the sizable loss of stiffness occurring after cracking.

One of the limitations in the evaluation of the flexural stiffness by using a fraction of the gross moment of inertia (e.g. 0.3 $I_g$) is that in this way the span-to-depth ratio has no role on cracked stiffness. Paulay and Priestley (1992) indicated that the moment of inertia of cracked sections in coupling beams is a function of beam aspect ratio, and recommended that in conventionally-reinforced coupling beams $I_{cr}$ be calculated using Eq.(4):

$$I_{cr} = \frac{0.2I_g}{\left[1+3\left(\dfrac{h}{l_n}\right)^2\right]} \tag{4}$$

Alternatively, *ASCE/SEI 41-06* allows experimental results to be used to generate the backbone response of the structural members instead of using tabulated modelling parameters. These two approaches are schematically illustrated in Fig. 3, where Fig. 3a shows the shape of the backbone curves as obtained by using the values from Table 1, and Fig. 3b indicates a possible way of generating an experimentally-derived backbone curve and a simplified curve that one might obtain with the tabular procedure suggested in *ASCE/SEI 41-06*.

(a) (b)

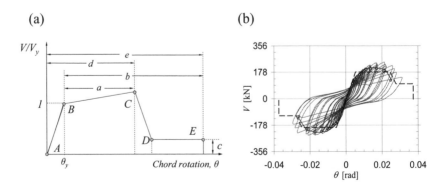

Figure 3 – Construction of the backbone curves using (a) tabulated values; and (b) experimental results (Ihtiyar and Breña 2007).

### 1.2.3 Components of chord rotation in coupling beams

It has been mentioned that chord rotation is used as the primary deformation parameter in *ASCE/SEI 41-06* to work out the backbone envelopes in coupling beams. In short deep members, deformation components other than those induced by bending may play an important role in the deformed shape. In the case of coupling beams, shear forces and bar slip markedly affect structural deformability, and substantially contribute to chord rotation, as graphically illustrated in Fig. 4. In particular, the chord rotation resulting from flexural and shear deformations after cracking should be included, to describe the ascending branch of the shear force-chord rotation curve. As for bar slip (Fig. 4c), its contribution to the total deformation may be substantial at large displacements, but is negligible in the post-cracking pre-yielding phase (at small displacements).

(a)                          (b)                          (c)

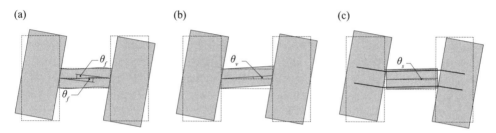

Figure 4 – Contributions to chord rotation in a coupling beam: (a) flexural deformation; (b) shear deformation; and (c) bar slip.

## 2. ROLE OF THE REINFORCEMENT LAYOUT: EXPERIMENTAL RESPONSE AND COMPARISON WITH *ASCE* BACKBONE CURVES

A number of specimens were designed and tested in Amherst (University of Massachusetts) primarily aimed to investigate the effects that both the reinforcement layout and the geometry have on the failure mode, and to evaluate the quality of the backbone curves worked out by using the procedures proposed in *FEMA 356* (parent document of *ASCE/SEI 41-06*). Although these specimens refer to no particular prototype building, their dimensions are consistent with ¾-scale models of typical coupling beams. Concrete nominal compressive strength and steel yield strength were 30 MPa and 410 MPa (longitudinal and transverse reinforcement), respectively. Only in Specimen CB-2 the transverse reinforcement consisted of deformed wire with a nominal yield strength of 580 MPA. Table 2 lists the main geometric and as-built material properties of all specimens. Figure 5 illustrates the geometry and reinforcement layout of the four specimens tested in this research project. The main variable parameters were: beam span, and the amounts of the transverse/ longitudinal reinforcement (see Ihtiyar and Breña, 2007, for further details). The specimens represent two groups of beams: short (specimens CB-1 and CB-3) and long (specimens CB-2 and CB-4). Since all coupling beams had the same depth, the shear span-to-depth ratio ($a/d$) changed from 0.75 to 1.50 by simply doubling beam length.

The load was applied to the coupling beams by means of two stiff concrete walls built at each end of the specimens. The lateral load was applied to the top of the walls by using a stiff steel element that imposed equal lateral displacement to both walls (Fig. 6). Given the geometry of the test setup, the applied lateral force $Q$ generated shear forces at the ends of the coupling beams equal to $Q\ h_{pin}/(l_b+l_w)$. These shear forces were 1.1 and 0.8 times the applied lateral force $Q$ for the short specimens (CB-1 and CB-3) and for the long specimens (CB-2 and CB-4), respectively. The same lateral-load history was used for the four specimens. Specimens were subjected to sets of three cycles of reverse cyclic loading at pre-defined amplitudes. The tests were force-controlled in the pre-yield stage and displacement-controlled in the post-yield stage. Below the estimated yield shear force ($V_y$), the amplitudes of the applied load were 1/3, 2/3, and 3/3 of $V_y$. The lateral displacement at the top of the walls at $V_y$ was defined as the *displacement at yielding*. In the displacement-controlled stage, the displacement increments were 0.5 times the displacement at yield. The loading process was stopped as soon as the specimens began to lose their strength at higher applied displacements since the primary intent was to evaluate the stiffness in the loading branch. Only Specimen CB-4 was subjected to much higher displacements, because in this case the test was aimed to investigate the shear-retention capacity under large displacements and – to this end – the design was controlled by bending.

Instrumentation consisted of linear potentiometers to measure the global displacement at the top of the walls, the relative displacement between beam end sections and concrete walls, and the displacements at the base of the walls. String potentiometers were positioned longitudinally and diagonally on the back face of the coupling beams to measure shear distortions. Strain gages were used to monitor the strains in the longitudinal and transverse reinforcement. A load cell was used to monitor the applied load during each test. The linear potentiometers measuring the relative displacement between the beam end sections and the walls were used to evaluate the chord rotation throughout each test.

Table 2 – As-built parameters of the coupling beams tested in this project.

| Specimen | $d$ [mm] | $l_n$ [mm] | Longitudinal steel | | | Transverse steel | | | $f_c$ [MPa] |
|---|---|---|---|---|---|---|---|---|---|
| | | | $A_s$ [mm$^2$] | $f_{yl}$ [MPa] | $\rho_l$[a] [%] | $A_v$ [mm$^2$] | $f_{yt}$ [MPa] | $\rho_v$ [%] | |
| CB-1 | 340 | 510 | 600 | 517 | 0.69 | 142 | 524 | 1.1 | 39 |
| CB-2 | 340 | 1020 | 851 | 448 | 0.99 | 52 | 607 | 0.13 | 39 |
| CB-3 | 270 | 510 | 860[b] | 517 | 1.25 | 142 | 524 | 1.1 | 31 |
| CB-4 | 340 | 1020 | 400 | 517 | 0.47 | 142 | 524 | 1.1 | 30 |

[a] $\rho_l = A_s/bd$; $\rho_v = A_v/b_w s$; [b] Includes the lowermost layer of the distributed longitudinal web reinforcement (2 No. 4 bars, Fig. 2.1a).

## 2.1 Measured hysteretic response

Specimen response was primarily evaluated by examining its shear force-chord rotation response. The measured shear force in the coupling beams was compared with the calculated values obtained from the backbone curves worked out according to *ASCE/SEI 41-06* and on the basis of the failure mode observed during the tests.

All calculated strengths (bending or shear capacities) were obtained using the measured materials properties of each specimen, taking into account the additional web reinforcement (if any).

Only Specimen CB-2 had insufficient shear strength, according to Eq. 2, and failed before the yielding of the longitudinal reinforcement (Table 3). All other specimens were expected to develop their flexural capacity, by attaining their bending strength at the end sections. (Compare $V_{end}$ – measured shear at the beam-wall connection – with $V_n$ = calculated strength according to Eq. 2, Table 3). Plastic hinges were not expected to form in any specimen except in Specimen CB-4, which was characterised by a low flexural steel-ratio and by a relatively long span.

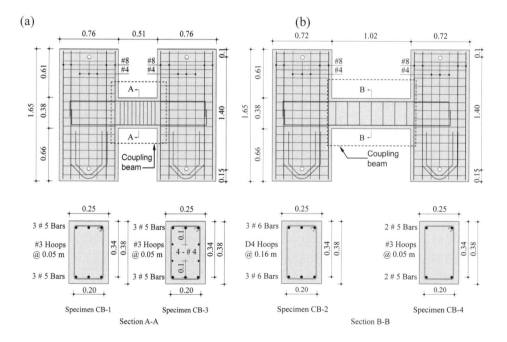

Figure 5 – Tests by Ihtiyar and Breña (2007): geometry and reinforcement (dimensions in [m]): Specimens CB-1 and CB-3 in (a); and CB-2 and CB-4 in (b).

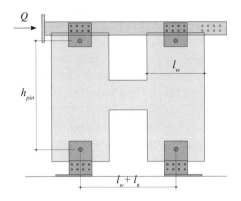

Figure 6 – Experimental setup in the tests by Ihtiyar and Breña (2007): geometry (a); and specimen assembled within the test rig (b).

The cyclic (hysteretic) shear force-chord rotation behavior of the four beams tested in the experimental program (Fig. 7) has several interesting aspects. Specimens CB-1 and CB-3 (short span) have similar hysteretic behaviours. Both specimens reached approximately the same shear force and were able to develop similar chord rotations at yielding and at the peak shear force. The influence of the horizontal web reinforcement in Specimen CB-3 did not significantly affect the hysteretic response.

Table 3 – Summary of measured shear force and chord rotations.

| Specimen | $Q_{test, pk}$ [kN] | $V_{y,test}$[a] [kN] | $V_{test,pk}$ [kN] | $\theta_{test,pk}$ [rad] | $V_{end}$[b] [kN] | $V_n$[c] [kN] |
|---|---|---|---|---|---|---|
| CB-1 | 436 | 371 | 480 | 0.0311 | 492 | 709 |
| CB-2 | 344 | 227 | 275 | 0.0076 | 319 | 187 |
| CB-3 | 460 | 447 | 506 | 0.0299 | 575 | 693 |
| CB-4 | 300 | 141 | 240 | 0.0214 | 168 | 647 |

[a]Determined using strain gauges attached to the flexural reinforcement
[b]Shear corresponding to development of the flexural strength at beam ends
[c]Using Eq. (2)

The highly-different behaviors of Specimens CB-2 and CB-4 (same span-to-depth ratio) were primarily caused by the significantly different amounts of transverse reinforcement. The transverse reinforcement in CB-2 was barely sufficient to maintain its shear strength after the formation of the first diagonal crack and led to a brittle failure with no yielding of the longitudinal reinforcement. On the other hand, Specimen CB-4 had a very ductile response because of its low flexural strength and its relatively high shear capacity. CB-4 was the only specimen that had a shear strength higher than that required to develop plastic hinges and to spread the plastic strains close to beam end sections.

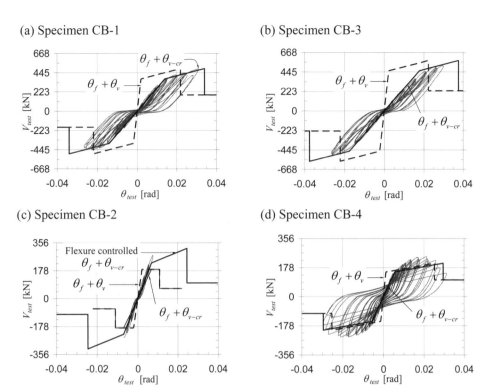

(a) Specimen CB-1    (b) Specimen CB-3

(c) Specimen CB-2    (d) Specimen CB-4

Figure 7 – Hysteretic response of the specimens tested by Ihtiyar and Breña (2007), and comparison with the backbone curves worked out in this project (the dashed curves correspond to *ASCE/SEI 41-06* and the solid curves include the proposed modifications).

## 2.2 Comparison of the backbone curves with the experimental force-deformation curves

The backbone curves are useful whenever static nonlinear analysis is carried out as a part of structural performance-based design or assessment The tests carried out by Ihtiyar and Breña (2007) provided an opportunity to evaluate the results of four coupling beams failing with different behaviors. The backbone curves of the four specimens were worked out on the basis of the recommendations from *ASCE/SEI 41-06* (dashed curves in Fig. 7 and Table 4).

The construction of these curves, however, required the introduction of several improvements, that were suggested by the test results. In details:

(1) The shear deformations based on the gross elastic properties were included to calculate the chord rotation at yielding, because the chord rotation at yield ing computed by means of Eq. (3) – which neglects the component of deformation due to shear forces – grossly underestimates the chord rotation measured in the tests.

65

(2) All specimens except CB-2 were initially assumed to be governed by bending.

(3) The shear force at yielding $(V_y)$ and the shear force at ultimate $(V_{end})$ were assumed to act at beam end sections, when yielding penetration was rather limited (less than $d/4$). However, for Specimen CB-4, with significant yielding penetration, the shear force at ultimate was assumed to act at the end section of the plastified region $(V_{hinge})$.

(4) To improve the fitting of the measured hysteretic curves (solid curves in Fig. 7) in terms of stiffness, the moment of inertia of the cracked section suggested by Paulay and Priestley (1992, Eq. 4) was adopted, and the shear deformation component based on the properties of cracked sections were used to evaluate the chord rotation at yielding. The cracked shear deformation component ($\theta_{v\text{-}cr}$) was evaluated using the shear deformation (Fig. 4b) measured during the tests (Ihtiyar and Breña, 2007).

Table 4 – Measured and calculated *(ASCE/SEI 41-06)* shear forces, and chord rotations at the peak load (the values between parentheses were calculated by adopting the four above-listed recommendations).

| Specimen | $V_{test,\,pk}$ [kN] | $\theta_{test,\,pk}$ [rad] | $V_{calc}^{(a)}$ [kN] | $\theta_{calc}$ [rad] | $\dfrac{V_{test,pk}}{V_{calc}}$ | $\dfrac{\theta_{test,pk}}{\theta_{calc}}$ |
|---|---|---|---|---|---|---|
| CB-1 | 480 | 0.0311 | 492 | 0.0219 | 0.98 | 1.42 |
|  |  |  | (492) | (0.0340) | (0.98) | (0.91) |
| CB-2 | 275 | 0.0076 | 187 | 0.0110 | 1.47 | 0.69 |
|  |  |  | $(320)^{(b)}$ | $(0.0245)^{(b)}$ | (0.86) | (0.43) |
| CB-3 | 506 | 0.0299 | 575 | 0.0223 | 0.88 | 1.34 |
|  |  |  | (575) | (0.0376) | (0.88) | (0.79) |
| CB-4 | 240 | 0.0214 | 205 | 0.0253 | 1.17 | 0.85 |
|  |  |  | (205) | (0.0296) | (1.17) | (0.72) |
|  |  |  |  | Average | 1.13 | 1.07 |
|  |  |  |  |  | (0.97) | (0.72) |
|  |  |  |  | CoV | 0.23 | 0.34 |
|  |  |  |  |  | (0.15) | (0.29) |

[a]Shear past the development of the beam flexural strength
[b]Using the curve corresponding to the bending-controlled beavior.

66

The shear forces at yielding and at ultimate were calculated using the measured materials properties. Chord rotations were obtained using the coefficients listed in Table 1 for bending-controlled beams (Specimens CB-1, CB-3, CB-4), as well as for shear-controlled beams (Specimen CB-2). For the sake of comparison, in the case of Specimen CB-2 the backbone curve based on the bending-controlled behavior was worked out as well (Fig. 7c).

A similar approach to work out the backbone curves according to *FEMA 356* (including the background of the proposed modifications) is discussed in Ihtiyar and Breña (2007).


## 3. EVALUATION OF TEST RESULTS AND BACKBONE ENVELOPES USING STRESS FIELDS

### 3.1 Stress fields for modelling reinforced-concrete shear walls

Stress fields were developed from the direct application of the lower-bound theorem of the theory of plasticity to reinforced-concrete members, as proposed by Drucker (1961), Fig. 8c. In a reinforced-concrete member, a stress field is a state of stresses, which is in equilibrium with the external actions and that respects the plasticity criteria for the materials (steel and concrete).

In general, compression is carried by concrete (although in some cases the reinforcement comes into play as well) and tension by reinforcing steel.

Assuming a rigid-plastic behavior for the material (Figs. 8a,b) a series of stress fields can be developed for being used in the design and assessement of structural concrete (Nielsen et al., 1978; Müller, 1978; Marti, 1980; Muttoni, 1989; Muttoni et al., 1997). These stress fields, called also *rigid-plastic (discontinuous) stress fields* (Muttoni and Fernández Ruiz, 2007) generally provide safe estimates of the failure load and allow the designer to clearly understand the structural load-carrying mechanisms, as shown for instance in Figs. 9a,b, where two equally-admissible stress fields are sketched for the same structure (a deep beam subjected to distributed loading). In Fig. 9a, the load is carried by means of a *fan* action, whereas in Fig.9b the load is carried by an *arch* action. The corresponding truss models are shown in Figs. 9c,d.

Applying rigid-plastic stress fields may, however, have two drawbacks:

1. The solution of the problem is not unique (see for instance Figs. 9a,b); hence, a certain level of expertise is required to identify the most appropriate load-carrying mechanism.

2. No information is provided on the deformation capacity of the member in question, because of the assumption on the rigid-plastic behavior of the materials (Fig. 9e). This second drawback limits in principle the use of stress fields in the solution of all those problems, where displacements and rotations are the basic input in structural analysis (in our case, any coupling beam subjected to seismic excitation).

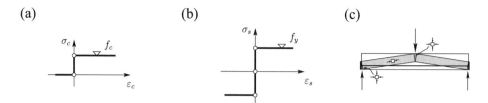

Figure 8 – Rigid-plastic stress fields: (a) rigid-plastic constitutive law for concrete (no tensile strength); (b) rigid-plastic constitutive law for steel; and (c) rigid-plastic stress field for a beam subjected to a mid-span load (Drucker, 1961).

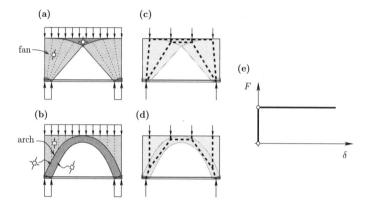

Figure 9 – Rigid-plastic stress fields for a deep beam subjected to distributed loading: (a) fan-shaped and (b) arch-shaped load-carrying mechanisms; (c,d) corresponding truss models; and (e) force-deflection curve.

In order to overcome the above-mentioned limitations, *elastic-plastic (continuous) stress fields* have recently been developed (Fernández Ruiz and Muttoni, 2007). The same hypotheses adopted in the case of rigid-plastic stress fields are still valid, but materials behavior is assumed to be elastic-perfectly plastic (Fig. 10). This allows calculating the strains in concrete, as well as the displacements of the member.

Since the longitudinal and transverse strains in the compression struts are known, the influence that transverse cracking has on concrete compressive strength can also be introduced by means of a strength-reduction factor affecting concrete strength, as suggested – for instance – by the "modified compression-field theory" (Vecchio and Collins, 1986):

$$f_{ce} = f_c \cdot \eta_\varepsilon \quad \text{where} : \eta_\varepsilon = \frac{1}{0.8 + 170\varepsilon_{tr}} \leq 1.0 \tag{5}$$

where $\varepsilon_{tr}$ is the transverse strain at right angles to the applied stress in concrete.

An efficient implementation of such fields using finite elements is described and discussed in Fernández Ruiz and Muttoni (2007).

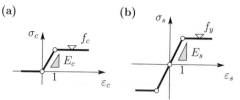

Figure 10 – Assumed materials behavior in elastic-plastic stress fields: (a) concrete; and (b) reinforcing steel.

The suitability of elastic-plastic (continuous) stress fields for describing the behaviour of shear walls and coupling beams subjected to monotonic loading has been investigated in this research project, with reference to the tests carried out by Maier and Thürlimann (1985). The geometry of Specimens S1 and S2 is shown in Fig. 11. Both specimens were subjected to various levels of axial and shear forces.

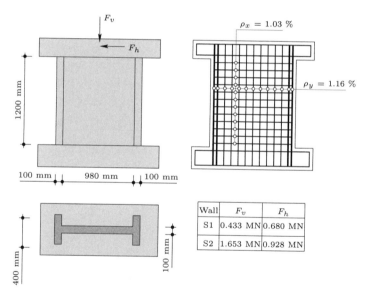

| Wall | $F_v$ | $F_h$ |
|------|-------|-------|
| S1 | 0.433 MN | 0.680 MN |
| S2 | 1.653 MN | 0.928 MN |

Figure 11 – Specimens S1 and S2 (Maier and Thürlimann, 1985), $f_c$ = 36 MPa, $E_c$ = 34 GPa, $f_y$ = 574 MPa, $E_s$ = 200 GPa: geometry (left), and reinforcement (right).

The results obtained using elastic-plastic continuous stress fields are shown in Fig. 12. Excellent agreement is obtained with respect to the failure load (the calculated values differ by +1% and -2% from the measured values in specimens S1 and S2, respectively). Furthermore, fair agremeent is obtained in terms of overal deformation capacity, steel deformation at yielding and concrete deformation at the onset of crushing (Fig. 12g). The corresponding rigid-plastic stress fields for the two specimens are shown in Figs. 12c,f. The force paths provide a tool for designing both the vertical and horizontal reinforcements.

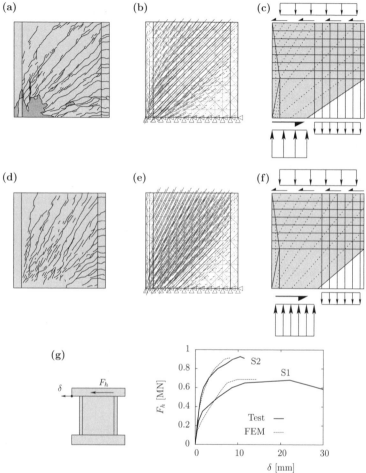

Figure 12 – Shear walls S1 and S2 (Maier and Thürlimann, 1985): (a) cracking pattern of S1 (after failure); (b) plot of the principal-stress directions for S1 according to the elastic-plastic stress-field approach; (c) rigid-plastic stress field for S1; (d) crack pattern in S2 (at 95 % of the failure load); (e) plot of the principal-stress directions for S2 according to the elastic-plastic stress-field approach; (f) rigid-plastic stress field for S2; and (g) comparison of measured/computed horizontal deflections for both shear walls.

## 3.2 Modelling coupling beams by means of elastic-plastic stress fields under cyclic loading, and comparison with test results

Applying elastic-plastic stress fields is investigated in this section with reference to the tests presented in Section 2.1. Figure 13 shows the calculated stress fields at the peak load for the four coupling beams tested by Ihtiyar and Breña (2007). The stress fields are consistent with the observed crack patterns and therefore represent of the actual force paths. For the different specimens, Figure 14 shows the shear force – chord rotation responses calculated by using (a) the materials properties described in Section 2, and (b) a reduced modulus for the concrete (1/4 of the actual value, to simulate the reduced stiffness after cracking). A summary of the main results can be found in Table 5.

(a) Specimen CB-1        (b) Specimen CB-3

(c) Specimen CB-2        (d) Specimen CB-4

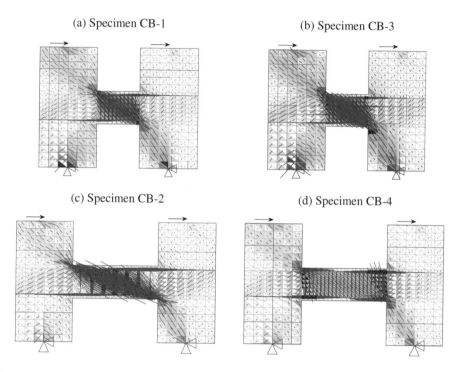

Figure 13 – Elastic-plastic stress fields calculated for the coupling beams tested by Ihtiyar and Breña (2007)

The fitting of the test results leads to the following observations:

1. The failure load is accurately predicted for all coupling beams, regardless of the slenderness, reinforcement layout and failure mode.

2. The failure load is little sensitive to any reduction of concrete modulus of elasticity. Nevertheless, small reductions of the failure load are obtained by decreasing the modulus of elasticity, because of the ensuing larger displacements, that reduce concrete strength through the factor $\eta_\varepsilon$.

3. Chord rotations are accurately predicted by using concrete elastic (uncracked) modulus of elasticity in the initial load cycles. At larger displacements, the degradation of the modulus of elasticity due to cyclic loading plays a significant role in terms of deformations, as confirmed by the better fitting of the measured cyclic response, particularly in the case of short coupling beams, whenever the elastic modulus is markedly reduced ($E_c/4$).

(a) Specimen CB-1

(b) Specimen CB-3

(c) Specimen CB-2

(d) Specimen CB-4

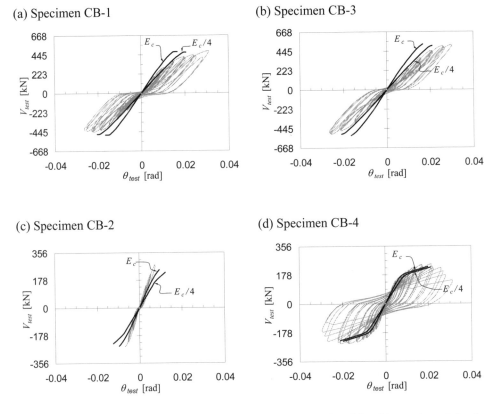

Figure 14 – Shear force – chord rotation curves obtained in this project (elastic-plastic stress fields) and measured curves (Ihtiyar and Breña (2007).

By comparing the results obtained via the stress-field approach with the backbone envelopes based on *ASCE/SEI 41-06*, the following considerations can be drawn:

(1) a significantly-better evaluation of the maximum load is obtained with a much lower value of CoV (Coefficient of Variation);

(2) a more reliable evaluation of the chord rotation at the maximum load is obtained with a similar scatter of the results.

Table 5 – Measured (by testing) and calculated (via stress fields) failure loads, and chord rotations at the maximum load. (Note that the values between parentheses were obtained by introducing a reduced modulus of elasticity for the concrete: $E_c/4$).

| Specimen | $V_{test-pk}$ [kN] | $\theta_{test-pk}$ [rad] | $V_{calc}$ [kN] | $\theta_{calc}$ [rad] | $\dfrac{V_{test}}{V_{calc}}$ | $\dfrac{\theta_{test}}{\theta_{calc}}$ |
|----------|---------|-----------|---------|-----------|---------|---------|
| CB-1 | 480 | 0.0311 | 479 | 0.0167 | 1.00 | 1.86 |
|  |  |  | (472) | (0.0206) | (1.02) | (1.51) |
| CB-2 | 275 | 0.0076 | 246 | 0.0096 | 1.12 | 0.79 |
|  |  |  | (229) | (0.0125) | (1.20) | (0.61) |
| CB-3 | 506 | 0.0299 | 524 | 0.0166 | 0.97 | 1.80 |
|  |  |  | (508) | (0.0211) | (1.00) | (1.42) |
| CB-4 | 240 | 0.0214 | 228 | 0.0197 | 1.05 | 1.09 |
|  |  |  | (225) | (0.0211) | (1.07) | (1.01) |
|  |  |  |  | Average | 1.03 | 1.39 |
|  |  |  |  |  | (1.07) | (1.14) |
|  |  |  |  | CoV | 0.06 | 0.38 |
|  |  |  |  |  | (0.09) | (0.36) |

The results show that R/C modelling by means of the stress fields is a promising technique, that can adequately describe the cyclic behaviour of the coupling beams, through the "backbone curves".

Stress fields are a consistent approach, that can take into account concrete and steel various mechanical and geometric properties by introducing a very limited number of hypotheses and parameters (Fernández Ruiz and Muttoni, 2007).

The stiffness reduction introduced for large displacements in rather short coupling beams (*deep beams*) is consistent with the conclusions of previous studies (e.g. Paulay, 1971a; Park and Ang, 1985; Ihtiyar and Breña, 2007).

## 4. FUTURE WORK

The authors are currently working on an improved formulation of the elastic-plastic stress-fields for computing concrete strength and stiffness degradation as a function of concrete loading history (number of cycles and maximum deformation demand).

The final objective is to develop suitable elastic-plastic stress fields for obtaining the backbone curves to be used in performance-based seismic design or assessment.

## CONCLUSIONS

This paper discusses various techniques to work out the backbone curves of coupling beams subjected to seismic loading, and compares the numerical results with those coming from an experimental campaign concerning large-scale coupling beams. The main conclusions are:

1. Slenderness, reinforcement layout, amount of transverse reinforcement and failure mode (bending- or shear-controlled) have a sizable influence on the ultimate bearing and deformation capacities of coupling beams.

2. The influence of the previous parameters, however, is not accurately taken into account in current performance-based methods for the design of such structural members. This leads to a significant scatter in the generation of the backbone curves.

3. The backbone curves generated by using the available seismic-assessment documents (e.g. *ASCE/SEI 41-06*) reasonably represent the entire behavior of the coupling beams, provided that several modifications are introduced, as suggested by the authors. In particular, all relevant deformation components should be introduced, to obtain a realistic description of the overal response represented by the backbone curves.

4. Modelling the envelope response of a coupling beam based on elastic-plastic stress fields provides a rational approach for evaluating the bearing and deformation capacities at both the yield and peak loads. This approach makes it possible to take care of the influence that the various mechanical and geometric parameters (including structural slenderness, and amount and layout of the reinforcement) have on the behavior of coupling beams.

5. The shear (diagonal tension) strength of coupling beams evaluated in accordance with *ACI 318-08* is not a good failure indicator in any of the coupling beams tested in the laboratory and mentioned in this paper. Shear strength degradation occurred in beams, that were cycled past the yielding of the longitudinal reinforcement. Hence, it is important to include shear-strength degradation in the design of short coupling beams subjected to cyclic loading.

6. The degradation of concrete stiffness under cyclic loads bringing in large displacements deeply affects the shear force – chord rotation relationship of the coupling beams.

## ACKNOWLEDGEMENTS

The authors would like to acknowledge the valuable cooperation of Onur Ihtiyar, who in 2007 performed the experimental work described in this paper, in partial fulfilment of the requirements for earning his MS Degree in Civil Engineering at the University of Massachusetts (Amherst, USA).

# NOTATION

$A_{cv}$ = shear-resistant concrete cross-section
$A_s$ = area of longitudinal steel
$A_v$ = area of transverse steel (spacing $s$)
$E_c$ = concrete modulus of elasticity
$E_s$ = steel modulus of elasticity
$F$ = force
$F_H$ , $F_V$ = horizontal, vertical force
$G_c$ = concrete shear modulus
$I_{cr}$ = moment of inertia of a cracked section
$I_g$ = moment of inertia of the solid section (gross moment of inertia)
$M_n$ = nominal flexural strength of coupling beams
$M_y$ = bending moment at bar yielding
$Q$ = lateral force
$Q_{test, pk}$ = maximum lateral force (peak force)
$V$ = shear force
$V_{calc}$ = maximum calculated shear force
$V_{end}$ = shear at beam ends corresponding to the development of the flexural strength
$V_{hinge}$ = shear force computed by using beam theory in the central section of a plastic hinge
$V_n$ = nominal shear strength of a beam
$V_s$ = contribution of transverse steel to shear strength
$V_{test}$ = shear force generated at the end sections of a coupling beam tested in the laboratory
$V_{test, pk}$ = maximum measured shear force (peak value)
$V_y$ = estimated shear force at the yielding of the longitudinal reinforcement
$V_{y, test}$ = measured beam shear at first yielding of the longitudinal reinforcement
$b_w$ = web width
$d$ = flexural (effective) depth of a beam
$f_{ce}$ = effective concrete compressive strength
$f_c$ = concrete cylindrical compressive strength
$f'_c$ = 28-day concrete compressive strength
$f_y$ = steel stress at yielding
$f_{yl}$ = strength at yielding in the longitudinal reinforcement
$f_{yt}$ = strength at yielding in the transverse reinforcement
$h$ = beam depth
$h_{pin}$ = vertical distance between the loading and support pins in the specimens tested in the laboratory
$l_n$ = clear length of coupling beam
$l_p$ = length of a plastic hinge
$l_w$ = wall length
$s$ = spacing of the transverse reinforcement

$\alpha_c$ = factor concerning the aspect ratio (Eq. 2)

$\delta$ = displacement

$v$ = Poisson's ratio

$\theta$ = chord rotation; in a coupling beam: angle between the tangents to the deformed shape in the end sections and the original undeformed axis (same rotations in the end sections); in a column: ratio between the interstorey drift and the interstorey height (no rotations at the end sections)

$\theta_{calc}$ = calculated chord rotation at the maximum load

$\theta_f$ = flexural component of the chord rotation

$\theta_v$ = shear component of the chord rotation

$\theta_{v-cr}$ = shear component of the chord rotation assuming cracked sections

$\theta_s$ = bar-slip component of chord rotation

$\theta_{test, pk}$ = measured chord rotation at the maximum load

$\theta_y$ = chord rotation at yielding

$\varepsilon_c$, $\varepsilon_s$ = axial strain in concrete, in a steel bar

$\varepsilon_{tr}$ = transverse strain in concrete

$\eta_\varepsilon$ = strength-reduction factor accounting for transverse cracking in concrete

$\rho_l$, $\rho_v$ = reinforcement ratio (longitudinal, transverse reinforcement)

$\sigma_c$, $\sigma_s$ = stress in concrete, in a steel bar

## REFERENCES

American Concrete Institute (ACI) (2008). *Building Code Requirements for Structural Concrete (318-08) and Commentary (318R-08)*. ACI 318-08, Detroit (MI, USA).

American Society of Civil Engineers (2000). *Prestandard and Commentary for the Seismic Rehabilitation of Buildings*. FEMA Publication 356, Washington (D.C., USA).

Applied Technology Council (ATC-43 project) (1999a). *Evaluation of Earthquake Damaged Concrete and Masonry Wall Buildings –Basic Procedures Manual*. FEMA Publication 306, Washington, D.C.

Barney G.B., Shiu K.N., Rabbat B.G., Fiorato A.E., Russell H.G. and Corley W.G. (1980). *Behavior of Coupling Beams under Load Reversals*. Research and Development Bulletin RD068.01B, Portland Cement Association, 22 pp.

Beck H. (1962). "Contribution to Analysis of Coupled Shear Walls." *ACI Journal*. Vol. 59, No. 8, pp. 1055-1070.

Canbolat B.A., Parra-Montesinos G.J. and Wight J.K. (2005). "Experimental Study on Seismic Behavior of High-Performance Fiber-Reinforced Cement Composite Coupling Beams." *ACI Structural Journal*, Vol. 102, No. 1, pp. 159-166.

Coull A. and Choudhury J.R. (1967). "Analysis of Coupled Shear Walls." *ACI Journal*, Vol. 64, No. 9, pp. 587-593.

Coull A. and Puri R.D. (1968). "Analysis of Coupled Shear Walls of Variable Cross-Section." *Building Science*, Vol. 2, No. 4, pp. 313-320.

Coull A., Puri R.D. and Tottenham H. (1973). "Numerical Elastic Analysis of Coupled Shear Walls." *Proceedings of the Institution of Civil Engineers. Part 1 – Design & Construction*, Vol. 55, pp. 109-128.

Drucker D.C. (1961). "On Structural Concrete and the Theorems of Limit Analysis." *Publications, Int. Ass. for Bridge and Structural Engineering*. Vol. 21, pp. 49-59

Elkholy I.A.S. and Robinson H. (1974). "Inelastic Analysis of Coupled Shear Walls." *Building Science*, Vol. 9, No. 1, pp. 1-8.

Fernández Ruiz M. and Muttoni, A. (2007). "On Development of Suitable Stress Fields for Structural Concrete." *ACI Structural Journal*. Vol. 104, No. 4, pp. 495-502.

Galano L. and Vignoli A. (2000). "Seismic Behavior of Short Coupling Beams with Different Reinforcement Layouts." *ACI Structural J.* Vol .97, No. 6, pp. 876-885

Glueck J. (1973). "Elasto-Plastic Analysis of Coupled Shear Walls." *Journal of the Structural Division, ASCE*, Vol. 99 (ST8), pp. 1743-1760.

Harries K.A., Mitchell D., Redwood R.D. and Cook, W.D. (1997). "Seismic Design of Coupled Walls – A Case for Mixed Construction." *Canadian Journal of Civil Engineering*. Vol. 24, No. 3, pp. 448-459.

Ihtiyar O. and Breña S.F. (2006). "Force-Deformation Response of Conven-tionally Reinforced Coupling Beams: Evaluation of FEMA 356 and FEMA 306." *2006 8th U.S. Nat. Conf. on Earthquake Engineering*. Paper No. 701. San Francisco (CA, USA).

Ihtiyar O. and Breña S.F. (2007). "Assessment of FEMA 356 Techniques for Orthogonally Reinforced Coupling Beams through Experimental Testing." *2007 ASCE Structures Congress: Structural Engineering Research Frontiers*. Long Beach (CA, USA).

International Conference of Building Officials (1997). *Uniform Building Code - Volume 2*. Whittier (CA, USA).

International Code Council (2009). *International Building Code*. Whittier (CA, USA).

Mahin S.A. and Bertero V.V. (1976). "Nonlinear Seismic Response of a Coupled Wall System". *Journal of the Structural Division, Proceedings ASCE*. Vol. 102, No. ST9, pp. 1759-1780

Maier J. and Thürlimann B. (1985). *Bruchversuche an Stahlbetonscheiben" (Tests on Shear walls, in German)*. Institut für Baustatik und Konstruktion ETH Zürich, Vol. 8003-1.

Marti P. (1980). *Zur plastischen Berechnung von Stahlbeton" (On the Plastic Analysis of Reinforced Concrete, in German)*. Institut für Baustatik und Konstruction, Vol. 104, ETH Zürich, 175 pp.

Muttoni A. (1989). *Die Andwendbarkeit der Plastizitätstheorie in der Bemessung von Stahlbeton (The Applicability of the Theory of Plasticity in the Design of Reinforced Concrete, in German)*. Institut für Baustatik und Konstruktion, ETH Zürich, Vol. 176, 159 pp.

Muttoni A., Schwartz J. and Thürlimann B. (1997). *Design of Concrete Structures with Stress Fields*. Birkhaüser / Springer, 145 pp.

Muttoni A., Fernández Ruiz M. (2007). "Dimensionamiento y verificación del hormigón estructural mediante el método de los campos de tensiones" (Design of Structural Concrete by means of Stress Fields, in Spanish). *Hormigón y Acero*, Madrid (Spain), No. 243, pp. 93-102.

Müller P. (1978). *Plastische Berechnung von Stahlbetonscheiben und –balken (Plastic Calculus of Reinforced Concrete Disks and Beams, in German)*. Institut für Baustatik und Konstruction, ETH Zürich, Vol. 83, 160 pp.

Nielsen M. P., Braestrup M. W., Jensen B. C. and Bach F. (1978). *Concrete Plasticity: Beam Shear, Shear in Joints and Punching Shear"*. Danish Society for Structural Science and Engineering, Special Publication, 129 pp.

Park Y-J and Ang A.H-S. (1985). "Mechanistic Seismic Damage Model for Reinforced Concrete." *Journal of Structural Engineering*, Vol. 111, No. 4, pp. 722-739.

Paulay T. (1970). "Elasto-Plastic Analysis of Coupled Shear Walls." *Journal of the American Concrete Institute*. Vol. 67, No. 11, pp. 915-922.

Paulay T. (1971a). "Coupling Beams of Reinforced Concrete Shear Walls." *Journal of the Structural Division, Proceedings ASCE*. Vol. 97, No. ST3, pp. 843-861.

Paulay T. (1971b). "Simulated Seismic Loading of Spandrel Beams." *Journal of the Structural Division, Proceedings ASCE*. Vol. 97, No. ST9, pp. 2407-2419.

Paulay T. and Binney J.R., (1974). "Diagonally Reinforced Coupling Beams of Shear Walls." *Shear in Reinforced Concrete, ACI Publication SP-42*, pp. 579-598.

Paulay T. and Priestley M.J.N. (1992). *Seismic Design of Reinforced Concrete and Masonry Buildings*. John Wiley & Sons, 744 pp.

Paulay T. and Santhakumar A.R. (1976). "Ductile Behavior of Coupled Shear Walls." *Journal of the Structural Division, Proceedings ASCE*, Vol. 102, No. ST1, pp. 99-108.

Takayanagi T. and Schnobrich W.C. (1979). "Non-linear Analysis of Coupled Wall Systems." *Earthquake Engineering & Structural Dynamics.*, Vol. 7, No. 1, pp. 1-22.

Tassios T.P., Moretti M. and Bezas A. (1996). "On the Behavior and Ductility of Reinforced Concrete Coupling Beams of Shear Walls." *ACI Structural Journal,* Vol. 93, No. 6, pp. 711-720.

Vecchio F. J. and Collins M. P. (1986). "The Modified Compression Field Theory for Reinforced Concrete Elements Subjected to Shear". *ACI Journal*, Vol. 83, No. 2, pp. 219-231.

STUDIES AND RESEARCHES – V. 29, 2009
Graduate School in Concrete Structures – Fratelli Pesenti
Politecnico di Milano, Italy

# PUNCHING - SHEAR STRENGTH:
# A MODEL STILL IN PROGRESS

Franco Angotti[1], Maurizio Orlando[2]

## ABSTRACT

Punching-shear is a failure mechanism typical of slabs and footings subjected to concentrated loads applied on very small contact areas. Punching resistance is mainly a function of concrete compressive strength and flexural reinforcement ratio, but it also depends on aggregate size and column side-to-slab depth ratio (size effect). Moreover, in shear-reinforced slabs, punching strength depends also on bond conditions in the transverse reinforcement, which in turn depends on slab depth and reinforcement type.

Because of punching-shear complexity, in Eurocode 2 (as in other Codes) the verification rules refer to a conventional failure surface, and the design parameters are chosen to fit the experimental evidence. Nevertheless, the calibration of some parameters looks inadequate, since – for instance - neither size effect nor bond conditions for different transverse-reinforcement types are introduced, and some design rules are hardly exhaustive, like those concerning the design of transverse reinforcement in footings.

Last but not least, both EC2 and EC8 are limited to static loading, while the effects of cyclic loading in slab-column connections under seismic excitation are never mentioned, something that is dealt with in other Codes (like ACI), whose provisions are briefly commented.

[1] Professor, Department of Civil and Environmental Engineering, Università degli Studi di Firenze, Firenze (Italy)
[2] Associate Professor, Department of Civil and Environmental Engineering, Università degli Studi di Firenze, Firenze (Italy)

## 1. INTRODUCTION

Punching-shear or two-way shear is typical of R/C slabs and footings subjected to high concentrated loads applied on very small contact areas. Different models have been proposed in the literature to describe the punching-shear mechanism, like those based on the theory of plasticity (for instance the strut-and-tie models) and on fracture mechanics (CEB-FIP, 2001). Nevertheless, a consistent analytical formulation is still badly needed, and the formulas adopted in many international codes (Eurocode 2 included, see CEN-EN1992-1-1, 2004) are mainly derived from the experimental results.

Within this framework, the verification of slabs and footings subjected to punching shear, with/without transverse reinforcement, is treated in this paper according to EC2, in order to highlight the doubts originating from the application of this code and the inconsistencies with respect to the tests. Such topics have already been discussed by the authors in a previous paper (Angotti and Orlando, 2009), but here are commented in more detail, with specific reference to the very recent Italian Design Recommendations (2008) and to the seismic design of slab-column connections, not covered by the Eurocodes.

## 2. PUNCHING-SHEAR MECHANISM

The punching-shear failure of a R/C slab or footing is characterized by the formation of inclined cracks, which start from the column perimeter and propagate until the formation of a typical truncated (Fig. 1). This failure mode is brittle and the flexural reinforcement may remain in the elastic field till the collapse.

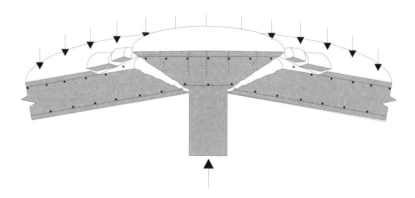

Figure 1 – Schematic section of the punching surface of a slab resting on a circular column.

In a typical test of a R/C slab resting on a circular column, the following steps can be observed under increasing load (Guandalini et al., 2009):

1. initial elastic bending without cracking;
2. formation of some circumferential cracks close to the column, visible along the upper face of the slab; these cracks are followed by the development of radial cracks, that – together with the circumferential cracks - form a series of circular sectors on the slab;
3. formation of further rather open circumferential cracks relatively far from column perimeter; at the same time, close to the column both the radial bending moment and the radial curvature remain roughly constant;
4. formation of internal inclined cracks, which coalesce into a single truncated-cone fractured surface followed by the separation of the slab from the column.

Once the peak load has been attained, no further cracks form, but the existing cracks widen, till the collapse of the slab, which occurs abruptly in the case of ordinary flexural-reinforcement ratios. After the collapse, a large circumferential crack appears at the extrados, whose radius is larger than the intersection of the punching surface with the extrados itself, because of the yielding and plastic deformation of the upper tensile reinforcement.

## 2.1 Shear transfer

The primary punching response is provided (a) by the inclined concrete struts, and (b) by the forces transferred across the shear cracks. Some mechanical models (Kinnunen and Nylander, 1960) explain the punching strength primarily by means of the action exerted by the inclined struts, while other researchers (Menetrey, 1996) rely more on the forces across the cracks. In all approaches, load transfer is described through a strut-and-tie (S&T) model, which extends from the load application point to the boundary of the failure region; in transversely-unreinforced slabs, the S&T model contains concrete ties. In Menetrey's model, which relies on the forces transferred across the cracks, a concrete tie is also active in the failure region (see the bold dashed line in Fig. 2). The punching strength is then obtained by projecting the tensile strength of this concrete tie in the vertical direction ($F_{ct}$ in Fig. 2). Other contributions are given by the flexural, transverse and bonded prestressing reinforcement crossing the punching surface.

Any reinforcement crossing the punching surface contributes to the shear transfer through dowel action (like in the case of the bars crossing a flexural crack in a beam). The mechanical ratio of the bonded prestressing steel crossing the punching surface is added to the mechanical ratio of the ordinary flexural reinforcement. The tests show that - in the slabs reinforced with an orthogonal grid of flexural reinforcement – the dowel-action contribution to the punching-shear strength is close to 34% (CEB-FIP, 2001). The punching capacity is also significantly affected by the flexural reinforcement ratio. The experimental load-displacement curves of the slabs with different reinforcement ratios are characterized by an initial linear elastic branch, which is the same for all slabs, and by a second branch, whose peak and ultimate displacement are increasing and decreasing functions of the reinforcement ratio, respectively.

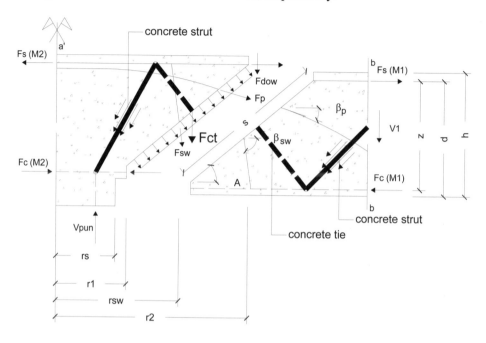

Figure 2 – Menetrey's model (Menetrey, 1996).

Furthermore, different flexural reinforcement ratios lead to different layouts for the resisting system (Fig. 3). For low reinforcement ratios, very high diagonal compressive stresses arise between each transverse reinforcement row and the two adjacent rows. The corresponding resisting mechanism can be appropriately described by means of a strut-and-tie model, whose struts extend from the top of each row to the bottom of the preceding row (Fig. 3a). For high flexural reinforcement ratios, the compression fields start from both the load-application zone and the upper end of each row and develop up to the column perimeter (Fig. 3b). This last model is confirmed experimentally by the occurrence of high tensile stresses in the flexural reinforcement (Beutel and Hegger, 2002), because the inclination of the struts is lower than in the case of low reinforcement ratios.

Punching strength depends on the distance between the first row of the transverse reinforcement and column perimeter: the maximum is reached for a distance equal to 0.8d (d = effective depth of the slab), which corresponds to a strut inclination of about 45°; for inclinations higher than 45°, the first reinforcement row has a smaller anchored length on each side of the punching surface and a smaller capacity.

82

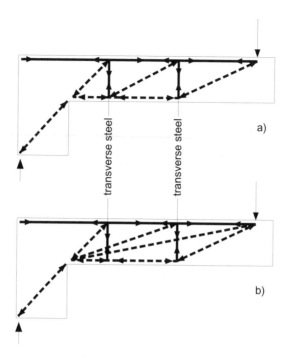

Figure 3 – Strut-and-tie models for low (a) and high (b) flexural-reinforcement ratios (CEB-FIP, 2001).

## 2.2 Size effect

The experimental evidence shows that punching-shear failures are characterized by size effect: the larger the slab depth, the smaller the strength per unit depth (that is the shear strength per unit length divided by the effective depth of the slab). Moreover, the larger the distance of the critical surface from column perimeter, the smaller the strength per unit depth.

EN1992-1-1 rules take into account only the dependence of the strength on the depth of the slab (§ 4.2).

## 3. PUNCHING-SHEAR VERIFICATION ACCORDING TO EC2

This paragraph summarizes the main provisions for punching-shear checks in slabs and footings according to EN1992-1-1, with the explanation of the meaning of the main variables and parameters. The empirical character of EC2 formulation for punching is also highlighted and EC2 results are compared with those obtained by testing or by means of mechanical models.

According to EN1992-1-1, the checks on structural members subjected to punching shear are performed by making reference to a conventional "control perimeter", which is called "basic control perimeter" (symbol $u_1$). In slabs, the perimeter $u_1$ is located a distance 2d from column perimeter or from the edges of the loaded area (Fig. 4), while in footings the distance is a ≤ 2d. The basic control surface $S_1$ ("critical surface"), consists of the lateral surface of the cylinder whose base perimeter coincides with the basic control perimeter $u_1$ and whose height is equal to slab effective depth d ($S_1 = u_1$ d); d is defined as the mean value of the effective depths of the two-way flexural reinforcement.

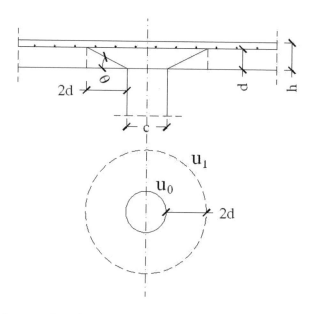

Figure 4 - Basic control perimeter $u_1$ according to EC2 for a slab resting on a circular column ($u_0$ is the column perimeter).

Besides the verification along the perimeter $u_1$, another verification should be performed along the perimeter $u_0$ of the column (or loaded area), where the design stress should be limited to the maximum punching-shear capacity $v_{Rd,max}$, which depends on concrete compressive strength.

### 3.1 Verification along the column perimeter $u_0$

The punching verification of a slab or footing, with/without transverse reinforcement, preliminarily requires the verification of the following condition along the perimeter $u_0$:

$$v_{Ed} \leq v_{Rd,max}, \tag{1}$$

where:

$v_{Ed} = \beta\, V_{Ed} / (u_0\, d)$ ($\beta \geq 1$ takes into account the eccentricity of the reaction exerted by the column and is defined with reference to the basic control perimeter $u_1$, see § 3.2.1);

$v_{Rd,max} = 0.5\, \upsilon\, f_{cd}$, where $\upsilon$ is a parameter related to concrete grade and $f_{cd}$ is concrete design compressive strength.

The design provisions for concrete crushing along column perimeter are supported by scanty experimental evidence, because in most of the tests punching-shear failure occurred far from column perimeter.

If Eq.(1) is not satisfied, one can adopt one or more of the following measures:
- increase column cross-section (or loaded area);
- increase slab thickness;
- adopt drop panels, which is the same as to increase slab thickness close to the columns;
- adopt a higher-grade concrete.

## 3.2 Verification along the basic control perimeter $u_1$ for slabs and footings without transverse reinforcement

Along the basic control perimeter $u_1$, the equation for punching-shear verification in slabs or footings without transverse reinforcement is as follows:

$$v_{Ed} \leq v_{Rd,c}, \tag{2}$$

where $v_{Ed}$ is the design stress and $v_{Rd,c}$ is the punching strength without transverse reinforcement.

According to EN1992-1-1, the design value of the punching stress $v_{Ed}$ along the perimeter $u_1$ is calculated using the following formula:

$$v_{Ed} = \beta\, V_{Ed} / (u_1\, d) \tag{3}$$

where:

$\beta = 1$ if column reaction (or applied load in directly-loaded areas) is centered with respect to the basic control perimeter;

$\beta > 1$ if column reaction (or applied load in directly-loaded areas) has a certain eccentricity with respect to the basic control perimeter;

$V_{Ed}$ design shear force; and

$u_1$ basic control perimeter located at the distance 2d in slabs and $a \leq 2d$ in footings.

The punching capacity without transverse reinforcement is given by:

$$v_{Rd,c} = C_{Rd,c}\, k \left(100\, \rho_1\, f_{ck}\right)^{1/3} + 0.10\, \sigma_{cp} \geq v_{min} + 0.10\, \sigma_{cp} \tag{4}$$

where:

$C_{Rd,c} = 0.18/\gamma_C$, with $\gamma_C = 1.5$ for persistent and transient loads, and $\gamma_C = 1.2$ for accidental loads;

$k = 1 + \sqrt{\dfrac{200}{d}} \leq 2.0$      size factor;

$\rho_1 = \sqrt{\rho_{ly}\, \rho_{lz}} \leq 0.02$      geometrical ratio of the tensile reinforcement (including both the ordinary reinforcement and the bonded prestressing strands/tendons – if any), calculated as the geometric mean of the ratios $\rho_{ly}$ and $\rho_{lz}$ of the tensile two-way reinforcement;

$\sigma_{cp} = \dfrac{\sigma_{cy} + \sigma_{cz}}{2}$      where $\sigma_{cy}$ and $\sigma_{cz}$ are the normal stresses in the critical section in the y- and z- directions (N/mm², positive if compression);

$v_{min} = 0{,}035\, k^{3/2} f_{ck}^{1/2}$      lower limit for punching strength; $v_{min}$ depends on the co-efficient k and on concrete characteristic strength ($v_{min}$ has been introduced in order to properly evaluate the punching-shear capacity of lightly-reinforced slabs, that is typical of prestressed slabs).

By comparing the strengths along $u_0$ and $u_1$, the values of slab effective depth for which the strength $v_{Rd,max}$ is higher or lower than $v_{Rd,c}$ can be worked out. In particular, the verification along the basic control perimeter $u_1$ is more severe than that along the column perimeter $u_0$, if the following condition is met:

$$\max(v_{Rd,c}) \cdot u_1 \cdot d \leq v_{Rd,max} \cdot u_0 \cdot d, \tag{5}$$

where $\max(v_{Rd,c})$ is the value of the punching strength without transverse steel obtained for $\rho_1 = 2\,\%$, which is the maximum value allowed by EC2 in Eq. (4).

Therefore, for any given value of concrete strength, size of column cross-section and flexural reinforcement ratio, Eq. (5) allows to find out a limit value $d_{lim}$ for slab effective depth, such as all values smaller than $d_{lim}$ make the check along $u_1$ more severe than that along $u_0$, while for $d > d_{lim}$ the check along $u_0$ is more severe than that along $u_1$.

The EC2 formulation for punching shear without transverse steel is largely empirical, and is based on the oldest and most widely used approach for punching capacity: a nominal shear stress is calculated on a specified control surface $S_1$ and it is compared with an empirical concrete strength parameter $v_{Rd,c}$. The distance of the critical perimeter $u_1$ from the column or loaded area determines the size of the control surface $S_1$ and the intensity of the nominal shear stress $v_{Ed}$.

In Eq. (4) the dependence on concrete compressive strength is formulated as $(f_{ck})^{1/3}$, while the role of the reinforcement ratio $\rho_l$ is introduced as $\rho_l^{1/3}$, and size effect and aggregate interlock are taken into account by introducing a coefficient k, that is a function of slab effective depth d.

In the previous version of EC2, the distance of the control perimeter from the column was 1.5d (2d in the last version). The updated distance has been adopted to make the punching strength less dependent of column size and to make it equal to the one-way shear strength. Moreover, the formulation is the same adopted for the shear strength of narrow beams without web reinforcement.

Although the shear stress on the control surface does not have any physical meaning, EC2 formulation fits well many experimental tests and agrees with the results provided by the mechanical models.

Walraven (2002) analyzed 112 tests according to the level II probabilistic method and found $C_{Rd,c} = 0.120$ (concrete class C25) and $C_{Rd,c} = 0.124$ (concrete class C90). Hence, Eq. (4), where $C_{Rd,c} = 0.18/\gamma_C$ (equal to 0.12 for $\gamma_C = 1.5$), provides a lower bound for the bearing capacity in punching of transversely-unreinforced slabs (Fig. 5).

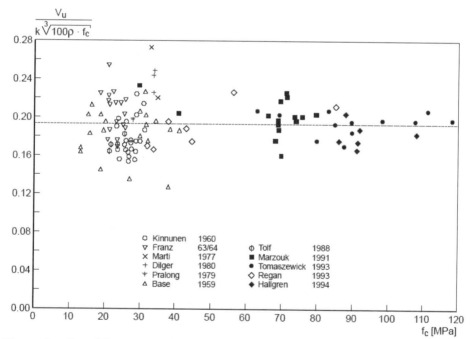

Figure 5 - Punching strength of transversely-unreinforced slabs: fitting of the test results by means of Eq. (4). Concrete compressive cylindrical strength: 14 - 120 MPa; effective slab depth: 100 - 275 mm; flexural reinforcement ratio: 0.4 - 2.5%; column diameter/effective slab thickness: 1.2 - 2.5, from Walraven (2002).

Fig. 6 shows the good agreement of EC2 predictions with the experimental results obtained by using the mechanical model based on the Critical Shear Crack Theory (CSCT), see Muttoni and Schwartz, 1991. Briefly, this model assumes that the punching strength of transversely-unreinforced slabs is governed by the width and by the roughness of an inclined critical shear crack (Fig. 7). This crack develops through the inclined compression struts; its width $w_c$ is assumed to be proportional to the slab rotation $\psi$, times the effective depth d of the slab: $w_c \propto \psi \cdot d$; the width $w_c$, however, is corrected by means of a factor to account for the maximum diameter of the aggregate. The punching load is determined by applying the failure criterion and a load-rotation relationship obtained via the nonlinear analysis of the slab in bending.

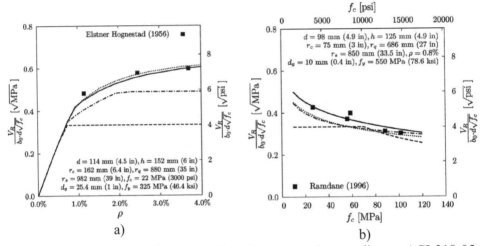

Figure 6 - Comparison of the punching shear strength according to ACI 318-05 (– –), to Eurocode 2 (– · – · –) and to the Critical Shear Crack theory (continuous and dotted curves) with various test results showing the influence of: (a) reinforcement ratio; (b) concrete strength. $V_R$ = punching strength; $b_0$ = control perimeter; d = effective slab depth; $f_c$ = concrete average compressive strength (measured on cylinders); and $\rho$ = flexural reinforcement ratio (Muttoni, 2008).

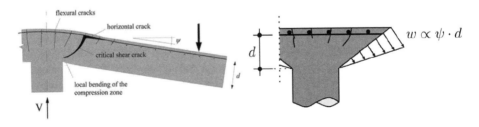

Figure 7 - Critical shear crack and slab rotation (Muttoni, 2008).

Anyhow the EC2 formulation does not take into account some parameters, which seem to influence significantly the punching capacity: e.g., according to the CSCT the punching strength reduces with increasing span-depth ratio of the slab (Muttoni, 2008), but this effect is not considered in Eq. (4).

### 3.3 Coefficient β for eccentric loads

Eurocode 2 takes into account the eccentricity of the shear force $V_{Ed}$, due to the moment $M_{Ed}$ transferred from the column to the slab, through a coefficient β≥1, which amplifies the shear stress induced by the shear force alone, see Eq. (3). The relation between β and the bending moment $M_{Ed}$ is discussed in § 4.1, where the shear stress is expressed as the sum of the shear stress $v_{Ed(V)}$ produced by $V_{Ed}$ and the shear stress $v_{Ed(M)}$ produced by $M_{Ed}$.

The moment $M_{Ed}$ to be considered for each direction (y and z) of the slab or footing ($M_{Ed,y}$ and $M_{Ed,z}$) is given by the sum of the moments acting in the end sections of the upper and lower columns (Fig. 8).

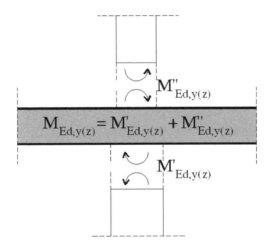

Figure 8 - Moments $M'_{Ed,y}$ and $M''_{Ed,y}$ transmitted to the slab by the upper and lower columns.

The stress produced by $M_{Ed}$ is calculated assuming a "plastic" distribution of the shear stresses ($v_{Ed(M)}=\pm$ const.) on the critical surface (Fig. 12).

For any structures where the lateral stability does not depend on frame action between the slabs and the columns, and where the lengths of the adjacent spans do not differ by more than 25 %, approximate values can be adopted for the coefficient β (Fig. 9).

The coefficient β is used for the checks concerning both the perimeter $u_1$ and the perimeter $u_0$; this fact represents one of the inconsistencies of EC2 provisions discussed in § 4.

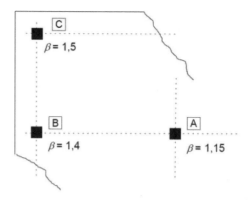

Figure 9 – Approximate values for β according to EC2.

### 3.4 Punching capacity for slabs and footings with transverse reinforcement

The punching-shear verification along $u_1$ for slabs or footings with transverse reinforcement is expressed by:

$$v_{Ed} \leq v_{Rd,cs}, \tag{6}$$

where $v_{Ed}$ is the design shear stress and $v_{Rd,cs}$ is the punching strength per unit area in transversely-reinforced slabs; $v_{Rd,cs}$ is given by the sum of two terms:

$$v_{Rd,cs} = v'_{Rd,cs} + v''_{Rd,cs}, \tag{7}$$

where $v'_{Rd,cs}$ and $v''_{Rd,cs}$ are the strengths provided by the concrete and by the steel, respectively.

As concrete can carry shear forces only if crack width is small, adding concrete and reinforcement contributions ($v'_{Rd,cs}$ and $v''_{Rd,cs}$, respectively) holds if the strains in the transverse reinforcement are small. In such a case, shear cracks are thin and their roughness guarantees the efficacy of aggregate interlock at the cracked interfaces (Ruiz and Muttoni, 2009).

In the literature, adding concrete and reinforcement contributions is performed according to two different approaches: some researchers propose to reduce the contribution of transverse reinforcement through the adoption of an "efficiency factor" to be applied to steel strength (= 0.25-0.8), while other researchers propose to reduce concrete contribution by about 20 – 40 %, that is to use efficiency factors for concrete strength in the range 0.6-0.8.

Eurocode 2 adopts the same formulation as Model Code 1990 (CEB-FIP, 1999, efficiency factor of 0.75 for concrete); this value has been calibrated on Regan's and Yitzhaki's results (CEB, 1985, Fig. 10). With this assumption, there is a good agreement between EC2 and the average values of the punching strength, while unsafe results may be obtained for the 5% fractile strength (Ruiz and Muttoni, 2009).

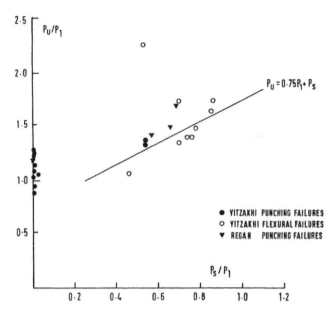

Figure 10 – Punching strength as a function of the resistances of shear reinforcement ($P_1$ = resistance of a similar slab without transverse reinforcement, $P_s$ = shear contribution of the steel at yielding, CEB, 1985).

The yield strength of the transverse reinforcement may not be attained because of inadequate anchoring of the transverse reinforcement on both sides of the critical punching crack. To take care of this aspect, EC2 defines the effective stress in the punching-shear reinforcement as a linear function of slab effective depth d, with he limit of steel stress at yielding ($f_{wd,ef}$ instead of $f_{wd}$ in Eqs. 8a,b).

Therefore, EC2 formula for $v_{Rd,cs}$ is as follows:

$$v_{Rd,cs} = 0.75 v_{Rd,c} + 1.5 (d/s_r) A_{sw} f_{ywd,ef} \frac{1}{u_1 d} \sin\alpha \tag{8a}$$

where:
- $A_{sw}$ is the area of each circumferential row of punching-shear reinforcement located around the column;
- $s_r$ is the radial spacing of the punching-shear reinforcement (that is the spacing between two adjacent rows);
- $f_{ywd,ef} = 250 + 0.25\, d \le f_{ywd}$ [N/mm$^2$] is the effective design strength of the punching-shear reinforcement; this effective design strength depends on slab effective depth d [mm], since the larger the depth d, the better the bond (better bond properties; longer anchored length of the punching reinforcement);
- $\alpha$ is the angle between the direction of the punching-shear reinforcement and the slab mean plane.

According to the most recent Italian design recommendations (NTC 2008, 2008), the punching-shear strength of slabs and footings with transverse reinforcement should be limited to the strength provided by the reinforcement, while the contribution provided by the concrete should be neglected:

$$v_{Rd,cs(NTC)} = 1.5(d/s_r)A_{sw}f_{ywd,ef}\frac{1}{u_1 d}\sin\alpha \tag{8b}$$

Therefore, according to NTC 2008 the area of the transverse reinforcement required to resist the design shear stress is higher than in EC2. By comparing Eqs. (8a) and (8b), the following relation can be easily derived between the area of transverse reinforcement calculated according to EC2 (Eq.8a) and to NTC 2008 (Eq.8b):

$$A_{sw(NTC)} = \frac{v_{Ed}/v_{Rd,c}}{v_{Ed}/v_{Rd,c} - 0,75}A_{sw(EC2)} \tag{9}$$

In Fig. 11 the ratio $A_{sw(NTC)}/A_{sw(EC2)}$ is plotted as a function of $v_{Ed}/v_{Rd,c}$. NTC 2008 is much more conservative than EC2 for any values of $v_{Ed}$ slightly higher than the punching strength $v_{Rd,c}$ without reinforcement (three times for $v_{Ed} \cong 1.1 v_{Rd,c}$ and two times for $v_{Ed}/v_{Rd,c} = 1.5$), while for $v_{Ed}/v_{Rd,c} > 4.5$ the values computed according to NTC 2008 are still larger than those computed according to EC2, but the difference is rather limited (less than 20%).

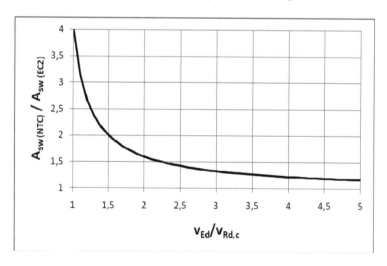

Figure 11 – Ratio between the area of transverse steel calculated according to NTC 2008 and EC2, as a function of $v_{Ed}/v_{Rd,c}$.

For further comments on neglecting concrete contribution in the calculation of $v_{Rd,cs}$ according to NTC 2008, see § 3.4.1.

## 3.5 Maximum area of the transverse reinforcement within each row

One should pay attention to the fact that - once the geometrical layout of the transverse reinforcement has been defined - there is an upper limit for the steel area within each circumferential row, above which the punching-shear strength does not increase anymore, because the failure (a) results from concrete crushing along the column perimeter; or (b) occurs beyond the region containing the transverse reinforcement.

In the case of transversely-reinforced slabs or footings, the punching-shear checks are satisfied if the following three conditions are met:

$V_{Ed} \leq V_{Rd,cs}$      along the perimeter $u_1$;

$V_{Ed} \leq V_{Rd,max}$      along the perimeter $u_0$ of the column or of the loaded area;

$V_{Ed} \leq V_{Rd,c,out}$      along the perimeter $u_{out}$ beyond which the transverse reinforcement is not required.

These three conditions can be synthesized through a single formal equation:

$$V_{Ed} \leq \min (V_{Rd,cs}; V_{Rd,max}; V_{Rd,c,out}) \tag{10}$$

In other words, punching-shear failure occurs when the design shear equals the lowest of the three above-mentioned strengths (or punching-shear capacities).

On the one hand the punching strength $V_{Rd,cs}$ increases with the amount of the transverse reinforcement, but - on the other hand - there is a maximum amount ($A_{sw,max}$) above which, even if $V_{Rd,cs}$ continues increasing, the punching strength does not increase anymore, because $V_{Rd,max} \leq V_{Rd,cs}$ or $V_{Rd,c,out} \leq V_{Rd,cs}$.

In the first case the problem is governed by concrete compressive strength along the column perimeter, while in the second case concrete tensile failure beyond the transversely-reinforced region becomes the dominant phenomenon.

For any given layout of the transverse reinforcement, the maximum area of the effective transverse steel within each row can be calculated, through the following equation:

$$V_{Rd,cs} \leq \min (V_{Rd,max}; V_{Rd,c,out}) \tag{11}$$

where:

$$V_{Rd,cs} = 0.75\, v_{Rd,c}\, u_1 d + 1.5 \left(d/s_r\right) A_{sw} f_{ywd,ef} \sin\alpha \tag{12a}$$

$$V_{Rd,max} = v_{Rd,max}\, u_0 d \tag{12b}$$

$$V_{Rd,c,out} = v_{Rd,c}\, u_{out} d \tag{12c}$$

The maximum area of $A_{sw}$ within each row, consistent with the condition $V_{Ed} \leq V_{Rd,max}$, is obtained by equating the strengths $V_{Rd,cs}$ and $V_{Rd,max}$:

$$A_{sw} = \frac{v_{Rd,max}\, u_0 d - 0.75\, v_{Rd,c} u_1 d}{1.5\left(d/s_r\right) f_{ywd,ef} \sin\alpha} \qquad (13)$$

while the maximum value of $A_{sw}$ consistent with the condition $V_{Ed} \leq V_{Rd,c,out}$ is obtained by equating $V_{Rd,cs}$ and $V_{Rd,c,out}$:

$$A_{sw} = \frac{v_{Rd,c}\left(u_{out} d - 0.75\, u_1 d\right)}{1.5\left(d/s_r\right) f_{ywd,ef} \sin\alpha} \qquad (14)$$

Finally, the maximum area of the transverse reinforcement which satisfies both conditions is the lowest between the two values given by Eqs. (13) and (14):

$$A_{sw,max(EC2)} = \min\left(\frac{v_{Rd,max}\, u_0 d - 0.75\, v_{Rd,c} u_1 d}{1.5\left(d/s_r\right) f_{ywd,ef} \sin\alpha}\; ;\; \frac{v_{Rd,c}\left(u_{out} d - 0.75\, u_1 d\right)}{1.5\left(d/s_r\right) f_{ywd,ef} \sin\alpha}\right) \qquad (15)$$

Table 1 lists the values of $A_{sw,max(EC2)}$ for a slab resting on a rectangular column, having two circumferential rows located around the column at the maximum distances prescribed by EC2 (first row at 0.5d from the column perimeter and second row at 0.75d from the first one). Concrete grade is C35/45 and the flexural-reinforcement ratio [$\rho_l = \sqrt{(\rho_{ly}\, \rho_{lz})}$] is 2 %.

Tab. 1 - Values of $A_{sw,max(EC2)}$ [mm$^2$]
(concrete class: C35/45, flexural reinforcement ratio: 2 %)

| $c_1+c_2$ [mm][1] | d [mm] | | | | | | | |
|---|---|---|---|---|---|---|---|---|
| | 200 | 250 | 300 | 350 | 400 | 450 | 500 | |
| 500 | 453 | 423 | | | | | | |
| 550 | 561 | 553 | | | | | | |
| 600 | 617 | 684 | 651 | | | | | |
| 650 | 625 | 814 | 803 | 749 | | | | |
| 700 | 633 | 867 | 955 | 921 | 848 | | | |
| 750 | 642 | 876 | 1107 | 1093 | 1039 | 948 | | |
| 800 | 650 | 886 | 1143 | 1265 | 1229 | 1156 | | line A |
| 850 | 658 | 895 | 1153 | 1429 | 1420 | 1363 | 1273 | |
| 900 | 666 | 904 | 1164 | 1440 | 1610 | 1571 | 1497 | |
| 950 | 675 | 914 | 1174 | 1452 | 1745 | 1779 | 1721 | |
| 1000 | 683 | 923 | 1184 | 1463 | 1757 | 1987 | 1945 | |
| 1050 | 691 | 933 | 1195 | 1474 | 1769 | 2077 | 2169 | |
| 1100 | 699 | 942 | 1205 | 1485 | 1781 | 2090 | 2393 | line B |
| 1150 | 707 | 951 | 1215 | 1497 | 1793 | 2102 | 2423 | |
| 1200 | 716 | 961 | 1226 | 1508 | 1805 | 2115 | 2437 | |

[1] $c_1$, $c_2$: dimensions of the column cross-section.

The empty cells above line A refer to punching failures on the column perimeter $u_0$ ($A_{sw}$ plays no role at all): for the related values of $(c_1+c_2)$ and d, the punching strength $V_{Rd,c}$ (provided by concrete along $u_1$) is higher than $V_{Rd,max}$, assuming that there is no transverse reinforcement.

For $A_{sw}$ values higher than those listed in Table 1, the punching failure takes place on the column perimeter $u_0$ for cells with grey background and on the basic control perimeter $u_1$ for cells under line B with no background.

Equation (15) changes if one refers to NTC 2008, because in this case the punching-shear strength with transverse reinforcement coincides with the strength provided by steel, while concrete strength is neglected; consequently, equation (15) becomes:

$$A_{sw,max(NTC)} = \min\left(\frac{v_{Rd,max}\, u_0 d}{1.5(d/s_r)f_{ywd,ef}\sin\alpha};\ \frac{v_{Rd,c}\, u_{out} d}{1.5(d/s_r)f_{ywd,ef}\sin\alpha}\right) \tag{16}$$

According to Eq. (16), the values of $A_{s,max}$ are much higher than those given by Eq. (15).

Table 2 lists the values of the ratio between the maximum area of transverse reinforcement on each row calculated according to NTC 2008 and to EC2 for rectangular columns (concrete grade C35/45; flexural reinforcement ratio 2 %). Only two circumferential rows have been considered at the maximum distances recommended by EC2.

Tab. 2 - Values of the ratio $A_{sw,max(NTC)}$ / $A_{sw,max(EC2)}$.

| $c_1+c_2$ [mm][1] | d [mm] | | | | | | | |
|---|---|---|---|---|---|---|---|---|
| | 200 | 250 | 300 | 350 | 400 | 450 | 500 | |
| 500 | 2.92 | 3.75 | | | | | | |
| 550 | 2.59 | 3.16 | | | | | | |
| 600 | 2.49 | 2.78 | 3.37 | | | | | |
| 650 | 2.51 | 2.53 | 2.96 | 3.57 | | | | |
| 700 | 2.53 | 2.47 | 2.68 | 3.13 | 3.74 | | | |
| 750 | 2.55 | 2.49 | 2.48 | 2.82 | 3.27 | 3.90 | | |
| 800 | 2.57 | 2.50 | 2.46 | 2.60 | 2.95 | 3.41 | | line A |
| 850 | 2.58 | 2.52 | 2.48 | 2.44 | 2.71 | 3.07 | 3.53 | |
| 900 | 2.60 | 2.54 | 2.49 | 2.45 | 2.53 | 2.82 | 3.18 | |
| 950 | 2.62 | 2.55 | 2.50 | 2.47 | 2.44 | 2.63 | 2.92 | |
| 1000 | 2.63 | 2.57 | 2.52 | 2.48 | 2.45 | 2.48 | 2.72 | |
| 1050 | 2.65 | 2.58 | 2.53 | 2.49 | 2.46 | 2.43 | 2.56 | |
| 1100 | 2.67 | 2.59 | 2.54 | 2.50 | 2.47 | 2.44 | 2.43 | line B |
| 1150 | 2.68 | 2.61 | 2.55 | 2.51 | 2.48 | 2.45 | 2.43 | |
| 1200 | 2.70 | 2.62 | 2.57 | 2.52 | 2.49 | 2.46 | 2.44 | |

[1] $c_1$, $c_2$: dimensions of the column cross-section.

From Table 2, for a column with a 500x350 mm cross-section ($c_1+c_2 = 850$ mm), the ratio $A_{sw,max(NTC)}$ / $A_{sw,max(EC2)}$ varies from 2.58 to 3.53 with increasing slab effective depth from 250 to 500 mm. Moreover, in this case, when $A_{sw}$ values are higher than the listed values, the punching failure takes place on the control perimeter $u_1$ (if d $\leq$ 350 mm) and on the column perimeter $u_0$ (if d $\geq$ 400 mm). As a matter of fact, $d_{lim}$ is 351 mm ($d_{lim}$ is the value of d which satisfies Eq.5).

## 3.6 Footings

For footings, the basic control perimeter is not known a priori, since it is located at a distance not higher than two times the effective depth from the column perimeter (as recommended in Model Code 1990, CEB-FIP, 1999). Therefore the basic control perimeter should be identified by trials and errors.

The different position of the critical perimeter in footings comes from the lower aspect ratio of footings with respect to slabs. Furthermore, there is not enough experimental evidence for footings, since most of the tests were carried out on thin slabs, with shear span-to-depth ratio higher than 3 - 4.

This ratio is generally lower in footings. Moreover, the vertical soil pressure modifies the inclination of the punching cone, which is higher than in slabs.

Therefore the distance a $\leq$ 2d of the critical perimeter from the column has to be found by means of the following procedure: for an assigned value of the distance a, one gets a different inclination of the failure surface and consequently a different values of the design shear stress and unit shear strength. After a few trials with different values for the distance a, the perimeter along which the ratio between the design shear stress and the shear strength is a maximum can be identified. This perimeter is the critical perimeter u(a) of the footing.

In the case of an axial force without any eccentricity, the shear force is given by:

$$V_{Ed,red} = V_{Ed} - \Delta V_{Ed} \tag{17}$$

where:

$V_{Ed}$ is the design shear force (equal to the axial force transmitted by the column);

$\Delta V_{Ed}$ is the net upward force acting on the base surface delimited by the critical perimeter; this force is equal to the resultant of the soil pressure due to all loads minus the resultant of the soil pressure due to the footing dead weight.

The design value of the punching-shear is given by:

$$v_{Ed} = \frac{V_{Ed,red}}{u\,d} \tag{18}$$

while the punching strength is:

$$v_{Rd} = C_{Rd,c}\,k\left(100\rho\,f_{ck}\right)^{1/3}\frac{2d}{a} \geq v_{min}\frac{2d}{a} \tag{19}$$

where a is the distance of the critical perimeter from column perimeter; $C_{Rd,c}$, k, $v_{min}$ are defined above (see Eq.4).

For an eccentric load, the design shear stress is obtained similarly to slabs, using the coefficient $\beta$; when the transverse reinforcement is required, the shear strength per unit area is calculated with the same rules used for slabs. Nevertheless EN1992-1-1 does not give any recommendation about the design of punching-shear reinforcement for footings (see § 4.3).

## 4. INCONSISTENCIES IN EC2 FOR PUNCHING-SHEAR

The application of EC2 provisions to the design of R/C slabs subjected to punching shear shows a number of inconsistencies::

- the questionable use of the coefficient $\beta$ calculated with reference to the critical perimeter $u_1$, for the verification along the column perimeter $u_0$;

- inadequate calibration of the parameters related to size effect;

- inadequate provisions for the design of transverse reinforcement in footings;

- no specific provisions in the calculation of the design strength (type of transverse reinforcement - studs, stirrups, bent-up bars - and quality of bond).

### 4.1 Coefficient $\beta$ for eccentric loads

The formulation of the coefficient $\beta$ comes from the hypothesis of a uniform distribution of the shear stresses along the perimeter $u_1$, so that its use appears correct only for the calculation of $v_{Ed}$ along $u_1$. Nevertheless, in the calculation of $v_{Ed}$ along the column perimeter $u_0$, EC2 refers to the same coefficient $\beta$ used in the verification along $u_1$, so that the EC2 model is inconsistent.

The meaning of $\beta$ is clear if one writes the shear stress on the critical surface at the distance 2d from the column, as the sum of the shear stress $v_{Ed(V)}$ produced by $V_{Ed}$ and the shear stress $v_{Ed(M)}$ due to $M_{Ed}$:

$$v_{Ed} = v_{Ed(V)} + v_{Ed(M)} = V_{Ed} / (u_1\, d) + v_{Ed(M)} \qquad (20)$$

Comparing this expression with Eq. (3), one gets:

$$\beta = 1 + v_{Ed(M)}\, u_1\, d / V_{Ed} \qquad (21)$$

Moreover, the stress produced by $M_{Ed}$ can be calculated by equating the unbalanced moment $M_{Ed}$ between the slab and the column, and the moment produced by the shear stress $v_{Ed(M)}$ distributed on the critical surface $S_1$:

$$M_{Ed} = \int_0^{u_1} \left(v_{Ed(M)}d\right)\cdot e\cdot du \qquad (22)$$

where:

$du$ = infinitesimal length of the critical perimeter $u_1$;
$e$ = distance of the length $du$ from the bending axis.

Assuming a rectangular distribution for the shear stresses on $u_1$ ($v_{Ed(M)} = \pm$ const.), the moment equilibrium equation can be written as:

$$M_{Ed} = v_{Ed(M)} \, d \int_0^{u_1} |e| \, du = v_{Ed(M)} \, d \, W_1 \qquad (23)$$

where $W_1$ is the moment corresponding to the rectangular distribution of unit shear stresses ($v_{Ed(M)}=1$) on the critical surface $S_1$ (Fig. 12).

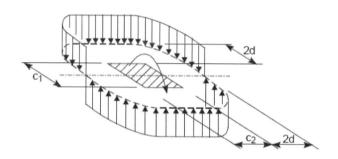

Figure 12 – Shear distribution due to an unbalanced moment at a slab-column connection (CEN-EN1992-1-1, 2004); the column is assumed to be an internal column.

From the previous expression one gets:

$$v_{Ed(M)} = M_{Ed} / (d \cdot W_1) \qquad (24)$$

and substituting equation (24) in equation (21):

$$\beta = 1 + v_{Ed(M)} \, u_1 \, d / V_{Ed} = 1 + M_{Ed} \, u_1 \, d / (d \, W_1 \, V_{Ed}) =$$
$$= 1 + (M_{Ed} / V_{Ed}) (u_1 / W_1). \qquad (25)$$

Finally the coefficient $\beta$ can be rewritten in the following form:

$$\beta = 1 + k (M_{Ed} / V_{Ed}) (u_1 / W_1) \qquad (26)$$

where the coefficient $k$ is introduced to take into account that $M_{Ed}$ is balanced not only by the shear stresses. In fact the bending moments in the slab strips parallel to the plane of bending and the twisting moments in the orthogonal strips balance $M_{Ed}$. Moreover, the coefficient $k$ takes into account that the effective shape of the shear-stress distribution is not rectangular.

From the above equations, it is clear that the calculation of the shear stresses due to $M_{Ed}$ with reference to a control perimeter different from $u_1$ requires a different definition of $\beta$. Nevertheless, as anticipated, EC2 does not take into account the dependence of $\beta$ with the control perimeter and allows the verification to be carried out along $u_0$ with the same coefficient used for $u_1$. Since this assumption may lead to an unconservative evaluation of the shear stresses along $u_0$, appropriate modifications are required to mend this inconsistency.

To this aim, in the absence of experimental evidence, some authors performed linear-elastic numerical analyses concerning rectangular slabs subjected to eccentric loads, for different restraint conditions; as a result, the following two alternative approaches were proposed for the verification along the column perimeter $u_0$ (Mancini and Bertagnoli, 2008):

1. $\beta$ is defined with reference to the perimeter located at the distance d from the column perimeter, or

2. the maximum punching-shear strength on the perimeter $u_0$ is reduced by 20 % with respect to the present definition, while EC2 definition of $\beta$ along $u_1$ is not modified.

The first approach requires the calculation of two different values of $\beta$, one for $u_0$ and one for $u_1$, while the second approach leads to the evaluation of a single value for $\beta$, with reference to $u_1$.

The second approach has also been discussed and approved by CEN/TC 250/SC 2, so that the revised version of EC2 will contain the following reduced value for $v_{Rd,max}$:

$$v_{Rd,max} = 0.4 \, \upsilon \, f_{cd}, \tag{27}$$

instead of $v_{Rd,max} = 0.5 \, \upsilon \, f_{cd}$ (see Eq.1)

## 4.2 Size effect

The expression given in EN1992-1-1 for the calculation of the strength $v_{Rd,c}$ for transversely-unreinforced slabs takes into account size effect through the parameter $k = 1+\sqrt{(200/d)}$. This coefficient considers only slab effective depth. Nevertheless, as already mentioned, the strength $v_{Rd,c}$ depends also on the radius of the punching surface, but this last effect is not taken into account in the EC2.

For this reason some authors (Leskelä, 2007) proposed to take into account the radius of the punching surface, assuming that the coefficient $C_{Rd,c}$ is not constant, but varies with the size of column cross-section and slab effective depth:

$$C_{Rd,c} = 0.3 \cdot (c + 1.5 \, d) / (c + 4d) \tag{28}$$

where

$c = \sqrt{(c_1 \, c_2)}$ for rectangular columns with cross-section size $c_1$ and $c_2$;

$c = D$ for circular cross-sections of diameter D.

## 4.3 Design of punching-shear reinforcement for footings

EN1992-1-1 gives no recommendations about the choice of the control perimeter to be used for the design of transverse reinforcement in footings. If Eq. (8a) is inverted, the following expression for the area $A_{sw}$ of the steel within each row around column perimeter is obtained:

$$A_{sw} = \frac{\left(v_{Ed,red} - 0.75\, v_{Rd,c}\right) u_1\, d}{1.5\left(d/s_r\right) f_{ywd,ef}\, \sin\alpha} \tag{29}$$

where the symbols have the usual meaning.

In the absence of EC2 recommendations and to keep on the safe side, it is possible to calculate the area $A_{sw}$ of the transverse reinforcement by means of the following procedure:

- assume $v_{Ed,red} = v_{Ed}$ (the upwards shear stress due to soil pressure should not be subtracted from the shear stress induced by the axial load of the column);

- assume for $v_{Ed}$ the maximum value among all the values calculated with respect to those control perimeters where the verification is not satisfied without transverse reinforcement and whose distance from column perimeter is less than 2d;

- calculate $v_{Rd,c}$ along the perimeter $u_1$, in order to minimize the second term in parentheses [for a<2d, $v_{Rd,c}(u_1) < v_{Rd,c}(a) = (2d/a)\cdot v_{Rd,c}(u_1)$] and to maximize the difference $(v_{Ed,red} - 0.75\, v_{Rd,c})$.

With reference to NTC 2008, the same comments made for slabs in § 3.4 could be repeated for footings.

## 4.4 Anchorage of transverse reinforcement

Bond conditions are not the same for all types of transverse reinforcement (Beutel and Hegger, 2002). The EC2 formula to calculate the effective strength of transverse reinforcement does not take into account bond-related problems, since it only considers the dependence of the strength on the effective depth, whatever the reinforcement type might be.

Even in Model Code 1990 the strength of the punching-shear reinforcement does not depend on the reinforcement type and is assumed to be constant ($f_{ywd,eff} = 300$ N/mm$^2$). Comparing the expressions for the strength of transverse reinforcement of EC2 and MC'90, EC2 expression gives the same value as MC'90 if d = 200 mm, while the values are lower or higher for d < 200 mm and d > 200 mm, respectively.

To improve EC2 provisions, the effective steel strength should be diversified on the basis of the type of the transverse reinforcement (for instance, because of their reduced anchored length, stirrups may not be as effective as mechanically-anchored studs, unless the stirrups are bent around the flexural top-and-bottom reinforcement, something hardly feasible in thin slabs).

## 5. PUNCHING SHEAR IN SEISMIC AREAS

This paragraph deals with slab verification in punching-shear under seismic excitation.

EN1992-1-1 refers only to the design of R/C structures in non-seismic areas; consequently, no recommendations are given about the behavior of slab-column connections or column-footing connections under seismic loading. Neither EN1998, nor the recent Italian design recommendations (2008) mention this issue, although both codes include R/C design in seismic areas.

The main problems concerning the punching-shear verification in slab-column connections under seismic excitation may be synthesized as follows:

a. Is a slab-column frame system adequate to resist horizontal loads?

b. Is it possible to design earthquake-resistant slab-column connections without transverse reinforcement?

c. Is it possible to apply EN1992-1-1 provisions, with some modifications, to evaluate the strength of the connections under cyclic loads?

d. Should further provisions for the transverse reinforcement be introduced, in order to guarantee the ductility of the connections?

### 5.1 Slab-column frames as earthquake-resistant systems

Some provisions for designing slab-column frames as earthquake-resistant systems can be found in certain codes, like – for instance - ACI Code, and may be adopted by Eurocodes with some minor modifications. Slab-column frames without beams may be used in low- or moderate-seismicity regions, while in high-seismicity regions a proper bracing system is a must, as specified by the Eurocodes.

In the first case, being slab-column connections a part of the earthquake-resistant system, they should be designed to resist the shear forces produced by the gravity loads combined with the earthquake-induced unbalanced moments.

In the second case, slabs exhibit the same lateral displacements of the earthquake-resistant system, and the connections should be designed to keep their capacity to support gravity loads under these displacements.

## 5.2 Seismic design of slab-column connections without shear reinforcement

Under unbalanced slab-column cyclic moments, the shear strength provided by concrete diminishes like in beams. Nevertheless, contrary to beams, slabs are subjected to a degradation of concrete shear strength, that is limited to a critical area in the zones closest to the column, while the surrounding concrete exerts a confining action on the joint region (something non existing in beam-column connections). For such a reason, in slab-column connections (without shear reinforcement) the strength per unit area is not negligible. With regard to this point, ACI Code allows nonprestressed slab-column connections to be designed without shear reinforcement, if one of the following two criteria is respected:

1. the shear stress due to gravity loads combined with the unbalanced moments does not exceed the punching-shear strength provided by the concrete alone;

2. the drift storey ratio (= storey drift divided inter-storey spacing) does not exceed a limit value, which depends on the ratio between the shear force due to gravity loads and the nominal punching strength.

Concerning the first criterion, ACI 318-08 (2008) does not require the introduction of any shear reinforcement in slab-column connections subjected to moment reversals, if the maximum shear stress does not exceed the unit shear strength of the concrete at the critical section. The maximum shear stress is due partly to the shear force $V_u$ produced by gravity loads and partly to the unbalanced moments $M_u$ transferred by the columns to the slab under the design storey-drift ratio. Therefore, the verification is similar to that without lateral forces, but requires the calculation of the moments occurring at the slab-column connections, when subjected to the design displacement. In this calculation, the designer should correctly select the stiffness of the slab-column connections, taking into account the effects of cracking and the reinforcement (with regard to this last point, some comments are reported at the end of this chapter).

The second criterion does not require the calculation of the unbalanced moments, but requires the calculation of the design storey drifts of the bracing system. This criterion ensues from the results of many tests carried out by different authors (Hueste and Wight, 1999; Pan and Moehle, 1989; Robertson and Durrani, 1992). They showed that the ability of slab-column connections to withstand sizable storey drifts without punching failures decreases with increasing gravity loads.

The ultimate storey drift ratio ($DR_u$) varies with the ratio [$V_u / (\phi V_n)$], where $V_u$ is the maximum shear force transferred from the column to the slab and $V_c$ is the nominal punching-shear strength without shear reinforcement ($\phi$ is the strength reduction factor for punching, equal to 0.75). The tests showed also that studs are more efficient than stirrups as a shear reinforcement, since studs allows for higher drift ratios (Fig. 13).

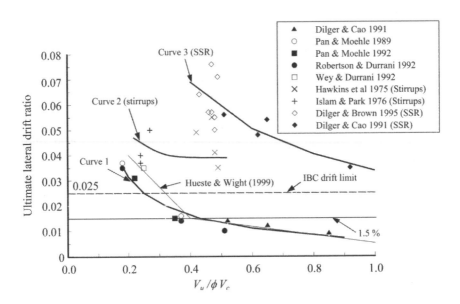

Figure 13 – Effect of gravity loads on the lateral drift capacity of internal slab-column connections (ACI 421.2R-07, 2007).

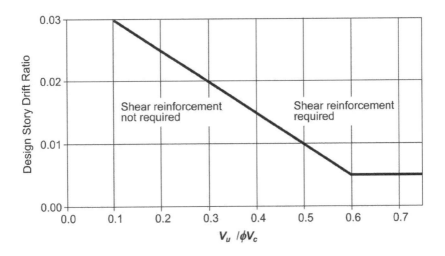

Figure 14 – Criterion of the storey drift ratio (ACI 318-08, 2008).

Based on the previous results, ACI 318-08 proposes a simplified relationship between $DR_u$ and $(V_u / \phi V_c)$, regardless of the type of transverse reinforcement (Fig. 14):

$$DR_u = \max [0.005; 0.035 - 0.05(V_u / \phi V_c)] \tag{30}$$

where the design storey drift ratio is taken as the largest between the two design storey-drift ratios of the adjacent storeys (above and below the slab-column connection).

As an example, for $(V_u / \phi V_n) = 0.3$ the drift ratio $DR_u$ amounts to 2 %, which means that - should the design storey drift ratio be lower than 0.02 - the shear reinforcement would not be required, while for $DR_u$ higher than 0.02, the slab-column connections would require an appropriate shear reinforcement. For any values of $(V_u / \phi V_n)$ higher than 0.6, the transverse reinforcement is not required if the design storey drift ratio is lower than 5 ‰.

Slab-column connections satisfying neither Criterion No. 1 nor Criterion No. 2 require a shear reinforcement.

Moreover, according to ACI Code, in each direction of the slab at least two continuous bottom bars or wires should pass through the region bounded by the longitudinal reinforcement of the column. At each storey, these continuous bars should be adequately anchored to the first and last columns. These bottom bars are termed "integrity reinforcement", since they are aimed to give the slab some residual flexural capacity after a punching failure (in other words, the loads - that cannot be transmitted to the underneath column after the punching failure – may still be partly transferred to the nearby columns via the residual stiffness of the slab).

According to the authors, similar criteria should be introduced into the Euro-codes, in order to allow their use in the design of slab-column frames in seismic regions.

As an example, a criterion similar to the second criterion suggested by ACI looks very appropriate, because the calculation of the unbalanced moments is not required. As a matter of fact, the calculation of these moments is not an easy task due to the effects of cracking, which reduces the stiffness of the slab and increases the lateral flexibility of the structure under lateral loads.

Different models can be used to perform the calculation: finite-element discretization, effective beam-width model or equivalent frame model. In all cases, the calculation may give reliable results only if the reduction of slab stiffness due to cracking is correctly taken into account.

To take care of cracking, the analysis should be performed several times, with different assumptions on the effective moment of inertia of slab sections, because of the uncertainties due to cracking, that affects the interaction of the slab with the contiguous structural members (e.g. walls), as well as the stress state in the slab.

On the contrary, if a criterion based on the storey drift ratio is adopted, a single analysis is sufficient.

If there is no bracing system, a very low slab stiffness should be assumed (e.g. effective moment of inertia of the slab section = 1/3 of the gross moment of inertia, Kang and Wallace, 2005).

If there is an adequate bracing system, slab stiffness should be totally neglected.

## 5.3 Detailing of transverse reinforcement for ductility

Detailing the transverse reinforcement for ductility requires both the calibration of existing EC2 provisions for transverse steel and the addition of new provisions to take into account the experimental evidence about the ductility demand of transverse steel.

To this aim the results of the tests on slabs subjected to a constant shear force and to moment reversals should be considered (Ritchie and Ghali, 2005; Gayed and Ghali, 2006). Many authors showed that slab-column connections behave in a ductile fashion, if the shear reinforcement is based on studs. These connections may withstand drift ratios from 3 to 7%, depending on the magnitude of the shear force (ACI 421.1R-08, 2008).

In flat slabs, stirrups are not as effective as studs because of their inadequate anchored length, especially in thin slabs (effective depth lower than 250 mm). For this reason, the punching-shear strength of thin slabs slightly increases if stirrups are used, but significantly increases if studs are used; in the latter case, the failure can be considered ductile (Megally and Ghali, 2000).

The above-mentioned test results should be the basis for improving the Eurocodes, in order to allow the designer to identify the most suitable transverse reinforcement, and to guarantee the required ductility in slab-column connections.


## 6. CONCLUSIONS

A critical review of EC2 provisions for punching-shear verifications in slabs and footings, with/without transverse, reinforcement, is presented in this paper, where the punching shear mechanism is briefly described with reference to a typical test of a R/C slab resting on a circular column. Cracking from the formation of circumferential and radial cracks followed by internal inclined cracks is described as well up to the coalescence of the cracks into a mostly-conical fractured surface. The effects that a number of parameters (like concrete strength, flexural steel ratio and dimensions) have on punching strength are also presented and commented.

Due to the complexity of the punching phenomenon, no universally-accepted models have been formulated so far. (Some models are focused on the action of the inclined concrete struts, while other models mainly take care of the forces transferred across the shear cracks).

EC2 equations for punching are largely empirical, being based (a) on a nominal shear stress calculated on a conventional control surface and (b) on an empirical concrete strength parameter.

The control surface was chosen to use the same strength parameter introduced in the checks concerning the shear in one-way slabs and in narrow beams without web reinforcement. In spite of its empirical nature, however, EC2 approach leads to rather reliable results, that closely fit those obtained from the tests or provided by mechanical models.

Nevertheless, inconsistencies have been found in some parameters and provisions, with reference to experimental evidence.

Some of these inconsistencies may be eliminated simply by modifying the definition of the relevant design parameters, but other inconsistencies might be mended only by adopting different formulations involving further parameters. For instance, according to some mechanical models, the span-depth ratio seems to have a sizable influence on the punching strength, but it is ignored in EC2. In particular, increasing the span-to-depth ratio decreases the punching strength (hence, very thin slabs exhibit lower punching strengths than those predicted by EC2). Furthermore, the lack of such critical design recommendations as those concerning the transverse reinforcement in footings, has been high-lighted.

Summing up, the actual empirical approach of EC2 should be replaced with a more rational approach based on a consistent physical model, in which all the parameters influencing the punching capacity are taken care of.

Finally, the paper has stressed the necessity of extending EC2 provisions on punching-shear to earthquake-induced cyclic-drift reversals, in order to take care of the ensuing bending moments. To this aim a criterion based on the storey drift ratio may be adopted, together with further provisions for the detailing of the transverse reinforcement, since different types and layouts of the transverse reinforcement have different effects on the ductility of slab-column connections.

## REFERENCES

1. ACI Committe 318-08 (2008). *Building Code Requirements for Structural Concrete (ACI 318-08) and Commentary.* American Concrete Institute, Farmington Hills (Mich., USA).

2. ACI 421.1R-08 (2008). *Guide to Shear Reinforcement for Slabs.* American Concrete Institute, Farmington Hills (Mich., USA).

3. ACI 421.2R-07 (2007). *Seismic Design of Punching-shear Reinforcement in Flat Plates.* American Concrete Institute, Farmington Hills (Mich., USA).

4. Angotti F. and Orlando M. (2009). "Punching, Modelling and Testing: Critical Issues" (in Italian). *Proc. Nat. Conf. of AICAP (Italian Soc. for R/C and P/C),* ed. and pub. by AICAP, May 2009, Pisa (Italy), pp.49-56.

5. Beutel R. and Hegger J. (2002). "The Effect of Anchorage on the Effectiveness of the Shear Reinforcement in the Punching Zone", *Cement & Concrete Composites,* V. 24, pp. 539-549.

6. CEB (1985). *Punching Shear in Reinforced Concrete.* Bulletin 168, Lausanne (Switzerland).

7.  CEB-FIP (1999). *Structural Concrete. Textbook on Behaviour, Design and Performance - Vol. 2, Basis of Design.* Lausanne (Switzerland).

8.  CEB-FIP (2001). *Punching of Structural Concrete Slabs.* fib Bulletin 12, Lausanne (Switzerland).

9.  CEN-EN 1992-1-1 (2004). *Eurocode 2: Design of Concrete Structures - Part 1-1: Genera lRules and Rules for Buildings.* Bruxelles (Belgium).

10. Gayed R.B. and Ghali A. (2006). "Seismic-Resistant Joints of Interior Columns with Prestressed Slabs". *ACI Structural Journal*, V. 103, No. 5, Sept.-Oct., pp. 710-719. *See also Errata in ACI Structural Journal*, V. 103, No. 6, Nov.-Dec. 2006, p. 909.

11. Guandalini S., Burdet O.L. and Muttoni A. (2009). "Punching Tests of Slabs with Low Reinforcement Ratios". *ACI Structural Journal*, V. 106, No. 1, pp. 87-95.

12. Hueste M.B.D. and Wight J.K. (1999). "Nonlinear Punching-shear Failure Model for Interior Slab-Column Connections". *Journal of Structural Engineering, ASCE*, V. 125, No. 9, pp. 997-1008.

13. Kang T.H.K. and Wallace J.W. (2005). "Dynamic Responses of Flat Plate Systems with Shear Reinforcement", *ACI Structural Journal*, V. 102, No. 5, pp. 763-773.

14. Kinnunen S. and Nylander H. (1960). *Punching of Concrete Slabs Without Shear Reinforcement.* Transactions of the Royal Institute of Technology, No. 158, Stockholm, Sweden, 112 pp.

15. Leskelä M.V. (2007). *Inconsistencies in the Punching-Shear Design Rules of EN1992-1-1.* University of Oulu, Finland.

16. Mancini G. and Bertagnoli L. (2008). "About the Maximum Punching-Shear Resistance Adjacent to a Column". *Proc. Symposium in honor of Prof. G.D. Toniolo, Politecnico di Milano*, December 5-2008, "Advances in R/C and Precast Constructions" (in press).

17. Megally S. and Ghali A. (2000). "Punching-Shear Design of Seismic-Resistant Slab-Column Connections". *ACI Structural Journal*, V. 97, No. 5, pp. 720-730.

18. Menetrey Ph. (1996). "Analytical Computation of the Punching Strength of Reinforced Concrete". *ACI Structural J.*, V. 93, No. 5, pp. 1-9.

19. Muttoni A. and Schwartz J. (1991). "Behaviour of Beams and Punching in Slabs without Shear Reinforcement". *Proc. IABSE Colloquium*, V. 62, Zurich (Switzerland), pp. 703-708.

20. Muttoni A. (2008). "Punching Shear Strength of Reinforced Concrete Slabs without Transverse Reinforcement". *ACI Structural Journal*, V. 105, No. 4, Jul.-Aug., pp. 440-450.

21. NTC-2008 (2008). *Decree of the Italian Ministry of Infrastructures - January 14th, 2008 "Updated Technical Provisions for Constructions", in Italian).*

22. Pan A.D. and Moehle J.P. (1989). "Lateral Displacement Ductility of Reinforced Concrete Flat Plates". *ACI Structural Journal*, V. 86, No. 3, pp. 250-258.

23. Ritchie M. and Ghali A. (2005). "Seismic-Resistant Connections of Edge Columns with Prestressed Slabs". *ACI Structural Journal*, V. 102, No. 2, pp. 314-323.

24. Robertson I.N. and Durrani A.J. (1992). "Gravity Load Effect on Seismic Behavior of Interior Slab-Column Connections". *ACI Structural Journal*, V. 89, No. 1, pp. 37-45.

25. Ruiz M.F. and Muttoni A. (2008). "Application of Critical Shear Crack Theory to Punching of Reinforced Concrete Slabs with Transverse Reinforcement". *ACI Structural Journal*, V. 106, No. 4, pp. 485-494.

26. Walraven J.C. (2002). *Punching Shear.* Background Document for prENV 1992-1-1: 2001.

STUDIES AND RESEARCHES – V. 29, 2009
Graduate School in Concrete Structures – Fratelli Pesenti
Politecnico di Milano, Italy

# STABILITY CHECKS IN SLENDER R/C COLUMNS ACCORDING TO RECENT CODE TRENDS

Ciro Faella[1], Enzo Martinelli[2], Emidio Nigro[3]

## ABSTRACT

Stability-related issues are becoming increasingly important in concrete structures, because of the availability of better and better concretes, that are nowadays accepted by the codes of practice for the design of R/C and P/C structures. Increasing concrete strength results in reducing cross sections and enhancing member slenderness, with a direct influence on structural sensitivity to second-order effects.

Structural codes currently provide designers with various proposals for the slenderness limits of concrete members. These limits are usually based on the assumption that second-order effects do not exceed 10% of the first-order ones. Consequently, simple theoretical considerations, based on the theory of elastic stability, allow defining the slenderness limits for concrete members. However, such nonlinear phenomena as concrete cracking and steel yielding make any simple approach in handling stability problems highly questionable.

In this paper, starting from rather simple theoretical considerations aimed at identifying the basic parameters necessary for defining consistent slenderness thresholds, various proposals available in the scientific literature are presented and discussed. Specific attention is devoted to two formulations recently adopted by both the European and the Italian design codes, for limiting the slenderness of concrete members. Numerical analyses, however, show that these formulations are often non-conservative.

---

[1] Professor, University of Salerno, Dept. of Civil Eng., Fisciano (Salerno, Italy)
[2] Assistant Prof., Univ. of Salerno, Dept. of Civil Eng., Fisciano (Salerno, Italy)
[3] Professor, University Naples "Federico II", DIST, Naples (Italy)

# 1. INTRODUCTION

The stability-related issues of R/C members are becoming increasingly important as concrete mechanical properties improve and the its specific strength achieves values rather close to those of structural steel, whose design is often controlled by stability. Among the many issues, the evaluation of the so-called "second-order effects" plays a major role. Design-oriented structural analysis is often carried out assuming the loads to be applied on the undeformed shape and neglecting the increase of the internal forces due to the displacements of the points of application of the loads, such displacements being caused by the deformation of the structure as a whole. The ensuing internal forces (for instance, the bending moments) are referred as "first-order" internal forces (first-order moments $M_I$). Nevertheless, different values for the internal forces can be obtained by considering that loads act on the "deformed shape" of the structure. Focusing once more on the bending moments, the total value of such internal forces $M_{tot}$ can be derived under this more general hypothesis and the so-called "second-order" moment $M_{II}$ can be easily defined as the difference between the total and the first-order moment. The case in which the total moment $M_{tot}$ is larger than $M_I$ is of practical interest and the $M_{tot}/M_I$ ratio (larger than the unity) can be defined as "magnification factor" $\mu$ (Bazant & Cedolin, 1991).

Focusing on isolated columns subjected to a sizable first-order moment (called beam-columns in the following), an approximate relationship can be easily established between such parameter and the critical load multiplier $\alpha_{cr} = N_{cr}/N$ (Timoshenko & Gere, 1961; Bazant & Cedolin, 1991):

$$\mu = \frac{M_{tot}}{M_I} = \frac{M_I + M_{II}}{M_I} = \frac{\alpha_{cr}}{\alpha_{cr} - 1} . \qquad (1)$$

As a matter of principle, the factor $\mu$ in any members subjected to compression is generally higher than the unit. Nevertheless, as a general rule (widely accepted in practice and by the design codes) the amplification of the design stresses can be neglected if $\mu \leq 1.10$. Based on the relationship (1), the previous limitation can be written with reference to the critical multiplier $\alpha_{cr}$ or to other variables related to the previous parameter, such as the slenderness or the applied axial load.

The magnification factor may be easily determined once the critical value $N_{cr}$ of the axial load $N$ has been evaluated. However, Euler's definition of $N_{cr}$ cannot be straightforwardly applied to concrete members because most of the key properties of R/C mechanical behaviour are not covered by the hypotheses assumed in Euler's theory. For instance, member stiffness cannot be easily defined because of several nonlinear phenomena, such as nonlinear stress-strain relationship of concrete in compression, cracking in tension, delayed deformations deriving by creep and shrinkage, yielding and hardening of the reinforcement.

Consequently, various criteria, more or less directly related to the conceptual relationship (1), have been formulated in the scientific literature for defining handy design rules to recognize whether a structure is "affected" or not by the second- order effects (i.e. μ larger or smaller than 1.10, respectively). In the case of beam-columns, such criteria usually provide the designer with a threshold value λ* of the slenderness: if the actual value λ is higher than such a threshold, the column has to be considered "slender" and the second-order effects have to be determined. On the contrary, if $\phi \lambda \leq \lambda^*$, the column is "short" (the total moment can be reasonably assumed to coincide with the corresponding "first-order" values).

Since several different proposals are currently available in the scientific literature, and the recently-published European Code (EC2, EN-1992, 2005) and Italian Code (N.T.C., 2008) make two rather close proposals for defining the slenderness threshold, this paper focuses on the assessment of such different proposals and on the evaluation of their sensitivity to the major mechanical parameters.

After an outline of the theoretical background, the possible definition of the slenderness threshold, and a review of six different definitions of λ* will be presented. Later, a numerical procedure is validated and utilized (a) to perform a parametric analysis aimed at assessing the handiness and accuracy of the various definitions, and (b) to check whether the limit value on the maximum $M_{tot}/M_I$ ratio at failure (= 1.10 considered as a threshold between short and slender columns) is reasonable.

## 2. DEFINITION OF A THRESHOLD VALUE FOR THE SLENDERNESS

As previously stated, a limit value for the slenderness $\lambda^*$ of beam-columns can be introduced by imposing that the second-order effects do not exceed 10% of the corresponding first-order ones. Referring to the relation (1), such condition corresponds to put $\alpha_{cr} \geq 11$, resulting in this case $\mu \leq 1.10$.

Considering Euler's definition for the critical multiplier $\alpha_{cr}$, the following expression (containing several relevant mechanical parameters) can be derived:

$$\alpha_{cr} = \frac{N_{cr}}{N_{Sd}} = \frac{\pi^2 \cdot E_{cd} \cdot (kI_c)}{l_o^2 \cdot N_{Sd}} = \frac{\pi^2}{\lambda^2} \cdot \frac{E_{cd}}{f_{cd}} \cdot \frac{k}{v} \,, \tag{2}$$

where k is a factor related to cracking and to other nonlinear phenomena, with the aim to reduce the moment of inertia $I_c$ of concrete gross section to take care of concrete cracking and steel yielding; $E_{cd} = E_{ck}/1.5$ (see Eurocode 2); and $v = N_{Sd}/A_c f_{cd}$ is the non-dimensional axial load. The following relationship is obtained by solving equation (2) in terms of slenderness $\lambda = l_o/I_c$:

$$\lambda = \sqrt{\frac{k \cdot \pi^2}{\alpha_{cr}} \cdot \frac{E_{cd}}{f_{cd}}} \cdot \frac{1}{\sqrt{\nu}} \cdot \qquad (3)$$

For $\alpha_{cr} = 11$ the following expression can be worked out for the limit slenderness:

$$\lambda^* \approx 0,947 \cdot \sqrt{\frac{E_{cd}}{f_{cd}}} \cdot \sqrt{\frac{k}{\nu}} \cdot \qquad (4)$$

Equation (4) has the merit of establishing a relationship between $\lambda^*$ and the most relevant parameters.

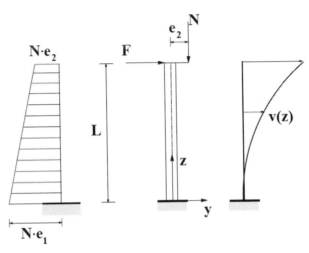

Figure 1 – Definition of the geometry and load conditions of a column subjected to a sizable first-order moment (*beam-column*).

Considering the column with a linear diagram of bending moment (Fig. 1), ranging from the value $N \cdot e_2$ on the top to the value $N \cdot e_1$ at the bottom (with $e_1 \geq e_2$), a more general expression of the magnification coefficient $\mu$ can be derived as a function of the shape of the bending moment diagram (which is described by the eccentricity ration $e_2/e_1$, see Migliacci & Mola, 1985; Faella & Nigro, 1992; Faella et al., 1998):

$$\mu = \frac{\alpha_{cr}}{\alpha_{cr} - 1} \cdot \left[ 1 + \frac{1}{\alpha_{cr}} \cdot \left( \frac{M_{I,1}}{M_I} - 1 \right) \right] =$$
$$= \frac{\alpha_{cr}}{\alpha_{cr} - 1} \cdot \left\{ 1 + \frac{1}{\alpha_{cr}} \cdot \left[ \frac{4}{\pi} \cdot \frac{e_2}{e_1} + \frac{8}{\pi^2} \cdot \left( 1 - \frac{e_2}{e_1} \right) - 1 \right] \right\} \qquad (5)$$

In equation (5) the quantity $M_{I,1}/M_I$ represents the ratio between the amplitude of the first harmonic of the first-order bending moment and the maximum moment $M_I = N \cdot e_1$. For a linear shape of the bending moment, the bottom expression (Eq.5) can be derived. It is interesting to observe that for $e_2/e_1 = 0.40$ expression (5) reduces to expression (1), because in this case $M_{I,1}/M_I \cong 1$.

Figure 2 shows the relationship between $\mu$ and $\alpha_{cr}$ for different values of $e_2/e_1$: for a given value of $\alpha_{cr}$, the smaller the ratio $e_2/e_1$, the smaller the second-order effects.

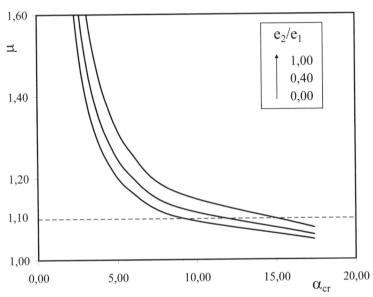

Figure 2 – Influence of $e_2/e_1$ on the magnification factor $\mu$.

Enforcing the limitation $\mu = 1.10$ in equation (5) leads to the following value of the critical multiplier:

$$\alpha_{cr} \approx 10 \cdot \left( 0.91 + 0.46 \cdot \frac{e_2}{e_1} \right) . \tag{6}$$

The following general expression can be obtained for $\lambda^*$ by introducing (6) into (3),

$$\lambda^* \cong \sqrt{\frac{E_{cd}}{f_{cd}}} \cdot \sqrt{\frac{k}{v}} \cdot \sqrt{\frac{1}{0.91 + 0.46 \cdot e_2/e_1}} . \tag{7}$$

The expression (7), although affected by the approximation assumed for deriving expression (5), shows how the threshold slenderness of isolated beam-columns is related to various geometrical and mechanical parameters. Figure 3 shows the ratio between the limit slenderness $\lambda^*$ given by (7) and the corresponding value obtained in the case of a uniform moment diagram ($e_2/e_1$=1.0). The diagram shows that $\lambda^*$ values increase as $e_2/e_1$ decreases, by roughly 20% in the case of a triangular diagram ($e_2/e_1$=0.0) with respect to the reference case of uniform bending moment.

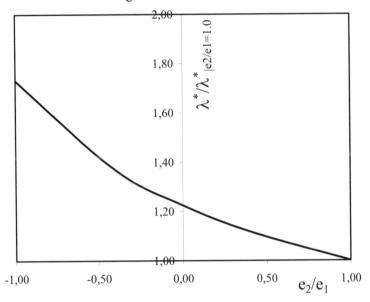

Figure 3 – Influence of $e_2/e_1$ on the value of the limit slenderness $\lambda^*$.

## 3. DIFFERENT FORMULATIONS FOR THE DEFINITION OF THE LIMIT SLENDERNESS

In this paragraph, six different proposals concerning the definition of the slenderness limits for isolated R/C beam-columns are presented and commented.

These proposals are drawn from either the scientific literature or recent design codes for R/C structures. The presentation of the different proposals shows to what extent they are linked to the general formulations given in (4) and (7), and based on simple mechanical models.

Preliminarily, one should note that some of the proposals mostly consist of a set of requirements concerning the evaluation of the effective sectional moment of inertia, to implicitly take into account some non-linear phenomena (such as concrete cracking), while other proposals directly provide the slenderness limit-values, beyond which second-order analysis is required for design purposes.

In the first case, the expression of the effective moment of inertia can be used:

- in (2), to evaluate the critical multiplier $\alpha_{cr}$ and to ascertain whether the structure is sensitive to second-order effects, or
- in (3) to derive the corresponding slenderness limit-value.

114

## 3.1 A.C.I. 318-89

The American Code ACI 318 (1989) suggests a conventional expression for the flexural stiffness, which is quite close to the expression for cracked sections in simple bending:

$$I_{ACI,89} = 0.20 \cdot I_c + n \cdot I_s \geq 0.40 \cdot I_c . \tag{8}$$

where $I_c$ and $I_s$ are the sectional moments of inertia of the concrete and of the reinforcement, respectively, while $n = E_s/E_c$ is the so-called (steel-concrete) "modular-ratio".

Since it is possible to choose other approximate expressions for the actual flexural stiffness of R/C sections (i.e. considering the possible influence of the normal stress and of the "shape" of the bending moment diagram) a comparative analysis among those different alternatives has been performed in Faella et al. (1998), in order to assess the role of each alternative in the definition of the limit slenderness.

The value provided by (8) generally ranges between the two extreme values of the flexural stiffness identified by the values $I_1$ and $I_2$ pertaining to the uncracked and to the cracked section, respectively, according to the notation adopted by Eurocode 2 (EN-1992-1 , 2005).

## 3.2 A.C.I. 318-05

The various proposals adopted in the review of the American code of practice confirm that defining consistent slenderness limits is still a highly-debated issue. To this regard, A.C.I. 318 (2005) proposes a different expression for the conventional flexural stiffness:

$$I_{ACI,05} = \frac{0.2 \cdot I_c + n \cdot I_s}{1 + \beta_d} , \tag{9}$$

where $\beta_d$ is the ratio between the normal stress due to the permanent loads (amplified) and the total normal stress. An approximate version of the above formula is also allowed in the cases in which the inertia of the reinforcement $I_s$ is unknown:

$$I_{ACI,05} = \frac{0.4 \cdot I_c}{1 + \beta_d} . \tag{10}$$

Since in the above-mentioned document the role of the eccentricity in defining the effective flexural stiffness is not explicitly mentioned, the relation (3) can be used to evaluate the critical multiplier $\alpha_{cr}$ assuming the following expression for the coefficient k:

$$k = \frac{0.4}{1+\beta_d} \ . \tag{11}$$

Similarly, by introducing expression (11) into expression (4), the limit value $\lambda^*$ of the slenderness can be obtained.

### 3.3 Method of the Inertia of the Cracked Sections (MISF)

A formulation proposed by Faella et al. (1998), concerning the definition of the effective flexural stiffness and the evaluation of the slenderness limit, is based on the "stiffness of the cracked section" in bending. As a matter of principle, this is a conservative assumption for the actual flexural stiffness, since the effects of the non-linearity in the constitutive law of the concrete are excluded.

With reference to the case of a rectangular section with bottom and top reinforcement, in Faella et al. (1998) the authors suggested the simplified expression (12) for the moment of inertia in a cracked section, showing that there are no major differences with respect to the corresponding "exact" value:

$$I'_2 = 0.10 \cdot I_c \cdot \left[ 1 + 36 \cdot (1 - 2 \cdot \delta)^2 \cdot n \cdot \rho \right] = 0.10 \cdot I_c \cdot (1 + k_\delta \cdot n \cdot \rho) \ , \tag{12}$$

where $\delta = d'/h$ is the ratio between the concrete cover and the depth of the section, involved into the definition of the coefficient $k_\delta = 36 \cdot (1 - 2 \cdot \delta)^2$, ranging between the value 23 for $\delta = 0.10$ and 29 for $\delta = 0.05$.

Assuming the approximate formulation (12) for the inertia and using the definition (3), the following expression can be derived for the threshold value of the slenderness:

$$\lambda^*_{MISF} = \sqrt{\frac{0.10 \cdot \pi^2 \cdot E_{cd}}{11 \cdot f_{cd}}} \cdot \frac{\sqrt{1 + k_\delta \cdot n \cdot \rho}}{\sqrt{v}} \cong 0.30 \cdot \sqrt{\frac{E_{cd}}{f_{cd}}} \cdot \frac{\sqrt{1 + k_\delta \cdot n \cdot \rho}}{\sqrt{v}} \ . \tag{13}$$

A general relationship between the slenderness threshold $\lambda^*$ and the ratio $e_2/e_1$ between the top and the bottom eccentricities can be introduced to take into account the influence that the top-to-bottom eccentricity ratio $e_2/e_1$ has on second-order effects (Figure 1). Thus, the following relationship can be derived by considering the relationship (5) instead of (1) for defining the magnification factor $\mu$ (Faella et al., 1998):

$$\lambda^*_{MISF} = \sqrt{\frac{0.1}{0.91 + 0.46 \cdot \dfrac{e_2}{e_1}}} \cdot \sqrt{\frac{E_{cd}}{f_{cd}}} \cdot \frac{\sqrt{1 + k_\delta \cdot n \cdot \rho}}{\sqrt{v}} \ . \tag{14}$$

A reduction factor can be applied to the above equation (14) with the aim of getting more conservative results covering the effects of the mentioned inelastic phenomena: to this purpose, a 0.90 factor has been calibrated by the authors through a wide numerical investigation.

The same formulation can be utilized as well to take into account creep effect, which is particularly sizable if the axial forces mostly ensue from gravitational loads or other permanent actions. On the one hand, creep may increase first-order effects, but, on the other hand, it may reduce structural flexural stiffness because of the development of delayed axial strains. Hence, a further reduction of the above-defined slenderness threshold should be introduced to cover creep effects.

Among the simplified methods available in the literature to model creep effects in R/C members, the well-known Effective-Modulus Method takes care of the "apparent" reduction of concrete elastic modulus because of creep strains. Furthermore, since the axial load is only partially due to permanent loads, a slightly generalized expression for concrete effective modulus $E_{c,eff}$ has been introduced by Faella et al. (1998):

$$E_{c,eff} = \frac{E_{cd}}{1+\alpha\beta\phi} = \frac{E_{cd}}{1+\phi_{eff}} , \qquad (15)$$

where $\phi_{eff} = \alpha\,\beta\,\phi$ is a reduced coefficient of viscosity, with $\alpha = N_g/N_{Ed}$ is the ratio between the permanent axial load and the design axial load, and $\beta = M_g/M_{Ed}$ is the ratio between the permanent bending moment and the corresponding design value.

Finally, the following relationship for the slenderness threshold can be derived directly from (14), by introducing the effective value $n_t$ of the (steel-concrete) modular ratio n at the time t:

$$\lambda^* = \frac{0.9}{\sqrt{\nu}} \cdot \sqrt{\frac{0.1}{0.91 + 0.46 \cdot \frac{e_2}{e_1}}} \cdot \sqrt{\frac{E_{c,eff}}{f_{cd}}} \cdot \sqrt{1 + k_\delta \cdot n_t \cdot \rho} =$$

$$= \frac{0.9}{\sqrt{\nu}} \cdot \sqrt{\frac{0.1}{0.91 + 0.46 \cdot \frac{e_2}{e_1}}} \cdot \sqrt{\frac{E_{cd}}{f_{cd}}} \cdot \sqrt{\frac{1}{1 + \phi_{eff}} + k_\delta \cdot n \cdot \rho} \qquad (16)$$

## 3.4   Decree by the Italian Ministry of Public Works (09/01/96)

The Decree by the Italian Ministry of Public Works (9/1/1996, "D.M. 1996" in the following) provides designers with a direct formulation concerning the slenderness threshold, in which the fundamental characteristics of the theoretical formulae derived in section 2 can be clearly recognized. According to this document, a R/C column is slender if its slenderness $\lambda$ is higher than $\lambda*$:

$$\lambda^* = 60 \frac{1 + 15\rho}{\sqrt{N_{Rd} / A_c}} \ . \tag{17}$$

In equation (17) there is a linear proportionality with the amount of the reinforcement $\rho$, which means that the slenderness limit is strongly dependent on the stiffness of the cracked cross section, significantly influenced by the amount of the reinforcement.. Furthermore, at the denominator there is the square root of the average axial stress, already found in equation (7).

Equation (17) is accompanied by the recommendation that special care should be taken in the design of any columns having a slenderness larger than $3\lambda^*$.


### 3.5   Eurocode 2

The idea that second-order effects could be ignored if smaller than 10% of the corresponding first-order effects is accepted - as a general principle - by Eurocode 2 (EN-1992-1, 2005). However, the definition of the slenderness limits is quite different from the definitions discussed in Section 2.

For isolated columns, second-order effects can be neglected if the slenderness $\lambda$ is smaller than a certain value $\lambda *$:

$$\lambda^* = \frac{20ABC}{\sqrt{v}} \ . \tag{18}$$

where:
- the parameter A is a function of the effective creep coefficient $\phi_{eff}$ via the following relationship:

$$A = 1/(1 + \phi_{eff}) \ , \tag{19}$$

  however, assuming $A = 0.7$ is allowed if $\phi_{eff}$ is not known;
- the parameter B takes into account the amount of the longitudinal reinforcement via the following relationship:

$$B = \sqrt{1 + 2\omega} \ , \tag{20}$$

  assuming $B = 1.1$ is allowed, as a default value;
- the parameter C takes in account the ratio $r_m = e_2/e_1$ between the top and bottom eccentricities of the column, via the following relationship:

$$C = 1.7 - r_m \ , \tag{21}$$

- the parameter $\nu$ is the design value of the axial force $N_{Ed}$ divided by concrete capacity in compression $A_c f_{cd}$ .

Although equation (18) assumes an inverse dependence of $\lambda^*$ on the square root of the axial stress $\nu$ and introduces the parameter B to consider the effect of the reinforcement, the two formulations (7) and (18) are based on significantly-different expressions for the role of the eccentricities. In (7) the dependence of the ratio $e_2/e_1$ is mitigated by the square root, while in (18) the linear relationship between C and $r_m$ results in a higher sensitivity of the slenderness threshold to the shape of the bending moment diagram.

In Fig. 4 the normalized values of the slenderness limits according to eqs. (18) and (7) are plotted as a function of $e_2/e_1$. Eurocode 2 provides much higher values for $\lambda^*$, especially in the case of triangular moment distributions or moment distributions with opposite eccentricity on the top and the bottom of the beam-column. For instance, in the case of a triangular diagram ($e_2/e_1 = 0.0$) the slenderness limit given by (18) is almost twice as much as that given by (7).

Consequently, there could be several cases of beam-columns supposed to be "theoretically slender" according to equation (7), which can be actually classified as "non-slender" (or "short") ones according to the EC2 definition of limit slenderness.

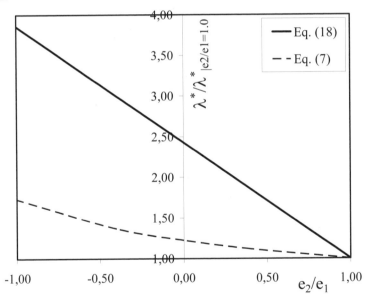

Figure 4 – Influence of the ratio $e_2/e_1$ on the slenderness limit $\lambda^*$ (EN-1992-1, 2005).

Thus, these preliminary observations suggest that the formulation of Eurocode 2 may be less conservative than (7), including the formulations more or less connected with (7), like the so-called MISF formulation (see Section 3.3). Comments on (7) compared to other formulations will be made in Section 5.

### 3.6 Decree by the Italian Ministry of Infrastructures and Transportation (14/01/2008)

The most recent version of the Italian Code for Buildings (see the Decree by the Ministry of Infrastructures and Transportation, 14/01/2008) provides a simplified expression for equation (18), by assuming for the parameters A and B the default values. Therefore the formulation of the slenderness limit is as follows:

$$\lambda^* = \frac{15.4C}{\sqrt{n}} \, , \tag{22}$$

where the parameter C defined in Eq.(21) is still explicitly mentioned. In the following, this proposal will be shortly referred as "NTC 2008".

### 4. PARAMETRIC ANALYSIS

An extensive parametric analysis has been carried out with the aim of comparing the limit values of the threshold slenderness given by the different codes and concerning the domains of slender and short columns. The analyses have been performed by means the so-called "general method" applied to the static solution of R/C beam-columns subjected to axial load and bending, and based on a finite-difference procedure.

The numerical procedure has been firstly validated by considering some experimental results available in the literature. In Figure 5 the numerical results are shown to fit rather well the test results in the case of Column "2A" tested by Levy and Spira (1971) and reported by Ferretti et al. (2002). The comparison is focused on the ascending branch of the load-displacement curve, because the prediction of the maximum capacity is of the utmost interest in this research project.

The proposed numerical procedure is utilized here for assessing the accuracy of the slenderness limitation indicated in Section 3. In particular, the maximum lateral displacement at the peak load under a given axial force is determined for a number of columns, whose slenderness is close to the limits specified in the various proposals reported in the previous section.

Several parameters affect the structural response of slender columns, as indicated in Section 2. Consequently, in the parametric analysis the following ranges have been considered:

- $e_2/e_1 = 1.0, 0.4, 0.0$;
- $f_{ck} = 20 - 50$ MPa;
- $\nu = 0.1 - 1.0$;
- $\rho = A_s/A_c = 0.005 - 0.05$;
- $\delta' = d'/h_c = 0.05 - 0.10$.

120

For any choice of the above parameters, the axial force N was derived as a function of the imposed normalized value $\nu$, and the limitations reported in Section 3 were assumed for deriving the values of the limit slenderness $\lambda^*$ and of the corresponding length L.

The normalized axial force $\nu$ was assumed as the main mechanical parameter. For each of the 140 "virtual" columns generated for as many values of $\nu$, and for each eccentricity ratio $e_2/e_1$, the value of the eccentricity $e_2$ causing the collapse was worked out.

Evaluating the second-order effects in each case and in collapse conditions was the final objective of the numerical investigation:

$$\frac{M_{II}}{M_I} = \frac{N \cdot v_{max}}{N \cdot e_2 + F \cdot L} = \frac{N \cdot v_{max}}{N \cdot e_1} \quad , \tag{23}$$

where $v_{max}$ is the value of the top displacement of the column in ultimate conditions.

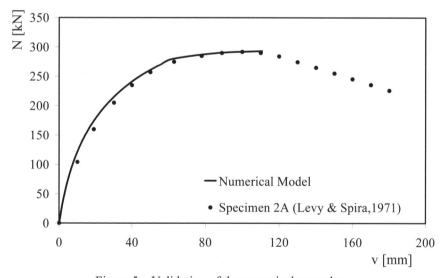

Figure 5 – Validation of the numerical procedure.

Second-order effects are assumed to be negligible if $M_{II}/M_I$ is lower than 0.10; consequently, the above condition has to be checked to assess the accuracy of the slenderness threshold reported in Section 3, that is not conservative, whenever the ratio $M_{II}/M_I$ is higher than 0.10.

## 5. DISCUSSION OF THE NUMERICAL RESULTS

About 1400 analyses have been carried out for each formulation of the limit slenderness reported in Section 3, considering 10 levels of the axial forces, with $v$ ranging from 0.10 to 1.0.

Figure 6 reports the median values of the ratio $M_{II}/M_I$ obtained for different values of $v$, assuming the limit values of the slenderness defined in the six proposals reported and commented in Section 3.

As already pointed out in a previous study (Faella et al., 1998), the values of the ratio $M_{II}/M_I$ resulting from the analyses are significantly lower than the commonly-adopted value 0.10, below which second-order effects may be neglected. Consequently, at least for $e_2/e_1 = 1.0$ all formulations are generally accurate and sometimes too conservative.

On the contrary, the above observation is not confirmed for other values of the ratio $e_2/e_1$. In particular, for the so-called "triangular" case (namely, $e_2/e_1 = 0.0$), the median values of $M_{II}/M_I$ move upward, and approach the limit value 0.10 or even exceed it for low axial-load levels (in the case of EC2 provisions).

In other words, the comparison between Figure 6 and Figure 7 confirms the theoretical considerations reported at the end of Section 3.5, about the too high sensitivity of EC2 proposal with respect to the parameter $e_2/e_1$.

Figures 8, 9 and 10 confirm such a sensitivity, showing how the mean, median and maximum values of $M_{II}/M_I$ (as a function of $v$) depend on the ratio $e_2/e_1$ (=1.0, 0.4, 0.0).

In the same figures, the standard deviation is reported as well, to give an idea about the scattering of the analytical results when the limit values on column slenderness are adopted according to EC2.

It should be observed that in the case $e_2/e_1 = 0.0$ (Fig.10) the mean and median values of $M_{II}/M_I$ are higher, and so the standard deviations.

The same trend is observed in Figs 11, 12 and 13 (NTC 2008); in particular, lower median values of $M_{II}/M_I$ have been obtained, since the terms A and B in (22) are introduced according to the default (and conservative) values accompanying the general formula (18). Nevertheless, the high sensitivity of $M_{II}/M_I$ to $e_2/e_1$ is confirmed.

Delayed effects (such as shrinkage and creep in concrete) have been neglected in the above analyses, that were focused on the most common case, in which the variable actions are significantly higher than the permanent actions. The delayed effects, however, can be introduced via - for instance - the parameter A (see the relationships 18 and 19). By varying A, the effects that delayed deformations have on the limit slenderness may be investigated.

The case of $\alpha \beta = 0.5$ defining $\phi_{eff}$ in equation (17) is considered in the following, as well as the value 2.0 for the creep coefficient $\phi$.

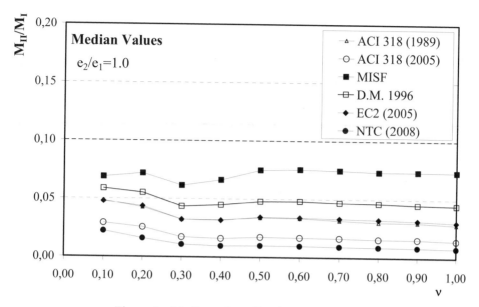

Figure 6 – Median value of $M_{II}/M_I$ ($e_2/e_1$=1.0).

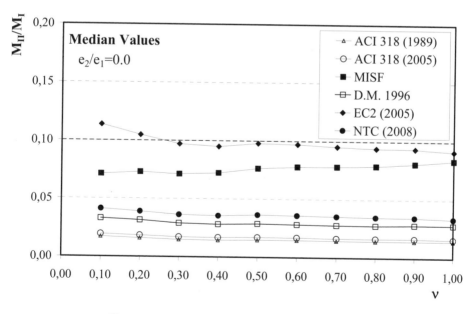

Figure 7 – Median value of $M_{II}/M_I$ ($e_2/e_1$=0.0).

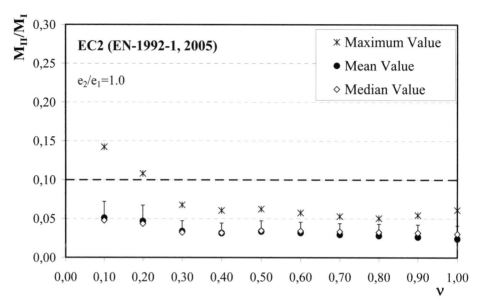

Figure 8 – Second-order effects for $e_2/e_1 = 1.0$  (EC2, see EN 1992-1, 2005).

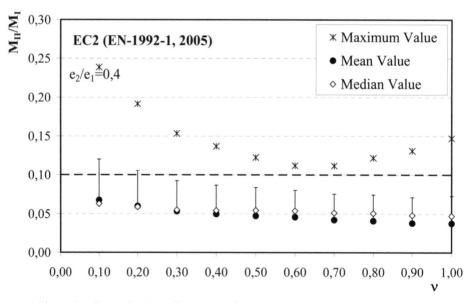

Figure 9 – Second-order effects for $e_2/e_1 = 0.4$ (EC2, see EN 1992-1, 2005).

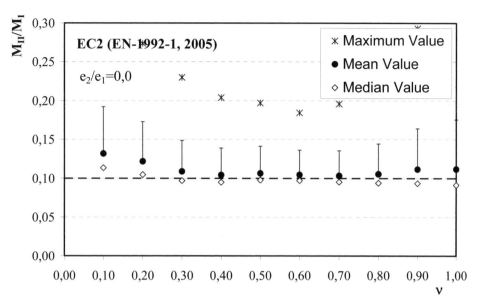

Figure 10 – Second-order effects for $e_2/e_1 = 0.0$ (EC2, see EN 1992-1, 2005).

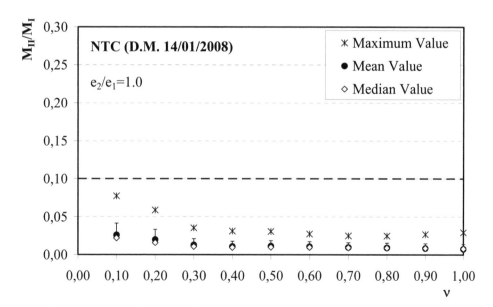

Figure 11 – Second-order effects for $e_2/e_1 = 1.0$ (NTC, see D.M. 14/01/2008).

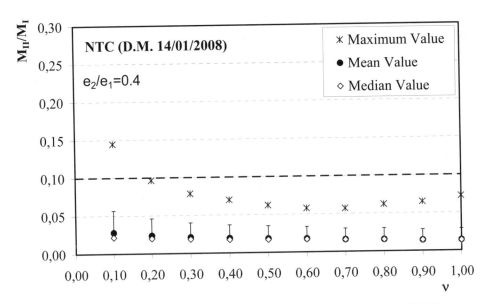

Figure 12 – Second-order effects for $e_2/e_1 = 0.4$ (NTC, see D.M. 14/01/2008).

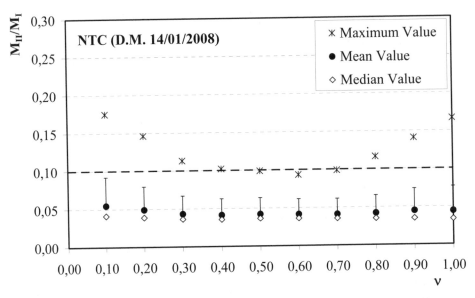

Figure 13 – Second-order effects for $e_2/e_1 = 0.0$ (NTC, se D.M. 14/01/2008).

The values of the threshold slenderness decrease by 50% compared to the corresponding values obtained by neglecting long-term deformations (Fig.14). The comparison with Figure 9 shows that including the long-term effects leads to a reduction of the $M_{II}/M_I$ ratio at failure.

It is worth noting that the numerical analyses including long-term deformations have been carried out on the basis of a simplified approach (Age-Adjusted Effective Modulus, AAEM).

In particular, a modified stress-strain relationship has been assumed for the concrete, by amplifying the elastic strains via the multiplying factor $(1+\phi_{eff})$, see Faella et al. (1998).

The above-mentioned figures, however, allow to conclude that in terms of stability instantaneous deformations are more critical than the long-term deformations.

Even in the case of short-term loading, this study confirms that the threshold values derived by Faella et al. (M.I.S.F. method, 1998) lead to $M_{II}/M_I$ values very close to 0.10 (and generally on the conservative side), with a limited scattering (Figures 15, 16 and 17).


# 6. CONCLUSIONS

Several formulations of the slenderness limits available in the technical literature for setting the threshold between slender and short R/C columns subjected to sizable first-order moments have been reported and compared in the present paper.

The main conclusions of a previous work with similar objectives are confirmed in the present paper, where the slenderness limitations provided by some of the most widely used codes of practice are shown to lead often to over-conservative results, whenever second-to-first order moment ratios $M_{II}/M_I$ are significantly lower than the 10% limit assumed as a tolerance threshold.

On the contrary, the most recent proposals (like the very recent Decree by the Italian Ministry of Infrastructures and Transportation, 2008; and Eurocode 2, see EN 1992-1, 2005) often lead to non-conservative results, because they overestimate the positive effect of non-uniform bending along the axis of the column.

Theoretical considerations as well as the parametric study carried out in this paper allow to recognize that these recent formulations are too sensitive to the bottom and top eccentricities, and to their ratio.

Moreover, including the long-term deformations into the analysis only results in a slight reduction of the errors in terms of second-order effects at failure, whose values are often larger than 10% of the corresponding first-order values.

In more details, creep influence on the overall response of R/C columns and creep contribution to second-order effects are generally overestimated by code proposals (particularly by the most recent two documents), since creep is

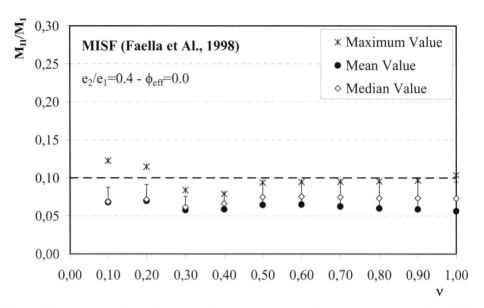

Figure 14 – Second-order effects considering long-term deformations for $e_2/e_1$=0.4 (EC2, see EN 1992-1, 2005).

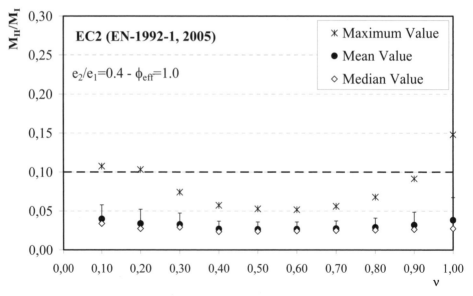

Figure 15 – Second-order effects for $e_2/e_1$ = 1.0 (MISF, see Faella et al., 1998).

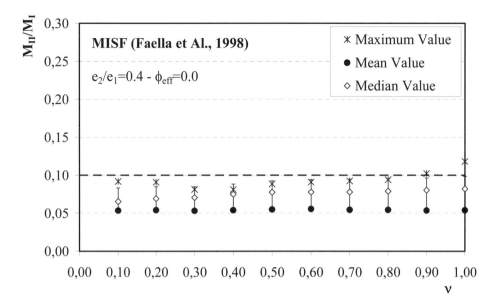

Figure 16 – Second-order effects for $e_2/e_1 = 0.4$ (MISF, see Faella et al., 1998).

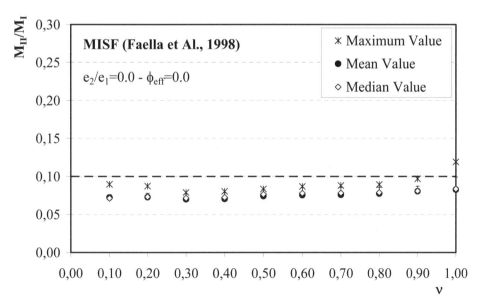

Figure 17 – Second-order effects for $e_2/e_1 = 0.0$ (MISF, see Faella et al., 1998).

introduced without considering the reinforcement. As it is well known, the reinforcement limits concrete creep, to such a point that creep is sizable only in lightly-reinforced members.

Finally, it is worth noting that the parametric analysis carried out in this study confirms the accuracy of the formulations based on simple mechanical considerations, as those proposed by the first and third authors in a previous paper (Faella et al., 1998).

## REFERENCES

A.C.I. 318-89 (revised 1992) / A.C.I. 318-05 (2005). *Building Code Requirements for Reinforced Concrete.* American Concrete Institute, Detroit (USA).

Bažant Z.P. and Cedolin L. (1991). *Stability of Structures: Elastic, Inelastic, Fracture and Damage Theories.* Oxford University Press, New York (USA).

EC-2 - EN 1992-1-1/2005 (2005). *Design of Concrete Structures, Part 1: General Rules and Rules for Buildings.*

Faella C., Nigro E. (1992). "Determinazione dell'eccentricità addizionale in regime elasto-viscoso lineare di elementi snelli di materiale omogeneo in presenza di armatura" (Evaluation of the Additional Eccentricity in Reinforced Homogeneous Elastic-Viscous Slender Members, in Italian). *Rendiconti Accademia Nazionale dei Lincei, Matematica e Applicazioni*, Series 9, Vol. 3.

Faella C., Consalvo V., Nigro E. (1998). "Alcune considerazioni sul limite di snellezza per le colonne in c.a. sensibili agli effetti del II ordine" (Some Considerations on Slenderness Limits in R/C Columns Sensitive to 2nd-Order Effects, in Italian). *Proc. XII Congress C.T.E.*, Padua (Italy), November 5-7.

Ferretti D., IORI I., Morini M. (2002). *La stabilità delle strutture – Il caso delle costruzioni in cemento armato (Stability of R/C Structures, in Italian).* McGraw-Hill Italia, Milan (Italy).

Levy M., Spira E. (1971). "Carrying Capacity of Plain- and Reinforced-Concrete Walls". *Proc. RILEM Int.l Symposium*, Buenos Aires, September 13-18.

Migliacci A., Mola F. (1985). *Progetto agli stati limite delle strutture in c.a. (Limit-State Design of R/C Structures, in Italian).* Pub. by Masson, Milan (Italy).

Ministry of Public Works, Decree 09/01/96 (1996). *Norme Tecniche per il calcolo, l'esecuzione ed il collaudo delle strutture di cemento armato normale e precompresso e per le strutture metalliche (Technical Provisions for the Design, Building and Inspection of R/C, P/C and Steel Structures).*

Ministry of Infrastructures and Transportation, Decree 14/01/08 (2008). *Nuove Norme Tecniche le Costruzioni (New Technical Provisions for the Constructions, in Italian).*

Timoshenko S. P., Gere J.M. (1961). *Theory of Elastic Stability*, 2nd Edition, pub. by McGraw-Hill, New York, (USA).

STUDIES AND RESEARCHES – V.29
Graduate School in Concrete Structures – Fratelli Pesenti
Politecnico di Milano, Italy

# CONCRETE RESIDUAL STRENGTH IN COMPRESSION : BLENDED CEMENTS VERSUS ORDINARY PORTLAND CEMENT

Eike Wolfram Klingsch[1], Andrea Frangi[2], Mario Fontana[3]

## ABSTRACT

The cement industry has been investing for several years in the development of new, environment-friendly blended cements, like supersulfated slag cement (SSC).

To allow this type of cement to be used in general-purpose constructions, basic information on the mechanical behavior of SSC concretes at elevated temperature and after cooling is needed. To this end, the results of an experimental research project on the compressive strength of two heat-exposed concretes containing blended cements are presented in this paper, and comparisons are made with a third ordinary concrete.

Three different types of cement were used during the tests: a supersulfated slag cement (SSC), a portland limestone cement (CEM II-A-LL) and an ordinary portland cement (CEM I). The compressive strength was measured at high temperature (hot tests), after cooling to ambient temperature (residual tests), and after a partial cooling to various temperatures comprised between the maximum temperature reached during each thermal cycle and ambient temperature (high-temperature residual tests). The specimens were concrete cylinders.

The results show that (a) SSC concrete exposed to high temperature has a mechanical behavior that is very close to those of limestone concretes and ordinary concretes containing portland cement; and (b) this similarity is confirmed by the high-temperature residual tests, whose results are the first published so far.

---

[1] Research Assistant, [2] Senior Researcher, [3] Professor
ETH, Institute of Structural Engineering (IBK), Zurich, Switzerland,

# 1. INTRODUCTION

The cement industry has been devoting a lot of efforts in the last decade to develop innovative, environment-friendly cement products, like - for instance - super-sulfated slag cement (SSC). In this type of cement up to 95% of the klinker is replaced with blast-furnace slag, a by-product of steel making. In this way, less energy is used for the production of klinker, and the emission of carbon dioxide is markedly reduced, compared to the production of ordinary portland cement.

As it is well known, concrete thermal and mechanical properties are deeply affected by the temperature. At high temperature, the mechanical properties exhibit a marked decay, generally followed by a reduction of the structural load-carrying capacity, while the structural deformability is enhanced. Since the rate of increase of the temperature in a concrete section is relatively low, the inner zones are protected against the heat. Therefore, reinforced concrete structures with adequate structural detailing (i.e. respecting certain minimum values like the size and the clear cover of the reinforcement) usually exhibit a satisfactory fire resistance, without any extra requirement for fire protection as mentioned in Eurocode 2 (2004).

Once the fire has been extinguished, however, heat penetration into the cross section generally continues for hours, since there is a thermal flux from the external hot layers, both inward and outward, with the possible formation of thermal stresses and cracks, as shown – for instance – by the numerical simulations carried out by Frangi et al. (2006). Additionally, chemical and physical phenomena, like the formation of calcium hydroxide and the re-hydration of the cement during the cooling phase, may cause the widening of the microcracks. The combination of these phenomena may lead to a significant reduction of concrete compressive strength past a fire. This topic was extensively analyzed in the past and among others the findings by Hertz (2005a; 2005b) and Khoury (1992) should be cited.

Investigations carried out by Felicetti and Gambarova (2008) found that the minimum strength is reached after 2-8 weeks since the end of the cooling process. (The strength loss is partly instantaneous - during the cooling process - and partly delayed - long-term loss; Li and Franssen, however, pointed out that the long-term loss is even more critical than the instantaneous loss).

The behavior of concrete at elevated temperature was extensively investigated in the past. An overview on concrete mechanical decay at high temperature, as well several recommendations for fire-resistant buildings were presented by Kordina and Meyer-Ottens (1999). Values for concrete strength at elevated temperature are given for example in Eurocode 2 (2004). Concrete strength is generally normalized with reference to the cold strength, for both siliceous and calcareous concretes. Little information, however, can be found on the development of the residual strength during the cooling process. According to Eurocode 4 (2005), concrete residual strength can be set to 90% of the hot strength.

This strength reduction is assumed to be independent from the maximum temperature previously reached by the concrete. For design purposes, the hot and residual strengths are upper- and lower-bound values. Any effect which might increase concrete residual strength above the hot strength is generally neglected.

During the mid 90s, many tests on concrete residual strength were carried out. These tests confirmed a strength reduction - compared to the hot strength - close to 10% for all the temperatures considered; these results, however, were never published and were seldom cited in other papers. With respect to these old tests, several recent tests carried out by such researchers as Li and Franssen (2009), and Felicetti and Gambarova (2008), suggest a larger reduction factor, comprised between 10% and 30%.

In general, the residual compressive strength after a partial cooling (from the maximum temperature reached during the heating process down to any temperature higher than the ambient temperature) has never been systematically investigated so far, though knowing more would be essential for refining the numerical analysis, whenever materials properties play a major role.

With reference to the specific case of the concretes containing supersulfated slag cement, there is a lack of basic knowledge on the mechanical behavior at elevated temperature and after cooling. Past studies have investigated the thermal properties of concrete made from either ordinary portland cement or portland blended cement (i.e. portland cement + blast furnace slag, fly ash or limestone powder). Only little attention has been devoted to SSC concrete.

Mendes (2008) analyzed at high temperature different cements with slag content up to 65%. He found that the residual strength increases at high slag contents, because of the reduced amount of calcium hydroxide, which causes the disintegration of ordinary hydrated portland cement.

A research project on the high-temperature behavior of concrete containing supersulfated slag cement is in progress at the Institute of Structural Engineering (IBK) at ETH Zurich. This research project aims to extend the theoretical and experimental database on the performance of SSC concrete at high temperature and after cooling. An extensive program using IBK electric furnace was performed to study the strength losses exhibited at high temperature by SSC, limestone and ordinary concretes, and to develop temperature-dependent stress-strain relationships at high temperature and past full/partial cooling. The stress-strain relationships can be used as input parameters in finite-element analysis and in the development of design models.

## 2. TEST SET-UP AND TESTING PROCEDURE

The experimental procedure is given in Table 1. All tests were carried out within a very short time-frame and the specimens were kept in controlled ambient conditions (T = 20°C; R.H. = 50%) to reduce the influence of concrete age and moisture content. The specimens were slowly heated up to the reference temperatures of 300°C, 500°C and 700°C. After a rest of two hours at the reference temperature, the specimens were cooled at a constant cooling rate.

The compressive strength at the reference temperature - hot strength -, as well as the strengths after full or partial cooling – residual strengths - were measured in displacement-controlled conditions. The typical thermal cycle is shown in Figure 1; the reference temperatures (hot and residual tests) are given in Table 1. The thermal cycles followed RILEM recommendations (Schneider, 1986), about the number of specimens to be tested at high temperature and after cooling.

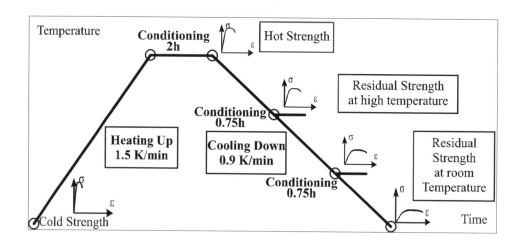

Figure 1 - Typical thermal cycle.

Table 1 - Testing procedure.

| Test Series | Max. Temperature | Reference temperatures | | | |
|---|---|---|---|---|---|
| 1 | 300°C | HS – 300°C | - | - | RS – 20°C |
| 2 | 500°C | HS – 500°C | - | RS – 300°C | RS – 20°C |
| 3 | 700°C | HS – 700°C | RS – 500°C | RS – 300°C | RS – 20°C |

HS = Hot Strength        RS = Residual Strength (after partial or full cooling)

In order to minimize the temperature gradients in the cross section and the ensuing thermal stresses, the heating and cooling rates were very low, and a "conditioning time" of 2 hours at the maximum temperature was adopted.

According to the test results presented in CEB-FIP Bulletin 46 (2008), heating and cooling rates should not exceed 5.0 and 1.0°C/min, respectively; higher values of the cooling rate would reduce the formation of calcium hydroxide, causing a higher residual strength, which decreases within days after the cooling process.

At first, a simple finite-element thermal analysis was carried out to predict the maximum thermal gradients during the heating and cooling phases. According to this analysis, as well as to literature results and preliminary tests, the heating rate at the concrete surface was set to 1.5°C/min and the cooling rate to 0.9°C/min respectively.

During the entire thermal cycle, the specimens were pre-loaded with a compressive stress close to 0.3 MPa (less than 0.75% of concrete cold strength). Concrete thermal expansion was practically unaffected by preloading and the specimens were assumed to be unloaded. As a matter of fact, concrete free thermal expansion during the thermal cycles may lead to some internal damage, to the detriment of the hot and residual strengths, because of the thermal incompatibility between the cement paste and the medium-coarse aggregates. (The role of preloading in compression, however, will be investigated in a further phase of this project).

After reaching the reference temperature, at the end of the conditioning period the specimen was tested in compression, and concrete strength at high temperature was evaluated. Since the furnace remained closed, concrete temperature was rather constant throughout each test. The loading process was displacement-controlled, with a constant rate of 0.005 mm/s measured between the press plates, as indicated in Figure 2.

The stress-strain curve was continuously monitored and the test was stopped manually after the fracture of the specimen. Usually two specimens were tested individually at each reference temperature. A total of 54 cylinders were tested. Concrete cold strength was determined in a similar manner, with the same displacement rate.

The tests were performed using an electric furnace ($T_{max} = 1000°C$). The maximum attainable heating rate measured on concrete surface (cylindrical specimens with a diameter of 150 mm and a length of 300 mm) was 4.5°C/min. The furnace consisted of two U-shaped vertical shells, allowing the specimen to be placed at mid-height inside the furnace; the specimens were surrounded by a steel cage to protect the furnace in case of concrete spalling.

Each concrete specimen was loaded by means of a hydraulic actuator, after being capped with thin layers of gypsum, to guarantee the uniform distribution and the centering of the axial load.

The test set-up is shown in figure 2. Figure 3 shows SSC concrete specimens before and after a full 500°C thermal cycle.

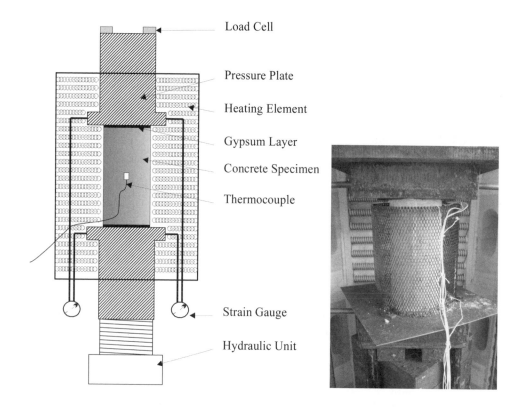

Load Cell

Pressure Plate

Heating Element

Gypsum Layer

Concrete Specimen

Thermocouple

Strain Gauge

Hydraulic Unit

Figure 2 - Test set-up and concrete specimen inside the furnace.

1) Untested      2) HS - 500°C      3) RS - 300°C      4) RS - 20°C

Figure 3 - SSC concrete specimens tested at 500°C and after partial/full cooling: (1) untested specimen, i.e. prior to testing; (2) test at 500°C; (c) test at 300°C after cooling from 500°C (partial cooling); and (4) test at 20°C after cooling from 500°C (full cooling).

## 3. TEST SPECIMENS

As previously mentioned, the tests were carried out using cylindrical specimens ($\varnothing = 150$ mm; $L = 300$ mm) made of three different concrete mixes. The mix design was the same, but for the cement, which was a superfulfated slag cement (SSC; slag content = 95%, Mix 1 = M1), a portland-limestone cement (CEM II-A-LL, Mix 2 = M2) and an ordinary portland cement (CEM I, Mix 3 = M3), as shown in Table 2.

The cement content and the water-cement ratio were 300 kg/m$^3$ and 0.55 in all three mixes. The aggregate was mixed (partly siliceous and partly calcareous, as explained later), with the maximum aggregate size $d_a = 32$ mm. The average mass per unit volume of the fresh concrete was 2420 kg/m$^3$, but after the storage at 20°C and 50% R.H. for 90 days a slight decrease was observed (2390 kg/m$^3$).

Table 2 - Mix designs and compressive strength.

| Concrete Mixture | - | M1 | M2 | M3 |
|---|---|---|---|---|
| Cement type | - | SSC | CEM II-A-LL | CEM I |
| Cement content | kg/m$^3$ | | 300 | |
| Water content | kg/m$^3$ | | 165 | |
| Water cement ratio | - | | 0.55 | |
| Concrete density (1 day) | kg/m$^3$ | 2424 | 2415 | 2451 |
| Concrete density (90 days) | kg/m$^3$ | 2391 | 2377 | 2407 |
| Maximum aggregate size $d_a$ | mm | | 32 | |
| $f_c$ at 90 days | MPa | 33.1 | 34.3 | 40.3 |

Before concreting, a petrographic analysis of the aggregate was carried out. Since the quarry was located close to a glacial moraine, a little less than 2/3 of the aggregate consisted of limestone gravel (close to 62%), while the remaining 1/3 (close to 38%) came from siliceous rocks (Table 3).

To guarantee the uniformity of the concrete inside each specimen, the rather large maximum aggregate size ($d_a = 32$ mm) required the cylindrical specimens to have larger dimensions than those usually adopted in high-temperature tests ($\varnothing = 150$ mm; h = 300 mm, contrary to the more usual $\varnothing = h/2 = 80\text{-}100$ mm).

The specimens were cast in ordinary laboratory conditions (T = 20°C and R.H. = 65%). Non-absorbent plastic cylinders were used for the formwork. Before concreting, four thermocouples were placed inside each formwork, two close to the mid-height section, and two at 30 mm from one of the end sections. The distance between the axes of each couple of thermocouples was not less than 30 mm, to minimize any possible perturbation caused by the electric fields.

Table 3: Petrographic analysis.

| Gravel constituents | % | Chemical nature |
|---|---|---|
| Limestone | 25 | Calcareous |
| Pebble Limestone | 32 | Calcareous |
| Sandstone (from flysch) | 28 | Siliceous |
| Granite, Gneiss | 6 | Siliceous |
| Chert, Quartz | 4 | Siliceous |
| Molasse | <5 | Calcareous |

The thermocouples were fixed to a 2 mm welding wire to guarantee their mutual position during concreting and compacting. (This set-up agrees with the guidelines published by the Institute for Material Research and Testing, BAM Berlin, 1990).

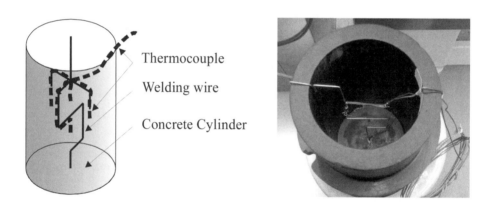

Thermocouple

Welding wire

Concrete Cylinder

Figure 4 - Thermocouples and formwork.

The concrete was poured into the formworks in two stages, and after each stage the specimen was compacted on the vibrating table. According to EN 12390-2 (2008) and EN 1363-1 (1999), the formwork was removed three days past concreting; then the cylinders were stored in very humid conditions (T = 20°C, R.H. 95%) for 28 days. At this age - and for further 90 days prior to heating - the specimens were stored in dry atmosphere (T = 20°C, R.H. 50%). The mass loss was monitored on a weekly basis until the specimens were heated in the furnace. At the time of testing, the specimens showed no significant mass loss.

# 4. TEST PROGRAM

The tests program is described in Table 3. While Steps 1 to 4 were carried out on all cement types, Steps 5 and 6 were limited to two cement types. After determining concrete strength in virgin conditions (Step 1), the same was done at high temperature (hot strength, Step 2). In Step 3, concrete residual compressive strength (past full cooling to 20°C) was evaluated. Step 4 concerned the evaluation of the high-temperature residual strength (past partial cooling).

Table 3: Test planning

| Step | Objective | Temperature Level | Number of specimens |
|------|-----------|-------------------|---------------------|
| 1 | Cold Strength | 20°C | $2^{1)}$ |
| 2 | Hot Strength | 300°C ; 500°C; 700°C | $2^{1)}$ |
| 3 | Residual Strength at 20°C | cooling to 20°C from the three temperature levels 300°C; 500°C; 700°C | $2^{1)}$ |
| 4 | Residual Strength at High Temperature | 500°C (cooling from 700°C); 300°C (cooling from 700°C); 300°C (cooling from 500°C) | $2^{1)}$ |
| 5 | Hot and Residual Strength past slow heating (limited to CEM-II-A-LL) | 500°C - hot strength 20°C - residual strength (cooling from 500°C) | 1 |
| 6 | Magnetic Resonance Imaging (limited to one CEM I specimen) | 20°C (cooling from 300°C) | 1 |

1) per concrete mixture and temperature level

# 5. TEST RESULTS

## 5.1 Stress-strain curves

The specimens containing the same type of cement showed no significant differences in terms of strength at room temperature, the average coefficient of variation being less than 5%. The average cold strength was 33.1 MPa for M1 (SSC concrete), 34.3 MPa for M2 (CEM II-A-LL) and 40.3 MPa for M3 (CEM I) after 90-day storage.

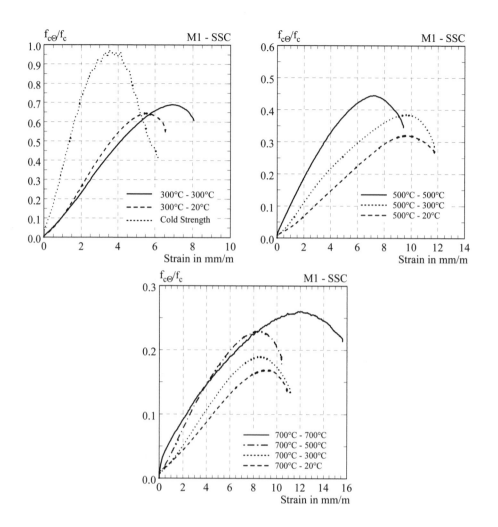

Figure 5 - Hot and residual stress-strain curves, Mix M1 (SSC concrete): first temperature indicated inside each figure = peak temperature reached at the end of the heating phase; second temperature = temperature during the test.

During the heating process, the temperatures at the concrete surface and in the core of the specimen were measured. The temperature development was controlled in such a way that the average temperature gradient between the surface and the core never exceeded 1°C/mm.

The stress-strain curves for the three different mixes are shown in Figures 5, 6 and 7, where the plots refer to the hot tests, as well as to the residual tests at high temperature and after cooling down to room temperature.

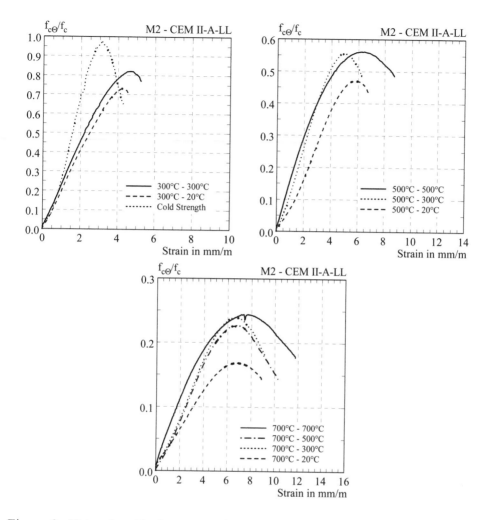

Figure 6 - Hot and residual stress-strain curves, Mix M2 (CEM II-A-LL concrete): first temperature indicated inside each figure = peak temperature reached at the end of the heating phase; second temperature = temperature during the test.

In general, the stress-strain curves are similar for all three mixes, even though SSC concrete exhibits higher strains at the stress peak. Furthermore, the hot stress-strain curves have a clearly defined loading branch, whose slope decreases monotonically with the strain, while the residual curves have an s-shaped loading branch, which is characterized by an upward concavity close to the origin. In general, the higher the maximum temperature, the more pronounced the s-shape after partial or full cooling. This is something that other authors did not experience in their tests, or were unable to detect, or decided to neglect, on the assumption that the initial upward concavity has to do with some inelastic settlements in the concrete close to the disturbed end sections.

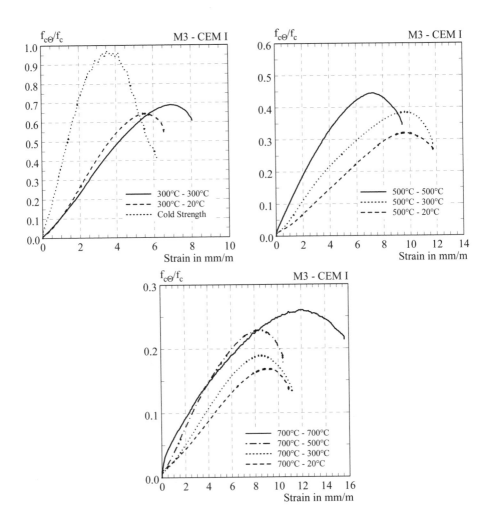

Figure 7 - Hot and residual stress-strain curves, Mix M3 (CEM 1 concrete): first temperature indicated inside each figure = peak temperature reached at the end of the heating phase; second temperature = temperature during the test.

A possible reason for the s-shaped stress-strain curves may be the loss of bond between the aggregate particles and the cement matrix during the cooling process. As a matter of fact, during the cooling process the thermal expansion of the aggregate particles decreases and gaps are formed between the matrix and the aggregate. Under increasing load during the following compression tests, the concrete is pressed together, and the gaps between the aggregate and the cement matrix are reduced or even closed. This effect tends to increase concrete own stiffness and may explain the s-shape of the stress-strain curves in residual conditions.

## 5.2 Magnetic Resonance Imaging

A number of preliminary tests with the help of Magnetic Resonance Imaging (MRI) was carried out in order to justify the previous hypothesis concerning the s-shape of the stress-strain curves in residual conditions. Using MRI at the University Hospital of Zurich, a concrete cylinder was scanned slice-by-slice. The higher-density particles inside the concrete cylinder appear brighter according to the grayscale, while cracks, cavities and air pores appear as black lines or dots (Fig. 8). After heating to 300°C, a concrete specimen containing CEM 1 was cooled and scanned. The main objective was to visualize the formation of possible cavities inside the specimen, between the cement matrix and the aggregate particles. As a matter of fact, Figure 8 shows that cavities form at the aggregate-matrix interface (the most affected zones are indicated by arrows).

Additional MRI scans are planned for the other two concretes, in order to have systematic information on the degree of bond loss between the cement matrix and the aggregate.

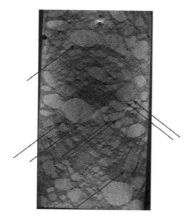

Figure 8 - Magnetic Resonance Imaging applied to a specimen made of mix M3 (CEM I) after a thermal cycle at 300°C.

## 5.3 Strength development with the temperature

Figure 9 shows the normalized results of both the hot and residual strengths of the three concretes. All results are normalized with reference to the strength before testing (cold strength = 1.0, virgin conditions). Starting at the relative cold strength of 1.0 at 20°C, the normalized hot strength as a function of the temperature is given by the continuous curve, while the dotted curves refer to the tests performed after partial or full cooling (at 20, 300, 500°C past a cycle at 700°C; at 20 and 300°C past a cycle at 500°C; at 20°C past a cycle at 300°C).

For instance, each of the intermediate dashed curves in Figure 9 shows that a specimen – heated up to 500°C and then cooled to 300°C - has a higher residual strength at 300°C than a specimen cooled to 20°C and tested at this temperature. In other terms, the residual strength at any temperature during the cooling phase is lower than the hot strength, but the higher the temperature in the residual test, the higher the residual strength. This is the novelty of this research project, since so far no residual strengths have been evaluated other than those corresponding to concrete full cooling (T = 20°C).

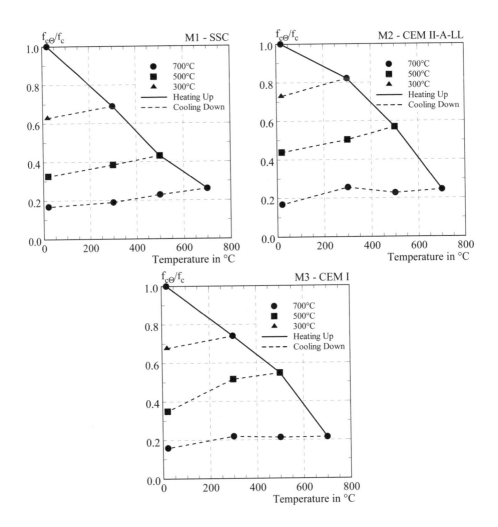

Figure 9 - Normalized plots of the compressive strength as a function of the temperature for the three concrete mixes investigated in this project.

As shown in Figure 9, SSC concrete shows slightly lower values for the hot strength compared to the concretes containing CEM II-A-LL and CEM I, at 300°C and 500°C. At higher temperature levels (700°C), all concretes behave similarly. While the strength loss during the cooling process is roughly linear in SSC concrete, this is not the case in the other two concretes, which are marginally more temperature-tolerant, especially below 500°C.

In general, the strength loss from hot conditions to residual conditions (room temperature) increases with the maximum temperature attained during the heating process. For instance, the specimens cooled from 300°C to 20°C have an average residual strength equal to 91% of the hot strength. After cooling from 500°C or 700°C to 20°C, the residual strength is down to 72% or 69%, respectively.

## 5.4 Influence of the heating rate

Any changes in the heating and cooling rates generally lead to significant changes in the development of concrete strength. Hertz (2005a) noticed that during the cooling phase, the formation of calcium hydroxide causes a deterioration in the concrete (voids and cracks), leading to a lower residual strength compared to the hot strength.

Fast cooling delays the formation of calcium hydroxide, leading to a higher residual strength in the short term, followed by a decrease in the next few days. Slow cooling of about 1.0°C/min or less enables a constant formation of calcium hydroxide and the minimum strength is attained some time past the end of the cooling process.

The sizable effects that the cooling rate has on the residual strength were observed by Mohamedbhai (1986), who recognized that the cooling rate is one of the main parameters influencing the residual strength. This influence was observed up to a maximum temperature of 600°C. At higher temperatures, the influence of the cooling rate becomes negligible. Mohamedbhai (1986) also observed that (a) the majority of the mechanical decay takes place within the first two hours of the exposure to high temperature, and (b) the higher the temperature, the lower the effect of exposure time.

Hertz (2005a) analyzed the influence of cooling conditions. Contrary to what happens when concrete is cooled in air, cooling concrete in water brings in a strength recovery, because the micro-cracks are filled by water, and calcium hydroxide can form inside the micro-cracks and the voids, which leads to a residual compressive strength even higher than the hot strength. Unfortunately, no temperature ranges for these recovery processes were given by Hertz (2005a).

Investigations carried out by Chan (2000) on ordinary concrete came to different conclusions. He adopted a "gradual cooling", i.e. natural cooling inside the furnace (after the electric power was switched off) and fast cooling by water drenching. The residual strength was only slightly affected by these rather harsh cooling conditions. After an exposure to 800°C, the slowly-cooled specimens exhibited a slightly higher (+11%) residual strength compared to the specimens subjected to both natural and in-water cooling.

To check whether the selected heating and cooling rates (+1.5°C/min and -0.9°C/min) lead to significant results in terms of mechanical decay, both, additional hot and residual tests were carried out. To this end, the influence of the heating and cooling rates was studied by carrying out two additional tests characterized by lower heating and cooling rates.

Two CEM II-A-LL cylinders were heated to 500°C; then the first was tested at this temperature (hot test) and the second was cooled to room temperature and tested (residual test). The 500°C thermal level was chosen, since at this temperature the mechanical decay of the concrete starts becoming sizable. The heating and cooling rates were reduced to 0.5°C/min and 0.3°C/min, respectively. At 500°C the temperature was kept constant for three hours.

The stress-strain curves in Figure 10 are very similar in both cases. As expected, the stress-strain curves referring to residual conditions show the typical s-shape. The specimen heated more slowly exhibits a slightly lower hot strength, compared to the specimen heated more rapidly.

As for the residual strength, the former specimen shows a slightly higher residual strength. The differences are very small and may be - at least partly - due to the natural dishomogeneity of the concrete. (The rest period of 3 hours at the reference temperature in the slower tests – compared to 2 hours in most of the tests – was expected to have no effect on strength development).

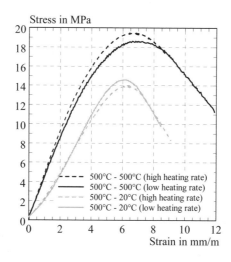

Figure 10 - Tests on CEM II concrete: stress-strain curves for two heating rates
Thick curves: standard heating and cooling rates = +1.5/-0.9°C/min.
Thin curves: low heating and cooling rates = +0.5/-0.3°C/min.

## 6. COMPARISON WITH STANDARDS AND LITERATURE

The values for the hot strength of concrete are given in Eurocode 2 (2004). Eurocode 4 (2005) gives also the values for the residual strength. In Eurocodes 2 and 4, the hot and residual strengths are given through normalized values, as a function of the maximum temperature reached by the concrete, for aggregate types (calcareous and siliceous aggregates, EC2).

Concrete with siliceous aggregate shows a higher reduction for the hot strength than concrete with calcareous aggregate. Since the mixes investigated in this project consisted of both aggregate types, the results of the tests were compared with the lower values based on siliceous aggregate. The values of the hot strength for CEM I and CEM II-A-LL concretes fit quite well those suggested by Eurocode 2, as shown in figure 11. The values relating to SSC concrete are affected by a higher loss at 300°C and 500°C, while at 700°C there is no practical difference between the three mixes and the predictions of Eurocode 2.

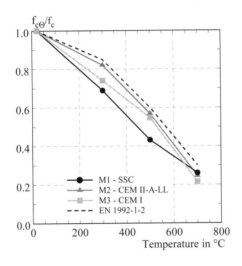

Figure 11 - Hot strength versus temperature: results from this project and predictions by Eurocode 2.

According to Eurocode 4, the residual compressive strength after cooling to room temperature can be estimated as 90% of the corresponding hot strength. This constant reduction factor can be used for all temperature levels. The tests performed in this project (as other tests available in the literature) show, however, something different, as indicated by Figure 12, where the normalized strength is plotted at high temperature and after cooling for all concrete types and temperature levels. At 300°C the residual strength is 9% less than the corresponding hot

147

strength, which is close to the suggested loss of 10% specified by Eurocode 4. At 500/700°C, the additional losses in the residual strength increases to 28%/31%, respectively. This implies that EC4 predictions seem to be acceptable for rather low temperatures, but overestimate the residual strength after a thermal cycle at higher temperatures (400°C - 500°C and onwards).

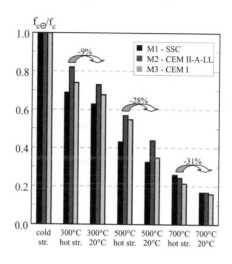

Figure 12 – Full cooling: strength loss in the tests performed in this project and percent decrease compared to the hot strength (average values of the 3 mixes).

In Figure 13 the normalized values of the residual strength obtained in this project are compared with those obtained by other authors (Chang et al., 2005; Sideris, 2007; Bamonte & Gambarova, 2009) and with Eurocode 4. There is an acceptable agreement among the tests performed by the different authors. All tests, however, confirm the overestimation of the residual strength by EC4. (Note that the tests performed by Sideris and Bamonte & Gambarova concerned both self-compacting concretes and ordinary concretes, but the authors came to the conclusion that there are no sizable differences between the high-temperature behaviors of SCC and ordinary concrete).

Concrete strength varied between 27 and 51 MPa. The results of the tests carried out by Chang et al. (2005) agree well with the values based on Eurocode 4, while all other results are lower, as already mentioned. Sideris' concretes contained a blended cement and crushed-granite aggregate ($f_c$ = 30 MPa). Bamonte & Gambarova's cylindrical specimens ($\varnothing$ = 100 mm, L = 200 mm; $f_c$ = 50-90 MPa) contained a limestone cement, and a mix of siliceous and calcareous aggregates; their concrete was very similar to Mix 2 of this project, as confirmed by the test results, that are very close.

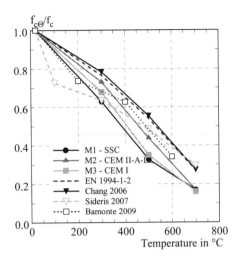

Figure 13 - Residual strength versus temperature: comparison with other results available in the literature and Eurocode 4.

Mendes et al. (2008) analyzed the residual compressive strength of blended cement with a slag content of 35%, 50% and 65%. The specimens were small cylinders ($\varnothing$ = 50 mm, L = 100 mm), heated up to 800C at a rather high heating rate (6.25°C/min). Then the cylinders were left inside the furnace, where they cooled naturally. The cold compressive strength was 45 MPa for 35% and 50% klinker replacement with slag, and 30 MPa for 65% klinker replacement. These results were compared with those concerning the SSC concrete (95% klinker replacement with slag) tested in this project as shown in Figure 14.

According to Mendes' results, replacing 35% and 50% of the klinker with slag slightly decreases the concrete strength up to 300°C, but replacing 65% of the klinker leads to a strength increase up to 400°C. Above 400°C, however, there is a rapid loss. Compared to Mendes' results, those of this project are much lower (Fig.14). A possible explanation may be found in an observation made by Mendes, that the reaction of slag with calcium hydroxide and hydrated cement paste may improve the resistance at elevated temperature. The rapid strength loss at temperatures above 400°C, however, was not discussed, as well as the scattering of the results.

## 7. OUTLOOK

The stress-strain curves obtained in this research project will be used as input data in the numerical analysis of R/C elements using finite elements. This information

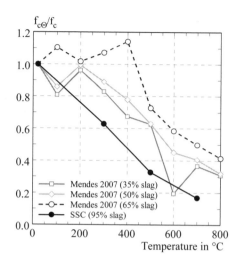

Figure 14 - Normalized residual strength of the SSC concrete tested in this project and comparison with the blended-cement concretes tested by Mendes et al. (2008).

is badly needed, since numerical models must consider concrete thermal history and should distinguish between the strength development during the heating and cooling processes.

Another aspect that should be investigated - since very little data is available on this issue - is the medium-term decrease of the residual strength, followed by a long-term recovery, which may even bring the residual strength to the same level of the hot strength. Some information on this is given in the CEB-FIP (2008) guidelines, with reference to rather low temperatures (250°C). In other tests by Poon et al. (2001), with concrete specimens heated up to 800°C, a recovery close to 93% of the original unheated strength was observed, but an appropriate post fire curing was required.

In future tests, the long-term effects will be analyzed. Concrete cylinders will be heated up to the three different target temperatures and then cooled to room temperature, as described in this paper. The residual strength will be evaluated after a number of months and up to one year. In addition, the re-hydration of the cement will be investigated, by examining and testing mortar prisms. These prisms will be exposed to the same thermal cycles of the concrete specimens, and will be stored in different conditions after cooling (sealed, unsealed, water-stored). The results will extend the knowledge on the long-term development of concrete compressive strength. Similar tests on concrete cylinders with different slag contents were carried out by Mendes et al. (2009). They observed that concrete containing ordinary portland cement and slag were not affected by re-hydration over a one-year period, and no changes occurred in the long-term development of the residual strength.

Due to unrestrained thermal expansion and crack formation, the specimens that are unloaded during the heating process (= unstressed specimens) exhibit lower hot and residual strengths than pre-loaded specimens, as mentioned in CEB-FIP Bulletin 46 (2008). Hence, a further test series is planned on pre-loaded concrete cylinders similar to the unloaded cylinders tested in this project.

## CONCLUSIONS

The results of this project on the hot and residual strength of concrete exposed to high temperature can be summarized as follows:

- The decay curves contained in Eurocode 2 and Eurocode 4 fit quite well the tests performed in this project in terms of hot strength, while Eurocode 4 definitely overestimates the residual compressive strength after full cooling.

- The loss in terms of compressive strength after cooling down to room temperature increases with the maximum temperature reached by the concrete during the heating process.

- All specimens showed extended cracking, but a sizable residual strength, even after cooling from very high temperatures.

- Even after cooling from moderate temperatures (300°C), debonding between the cement matrix and the coarse aggregate was observed by using Magnetic Resonance Imaging. Debonding may be the cause of the s-shaped loading branch of the residual stress-strain curves.

- The strength loss in supersulfated slag cement concrete (SSC concrete) at high temperature is slightly larger than that of concrete containing either ordinary portland cement or portland-limestone cement. However, the general performance of SSC concrete at high temperature is similar to that of the other concretes, in terms of stress-strain relationship and additional loss during the cooling process.

## ACKNOWLEDGEMENTS

The financial support by Holcim Group Support Ltd., who also supplied the test specimens, is gratefully acknowledged.

Special thanks should be conveyed to Dr. Med. Thomas Frauenfelder from the Institute for Diagnostic Radiology of the University Hospital Zurich, whose collaboration was instrumental in using the Magnetic Resonance Imaging facilities of the hospital.

# REFERENCES

ABM-Paper 2A (1990). *German Federal Institute for Materials Research and Testing.* BAM Berlin.

Bamonte P. and Gambarova P. (2009). "Self-Compacting Concrete at high Temperature: a Critical Survey and Recent Test Results". *Proceedings of Application of Structural Fire Engineering*, Prague, Czech Republic, pp.234-239.

Chan S. Y. N., Luo X. and Sun W. (2000). "Effect of High Temperature and Cooling Regimes on the Compressive Strength and Pore Properties of High Performance Concrete". *Construction and Building Materials* Vol 14, pp.261-266.

Chang Y. F., Chen Y. H., Sheu M. S. and Yao G. C. (2006). "Residual Stress-Strain Relationship for Concrete after Exposure to High Temperatures". *Cement and Concrete Research* Vol. 36, pp.1999-2005.

EN 12390 (2008). *Testing Hardened Concrete - Part 2: Making and Curing Specimens for Strength Tests.* EN 12390-2:2008, CEN European Committee for Standardization.

EN 1363-1 (1999). *Fire Resistance Tests - Part 1: General Requirements*, EN 1363-1:1999. CEN European Committee for Standardization.

Eurocode 2 (2004). *Design of Concrete Structures; Part 1-2: General Rules - Structural Fire Design EN 1992-1-2:2004.* CEN European Committee for Standardization.

Eurocode 4 (2005). *Design of Composite Steel and Concrete Structures - Part 1-2: General Rules - Structural Fire Design EN 1994-1-2:2005.* CEN European Committee for Standardization.

Felicetti R. and Gambarova P. (2008), "Expertise and Assessment of Materials and Structures after Fire". *CEB-FIP State-of-Art Report Bulletin 46 "Fire Design of Concrete Structures – Structural Behaviour and Assessment"*, Lausanne (Switzerland), pp. 63-114.

FIB State-of-Art Report Bulletin 46 (2008). *Fire Design of Concrete Structures – Structural Behaviour and Assessment.* Lausanne (Switzerland).

Frangi A., Tesar C. and Fontana M. (2006). "Bearing Capacity of Fire-Exposed Concrete Buildings" (in German). *Bauphysik,* Vol. 28, pp.170–183.

Hertz K. D. (2005a). "Concrete Strength for Fire Safety Design". *Magazine of Concrete Research,* Vol. 57, pp.445-453.

Hertz K. D. (2005b). "Assessment of Performance-based Requirements for Structural Design". *Proceedings of the 8th International Symposium on Fire Safety Science.* Beijing, pp.18-23.

Khoury G. A. (1992). "Compressive Strength of Concrete at High Temperatures: a Reassessment". *Magazine of Concrete Research,* Vol. 44, pp.291-309.

Kordina K. and Meyer-Ottens C. (1999). "Beton - Brandschutz-Handbuch". *Vbt Verlag Bau U. Technik,* 2nd edition.

Li Y.-H. and Franssen J.-M. (2009). "Residual Compressive Strength of Concrete after Heating from a Fire Situation". Private communication..

Mendes A., Sanjayan J. and Collins F. (2008). "Phase Transformations and Mechanical Strength of OPC Slag Pastes Submitted to High Temperatures". *Materials and Structures,* Vol. 41, pp.345-350.

Mendes A. and Sanjayan J. (2009). "Long-term Progressive Deterioration Following Fire Exposure of OPC versus Slag Blended Cement Pastes". *Materials and Structures,* Vol. 42, pp.95-101.

Mohamedbhai G. T. G. (1986). "Effect of Exposure Time and Rates of Heating and Cooling on Residual Strength of Heated Concrete". *Magazine of Concrete Research,* Vol 38, pp.151-158.

Poon C. S., Azhar S. Anson M. and Wong X.-L. (2001). "Strength and Durability Recovery of Fire-Damaged Concrete after Post-Fire Curing". *Cement and Concrete Research,* Vol 31, pp.1307-1318.

Schneider U. (1986). *Properties of Materials at High Temperatures-Concrete.* 3rd ed. RILEM Report. Kassel University, Kassel.

Sideris K. K. (2007). "Mechanical Characteristics of Self-Consolidating Concretes Exposed to elevated Temperatures". *ASCE Journal of Materials in Civil Engineering* Vol. 19, pp.648-654.

STUDIES AND RESEARCHES – V. 29, 2009
Graduate School in Concrete Structures
Politecnico di Milano, Italy

# REPAIR OF FIRE-DAMAGED R/C MEMBERS VIA HIGH-PERFORMANCE JACKETING

Angelo Leonardi[1], Alberto Meda[1], Zila Rinaldi[2]

## SUMMARY

A new repair technique, developed for fire-damaged R/C structures and based on the application of jackets made of high-performance fiber-reinforced concrete, is presented and discussed. The proposed technique may be in principle applied to both beams and columns, not only to restore the safety level after a fire, but also to increase fire safety in undamaged structures. (This aspect, however, is not treated in the paper, since R/C jacketing against fire is hardly cost-effective).

At first, the residual bearing capacity of a few "reference" members is determined for different values of the fire duration. Then, after discussing the pros and cons of the application of concrete jacketing to the structural cases in question, the performance of the composite structures is investigated, to make comparisons with the performance of the original undamaged structures, as well as with that of damaged structures.

Finally, the fire resistance of the repaired members is evaluated, to show the effectiveness of the proposed technique.

[1]Associate Professor, [2]Assistant Professor,
Rome University "Tor Vergata", Italy.

# 1. INTRODUCTION

Repair and strengthening of existing R/C structures is of great interest not only for extending their useful life, but also – and rather often – for their rehabilitation after being damaged during exceptional events such as earthquake and fire.

The preliminary question for any designer involved in the rehabilitation of fire-damaged structures is to check whether any specific repair strategy may be appropriate with respect to partial or total demolition, followed by reconstruction.

As a matter of fact, it has been shown recently that repairing fire-damaged structures, after a proper assessment campaign, may be the right choice (Taerwe et al., 2006; Mangoni et al., 2006). Hence, evaluating the residual bearing capacity of a fire-damaged structure is a necessary step before choosing any specific repair technique.

To this end, knowing materials residual properties after the fire is of primary importance for both concrete and steel (Felicetti and Gambarova, 1998; Felicetti et al., 2009; FIB Bulletin 46, 2008). Luckily, new techniques for the assessment of fire damage in R/C structures have been recently developed (Colombo and Felicetti, 2007), and deriving the residual properties of concrete and steel after a fire is nowadays much less uncertain than in the past.

For repairing fire-damaged structures, different solutions are available, such as partial reconstruction, adoption of R/C jacketing or use of externally-bonded fiber-reinforced polymers (FRP).

As should be expected, the choice of the repair technique has to do with the damage level and with the use of the structure after being repaired. At this stage, the designer should be aware of two requirements: the repaired structure should exhibit not only a sufficient bearing capacity in ordinary conditions, but also an adequate fire resistance, because a second fire cannot be ruled out.

A new technique has been recently proposed for strengthening R/C structures via thin jackets made of high-performance fiber-reinforced cementitious composites (HPFRCC, see Fisher and Li, 2006; Reinhardt and Naaman, 2007). These materials are characterized by a high compressive strength, which is accompanied by a rather high tensile strength, as well as by a hardening behavior in tension. Since the traditional reinforcement is no longer necessary, the usual limits specified for the cover do not apply to the jacket (no rebars and stirrups), and the thickness of the jacket can be as small as 30-40 mm.

The effectiveness of HPFRCC jackets for repairing fire-damaged R/C beams and columns is investigated in this paper, by performing a number of numerical analyses, where Coccia and Rinaldi's model (2006) - based on the direct integration of temperature-dependent materials constitutive laws – is adopted.

A first analysis is carried out for a number of selected "reference" sections of both beams and columns, subjected to different fire exposures under the standard fire ISO 834 (EN1991-1-2; 2004), in order to evaluate their residual behavior (Phase RES1). Subsequently, the behavior of the damaged sections, strengthened by means of HPFRCC jackets, is studied, in ordinary conditions (Phase REP) and then under a second fire (Phase REPHOT), to verify the effectiveness of the proposed repair technique.

## 2. HIGH-PERFORMANCE FIBER-REINFORCED JACKETING

Strengthening and/or repairing R/C beams with HPFRCC jackets has been investigated in previous research projects, by performing both numerical and experimental tests on full-scale members. The results are briefly described in this chapter, but more details can be found in Martinola et al. (2007), and in Maisto et al. (2007).

Three beams having a length of 4.55 m and a rectangular section with a depth of 500 mm and a width of 300 mm (Fig. 1) have been tested up to failure. The beams are longitudinally reinforced by means of 2 ∅ 16 mm bars at the bottom and 2 ∅ 12 mm at the top.

Two-leg stirrups (diameter = 8 mm; spacing = 150 mm) are placed at the extremities to resist the shearing force. Concrete grade was C20/25, and the combination of a rather low compressive strength with a rather light reinforcement (0.3%) was chosen in order to emphasize the positive effect of strengthening.

The first specimen (SP1) was considered as the "reference" case, while the second one (SP2) had a 40 mm-thick HPFRCC jacket (Fig. 2). The third specimen (SP3) was damaged by increasing the load up to the yielding of the tensile reinforcement, then the specimen was unloaded and repaired by applying a cementitious jacket. In this way it was possible to check the effectiveness of the jacket, as a means to strengthen and repair a typical R/C structure.

The HPFRCC jacket was cast directly on the surface of the original beam, after sandblasting to guarantee a perfect adhesion between the old concrete and the jacket (Martinola et al., 2007). With regard to this point, it is worth noting that HPFRCCs generally exhibit a rather low shrinkage; consequently, the interface stresses related to the possible different hygrothermal properties in the "new" and "old" materials are limited.

The HPFRCC was a micro-concrete (maximum aggregate size of 2 mm) reinforced with steel micro-fibers (content by volume = 2.5%; length = 15 mm and diameter = 0.18 mm). HPFRCC compressive strength was 180 MPa, while the uniaxial tensile strength – evaluated by testing dog-bone specimens according to the Italian Standard CNR DT 204 (2006) – was close to 12 MPa (Fig. 3; $f_{ct}/f_c$ = 1/15).

The load-deflection curves of the three specimens are plotted in Figure 4 (deflection = mid-span displacement). The HPFRCC jacket is very effective in increasing the bearing capacity and the stiffness in both the strengthened beam (no previous damage) and the repaired beam (previously loaded up to steel yielding). There is not much difference, however, between the strengthened and the repaired beams, but the former has a slightly larger peak load, while the latter has a slightly more extended and higher softening branch. Both have a much larger bearing capacity than the original un-jacketed beam, since after the application of the jacket the peak load becomes twice as much.

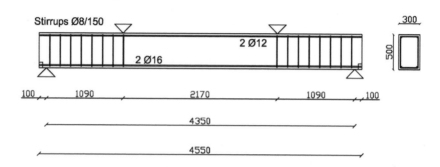

Figure 1 – Beam geometry.

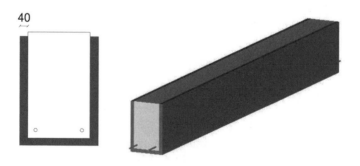

Figure 2 – Beam strengthening with HPFRCC jacketing (Martinola et al., 2007).

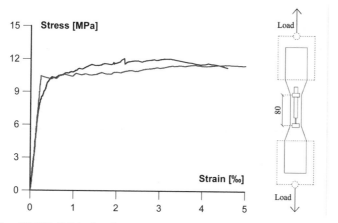

Figure 3 – HPFRCC behavior in uniaxial tension (Martinola et al., 2007).

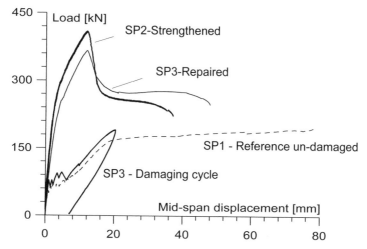

Figure 4 – Comparison among the reference undamaged un-jacketed beam SP1 (dashed curve), the undamaged strengthened beam SP2 (top curve), and the damaged repaired beam SP3 (damaging cycle and intermediate curve), from Martinola et al., 2007.

## 3. RESIDUAL BEARING CAPACITY OF R/C BEAMS

Jacketing by means of HPFRCC for repairing fire-damaged R/C members was firstly analytically investigated from a theoretical-analytical point of view. Initially, a beam with the same cross section (300x500 mm) adopted in a previous research project (Martinola et al., 2007) was considered. As for the longitudinal reinforcement, the bottom reinforcement consisted of four bars (∅16 mm), whose reinforcement ratio (0.6%) is typical of ordinary beams (Fig. 5).

Concrete behavior in compression ($f_c$ = 30 MPa) was modeled according to Kent and Park (1971), while steel behavior was described through an elastic-hardening law (strength at yielding 560 MPa and ultimate strength 670 MPa).

In order to assess the bearing capacity of the beam after the fire, the thermal analysis was performed by means of an available finite-element code (MAPTEMP, 1999) that can solve the conduction problem at the sectional level. Reference was made to the standard fire ISO 834 (EN1991-1-2, 2004) and to the thermal properties indicated in Eurocode 2 (EN1992-1-2, 2004). As shown in Figure 5, three of the four sides of the section were exposed to the fire. The fourth side (top side) was assumed to be in adiabatic conditions.

The after-fire capacity of the beam (phase RES1) was evaluated by means of the analytical procedure proposed by Rinaldi (2006) and extended to fire-damaged members by Coccia and Rinaldi (2006). According to this procedure, the temperature-dependent constitutive laws of the materials are directly integrated, in so providing the relationship between the bending moment and the mean curvature, for any given value of the axial load.

As a matter of fact, the cross-section is considered as a "composite" cross-section consisting of a number of layers (or "subsections"). Each subsection has a constant temperature at each step of the thermal analysis and is characterized by the constitutive relationship of the concrete at that temperature (Fig.6).

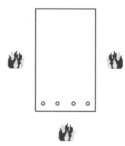

Figure 5 – Fire-exposed cross section of the reference beam considered in the numerical analysis.

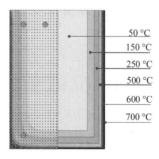

Figure 6 – Actual (left) and simplified (right) thermal fields (the latter was adopted in the mechanical analysis).

160

Concrete residual properties were assumed to coincide with the hot properties, and the values suggested by Eurocode 2 (EN1992-1-2, 2004) for siliceous aggregate were adopted (Fig. 7a). As for the residual strength of steel bars, reference was made to the first-hand experimental results published by Felicetti et al. (2009), concerning hot-rolled Tempcore bars (Fig. 7b).

The results are shown in Figure 8, in terms of ultimate resistant moment for different values of the fire duration.

A slight strength decrease occurs before the fire duration reaches 60 minutes (reduction of about 6%). Then the strength starts decreasing almost linearly, and after 90, 120 and 180 minutes the strength decay is close to 15%, 28% and 46%, respectively.

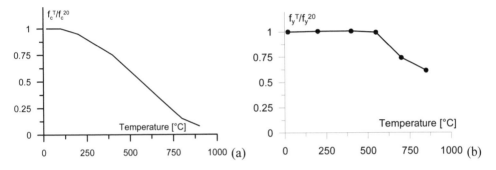

Figure 7 – Residual-strength decay for concrete (a); and steel rebars (b).

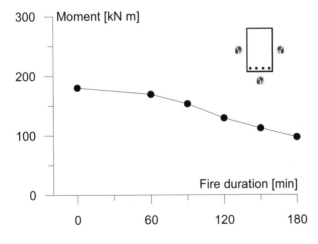

Figure 8 – Residual sectional capacity as a function of fire duration.

## 4. REPAIRING THE FIRE-DAMAGED BEAM

The damaged beam was repaired by applying a 40 mm-thick HPFRCC jacket along the lateral sides and the bottom side (Fig. 2).

The mechanical analysis was carried out with the same procedure used in the original beam, before and after the fire. Of course, the damaged part of the section was modeled on the basis of the temperature-dependent stress-strain relationships of concrete and steel, while the HPFRCC jacket was modeled as a virgin material, by adopting Kent and Park's formulation for the constitutive law in compression ($f_c$ = 180 MPa) and an elastic-plastic formulation in tension ($f_{ct}$ = 11 MPa, Fig.3).

The bearing capacity of the repaired beam at room temperature, before the second fire (Phase REP), is plotted in Figure 9, as a function of the fire exposure of the original beam. The bottom and top curves refer to the ultimate resisting moments of the section, after the fire and after being repaired, respectively. The bearing capacity of the repaired section is always larger than that of the original undamaged beam (dashed line in Fig. 9), and - for any fire duration - the jacket provides a 100% increase in terms of sectional bearing capacity.

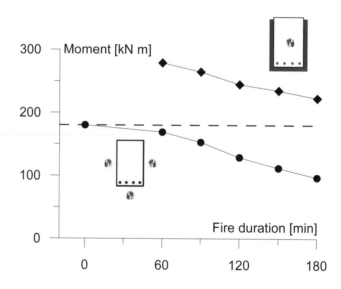

Figure 9 – Bearing capacity of the repaired beam (top curve) compared to those of the original beam, after being fire damaged (bottom curve) and in virgin conditions (dashed line), as a function of fire duration.

## 5. FIRE RESISTANCE OF THE REPAIRED BEAM

Any structure – after being repaired past a fire - should have a fire resistance higher than (or at least equal to) that in virgin conditions. Very often, however, fire resistance has to be increased in order to respect updated code provisions, in terms of fire safety, loads or use of the structure. Hence, it is imperative to investigate the hot behavior of the beam repaired by means of the HPFRCC jacket, should a second fire occur (Phase REPHOT).

A second thermal analysis on the repaired beam was performed, on the basis of reasonable values for the thermal properties of HPFRCC. These properties were taken from the literature.

As it is well known, HPFRCCs generally has a thermal conductivity higher than that of traditional concrete. For instance, according to Mindeguia et al. (2007), the thermal conductivity is almost twice as much in certain microconcretes. In the following, the HPFRCC conductivity is given a value that is exactly 100% larger than that suggested in Eurocode 2 (EN1992-1-2, 2004) for ordinary concrete (Fig. 10).

Due to the lack of available data, the mass per unit volume and the specific heat at different temperatures have been assumed equal to those of ordinary concrete (Eurocode 2).

After the thermal analysis, the mechanical analysis was performed. For the tensile strength of HPFRCC, the values reported in De Chefdebien et al. (2007) were adopted. Their tests showed a rapid decrease of the strength up to 150°C and a sort of plateau at higher temperatures (Fig. 11).

For any temperature higher than 950°C the tensile strength was neglected. (It is fair to say that HPFRCC mechanical properties at high temperature are still little known, as demonstrated by recent literature, see for instance Bamonte and Gambarova, 2008).

For concrete compressive strength and for steel properties at high temperature, reference was made to the decay laws given in Eurocode 2 (EN1992-1-2, 2004).

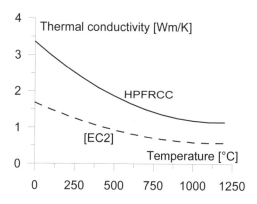

Figure 10 – HPFRCC: thermal conductivity as a function of the temperature.

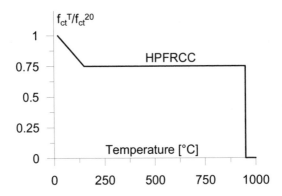

Figure 11 – HPFRCC: tensile strength as a function of the temperature.

As an example of the results obtained in this project, Figure 12 shows the response of a beam damaged by a 60-minute fire, repaired with a 40 mm-thick jacket and subjected to a second fire. The repaired beam can resist a new fire up to 180 minutes.

In Figure 13, the resistance of a fire-damaged and repaired beam is plotted as a function of the duration of a second fire, for three values of the duration of the first fire (60, 90 and 120 minutes).

As an example, a beam damaged by a first fire with a duration of 120 minutes and repaired with a HPFRCC jacket exhibits a bearing capacity that is higher than that of the virgin beam for any fire duration under 120 minutes.

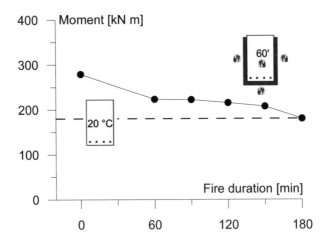

Figure 12 – Beam repaired after being exposed for 60 minutes to the standard fire: fire resistance during the exposure to a second fire.

# 6. REPAIR OF COLUMNS

In order to extend the analysis to the members subjected to an eccentric axial force, a number of columns having the same cross section as the previous beams (300x500 mm), reinforced with four bars per side (∅ 16 mm; total number of the bars = 12) has been studied. Each column was assumed to be exposed to the fire on all four sides.

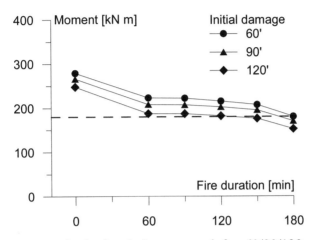

Figure 13 – Beam repaired after being exposed for 60/90/120 minutes to the standard fire: fire resistance during a second fire.

In order to define the bearing capacity of the columns, the $M_u$-$N_u$ envelopes were worked out by using the same procedure adopted for the beams. For different values of the fire duration and for a set of values of the axial force, writing the equilibrium equations of the section made it possible to work out a series of points of each envelope, by integrating the stresses and their moments, on the basis of the temperature-dependent constitutive laws. In this way, the $M_u$-$N_u$ envelopes, at ambient temperature ($T_a$) and the residual ones (Phase RES1) after a fire exposure of 60, 90, 120, 150 and 180 minutes were obtained (Fig. 14). By increasing the fire duration, the bearing capacity decreases and the $M_u$-$N_u$ envelopes shrink.

After being exposed to the fire, the section was repaired by applying a HPFRCC 40 mm-thick jacket along the four sides. For the thermal and mechanical properties of HPFRCC at high temperature, the same laws adopted in beam analysis were used in column analysis.

As an example, in Figure 15 the $M_u$-$N_u$ envelopes at ambient temperature, and the residual envelopes (Phase RES1) after 60 and 180 minutes of fire exposure are reported, together with the residual envelopes of the sections repaired after the above said fires (phase REP, symbols R-60 and R-180, respectively). Note the sizable increase in bearing capacity, because of the contribution of the strengthening jacket, that improves very much indeed the mechanical behavior of the column, compared to the original one.

As in the case of beams, the fire-resistance of the repaired section of the column is now evaluated (Phase REPHOT). To this end, a second standard fire was applied to the four sides of the repaired column, by adopting the same procedure and materials properties previously used in beam analysis.

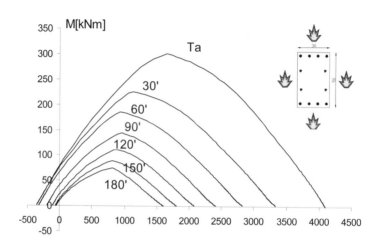

Figure 14 – Original section: $M_u$-$N_u$ envelopes for a section subjected to a four-side fire, for different values of the fire duration.

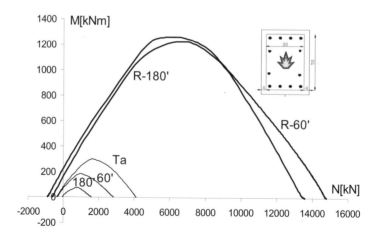

Figure 15 – $M_u$-$N_u$ envelopes of the original section (Ta), of the section subjected to a four-side fire having a duration of 60 and 180 minutes (60', 180', Phase RES1), and of the repaired section (R-60', R-180', Phase REP).

Figure 16 refers to the behavior of a section damaged by a fire exposure of 90 minutes, repaired and subjected to a second fire of 90 minutes. The same in Figure 17, where the duration of both the first and second fires is 180 minutes.

The results confirm the effectiveness of the proposed technique for repairing and strengthening fire-damaged columns.

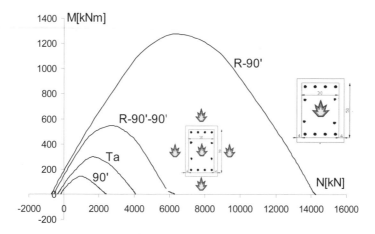

Figure 16 – $M_u$-$N_u$ envelopes of the original section (Ta), of the section subjected to a four-side fire having a duration of 90 minutes (90', Phase RES1), of the repaired section (R-90', Phase REP), and of the section subjected to a second four-side fire having a duration of 90 minutes (R-90'-90', Phase REPHOT)

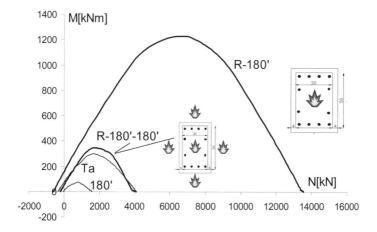

Figure 17 – $M_u$-$N_u$ envelopes of the original section (Ta), of the section subjected to a four-side fire having a duration of 180 minutes (180', Phase RES1), of the repaired section (R-180', Phase REP), and of the section subjected to a second four-side fire having a duration of 180'minutes (R-180'-180', Phase REPHOT)

# 7. CONCLUDING REMARKS

HPFRCC jacketing has been shown to be an effective repair and strengthening technique for existing R/C members exposed to high temperature and fire.

A jacket having a thickness of 40 mm applied to beams and columns with rather large sections (300 x 500 mm) makes it possible to significantly increase the bearing capacity in fire-damaged beams and columns, and gives the composite sections – and members – very good mechanical properties, should a second fire occur.

In particular, for a typical beam or column cross-section the following indications are given by the results obtained in this project:

- beams subjected to bending, damaged by a first standard fire of 120 minutes and later repaired, exhibit a bearing capacity higher than the original beams, for any duration of a second fire up to 120 minutes;

- columns subjected to an eccentric axial load, damaged by a first standard fire of 180 minutes and later repaired, exhibit a bearing capacity (expressed in terms of $M_u$-$N_u$ envelopes) higher than the original columns, for any duration of a second fire up to 180 minutes.

The proposed technique is advantageous also for its handiness, since – after removing and sandblasting the "old" fire-damaged concrete – it is possible to cast the high-performance fiber-reinforced cementitious composite directly on the surface of the old concrete (no need of coating the old concrete with a primer to guarantee the adhesion with the jacket). The new HPFRCC layers are not subjected to the usual limitations concerning concrete covers, since ordinary reinforcement is not required.

The results presented in this paper were obtained by means of a simplified analytical model, specifically developed for the evaluation of the residual bearing capacity of fire-damaged members. Nevertheless, albeit very promising, the results shown here require further checks, and improvements are needed with regard to concrete thermal behavior after a thermal cycle and during the reheating phase, as well as to HPFRCC thermal behavior.

# REFERENCES

Bamonte P. , Gambarova P.G. (2008). "Thermo-Mechanical Characterization of a UHPC Exposed to High Temperature and Application to a Two-Layered Apron". *Studies and Researches - Politecnico di Milano.* Vol.28, pub. by Starrylink (Brescia, Italy), pp.103-131.

CNR DT 204/2006 (2006). *Guidelines for the Design, Construction and Production Control of Fibre Reinforced Concrete Structures*, Italian National Research Council – CNR.

Coccia S., Rinaldi Z. (2006). "Residual Strength of R/C Beams after a Fire". *Proc. SiF' 06, Fourth International Workshop on Structures in Fire*, Aveiro, Portugal, 10 – 12 May, Vol.2, pp. 767-777.

Colombo M., Felicetti R. (2007). "New NDT Techniques for the Assessment of Fire-Damaged Concrete Structures". *Fire Safety Journal*, (42), pp.461-472.

De Chefdebien A., Robert F., Collignon C. (2007). « Performance of Ultra High-Strength Concrete Subjected to Fire". *Proc. 5th Int. Conf. on Concrete under Severe Conditions - CONSEC'07*, Tours (France). 4-6 June, Vol.2, pp. 1649-1658.

EN1991-1-2 (2004). *Eurocode 1: Actions on Structures. Part 1-2: General Actions – Actions on Structures Exposed to Fire*.

EN1992-1-2 (2004). *Eurocode 2: Design of Concrete Structures - Part 1-2: General Rules – Structural Fire Design*.

Felicetti R., Meda A., Gambarova P.G. (2009). "Residual Behavior of Steel Rebars and R/C Sections after a Fire". *Construction and Building Materials*, doi:10.1016/ j.conbuildmat.2009.06.050 (in press).

Felicetti R., Gambarova P.G. (1998). "Effects of High Temperature on the Residual Compressive Strength of Siliceous HSCs". *ACI Mat. Journal* 95(4), pp.395–406.

Fib Bulletin 46 (2008). *Fire Design of Concrete Structures – Structural Behaviour and Assessment*. Lausanne (Switzerland).

Fisher G., Li V.C. (2006). *Proc. Int. RILEM Workshop on High-Performance Fiber-Reinforced Cementitious Composites (HPFRCC) in Structural Applications*. RILEM Publications S.A.R.L., PRO 49.

Kent D.C., Park R. (1971). „Flexural Members with Confined Concrete". *Journal of the Structural Division*, ASCE 97(7), pp. 1969-1989.

Maisto L., Meda A., Plizzari G.A., Rinaldi Z. (2007). "R/C Beams Strengthening and Repair with High-Performance Fiber-Reinforced Concrete Jacket". *Proc. 4th Int. Conf. on the Conceptual Approach to Structural Design*, Venice (Italy).

Mangoni E., Spinelli P., Benedetti A. (2006). "R/C Structures Exposed to Fire: Damage Assessment and Efficient Structural Repairing with FRP". *FIB - Proc. 2nd Int. Congress*, Naples (Italy), 5-8 June 2006, ID12-6, Session 12 (on CD).

MAPPTEMP. (1991). *Thermal Analysis of Fire-Exposed Structures* (in Italian). User's Manual, ALPHARD S.r.l., Milan (Italy).

Martinola G., Meda A., Plizzari G.A., Rinaldi Z. (2007). "An Application of High-Performance Fiber-Reinforced Cementitious Composites for R/C Beams Strengthening". *Proc. FRAMCOS 6 - Sixth Int. Conf. on Fracture Mechanics of Concrete Structures*, Catania (Italy). 18-21 June 2007, Vol. 3, pp. 1541-1548.

Mindeguia J.C., Pimienta P., Simon A., Atif N. (2007). "Experimental and Numerical Study of an UHPFRC at Very High Temperature". *Proc. 5th Int. Conf. on Concrete under Severe Conditions - CONSEC'07,* Tours (France). 4-6 June 2007, vol. 2, pp. 1659-1666.

Reinhardt, H.W., Naaman, A.E. (2007). "High-Performance Fiber-Reinforced Cement Composites (HPFRCC5)". *Proc. 5th Int. RILEM Workshop*, RILEM Publications S.A.R.L., PRO 53.

Rinaldi, Z. (2006). "An Analytical Model for the Evaluation of the Local Ductility of R/C Members". *Studies and Researches - Politecnico di Milano*, Vol.26, pub. by Starrylink (Brescia, Italy), pp. 75-102.

Taerwe L., Poppe A., Annerel E., Vandevelde P. (2006). "Structural Assessment of a Pretensioned Concrete Girder after Fire Exposure". *FIB - Proc. 2nd Int. Congress*, Naples (Italy), 5-8 June 2006, ID 12-8, Session 12 (on CD).

STUDIES AND RESEARCHES – V. 29, 2009
Graduate School in Concrete Structures
Politecnico di Milano, Italy

# EXPERIMENTAL INVESTIGATION ON THE MECHANICAL BEHAVIOR OF CORRODED PRETENSIONED BEAMS

Zila Rinaldi[1], Stefania Imperatore[2], Claudio Valente[3]

## ABSTRACT

Corrosion phenomena and related effects, such as size reduction in both rebars and strands, bond decay at steel-concrete interface, and cracking in the surrounding concrete, are particularly critical in prestressed-concrete members, not only for safety reasons, but also for their huge possible socio-economic effects, since this technique has been used for the last 50 years in the majority of viaducts and bridges built in many countries like Italy.

In order to evaluate the influence that corrosion has on prestressed pretensioned beams, a number of tests has been carried out in the Laboratory of the University of Rome "Tor Vergata".

Nine prestressed beams (section size 200x300; total length 3000 mm; clear span 2700 mm) were first subjected to artificial corrosion, to obtain different damage levels, and then were tested in 4-point bending.

The results clearly show the sizable effects that corrosion has on the ultimate capacity (that is significantly reduced), on the failure mode and on the structural response, that turns from ductile to brittle.

---

[1] Assistant Professor, University of Rome "Tor Vergata", Italy.
[2] PhD, University of Rome "Tor Vergata", Italy.
[3] Associate Professor, University "Gabriele d'Annunzio", Chieti-Pescara, Italy.

# 1. INTRODUCTION

The influence that steel corrosion has on the global behavior of reinforced-concrete members is well known, but - in spite of the many studies on this topic - reliable equations and procedures for the assessment of structural residual life are still unavailable. The relevance of steel corrosion – and its economical implications - is witnessed by the many theoretical and experimental research projects documented in the literature, mainly concerning reinforced-concrete members (Rodriguez et al., 1996; Cairns, 1998; Castel et al., 2000; Coronelli and Gambarova, 2001, 2004; and Rinaldi et al., 2007).

On the contrary, even if prestressed concrete has been used in many constructions – and is increasingly used in new constructions - rather sensitive to steel corrosion (such as bridges and viaducts), limited attention has been devoted so far to the chemical and mechanical issues concerning P/C structures. A possible explanation of the scanty efforts devoted to the development of suitable methodologies for defining the safety level and for modeling the behavior of corroded P/C members is the complexity of the problem and the numerous parameters coming into play.

In prestressed structures, the possible consequences of steel corrosion are much more serious than in reinforced concrete, since strands are subjected to high mechanical stresses; consequently, the combination of corrosion-induced sectional reductions and notch effects can be fatal for structural safety (Bergsma et al., 1977; CUR, 1977; ACI, 2001).

Besides the classical pitting corrosion (due to chlorides), there is also a damage form called "environmentally-induced cracking" (EIC), that is related to the state of stress in the steel and may lead to a brittle failure even in a ductile material. EIC includes the so-called "stress-corrosion" or anodic corrosion, and the "brittleness by hydrogen" (hydrogen-induced cracking, HIC) or cathodic corrosion (Whiting et al., 1993; US Federal Highway Administration, 2000).

Last but not least, it is worth mentioning the "fretting corrosion", appearing as a damage of bond and occurring when the corroded surface of the strand is exposed to oxygen, as - for example - close to a crack (Nurnberger, 2002).

Cables and strands may fail in different ways depending on corrosion type, working conditions (static, dynamic, cyclic loads) and steel properties; further-more, according to Vehovar et al. (1998), increasing corrosion diminishes not only steel mechanical properties, but also its ductility, making the material more brittle.

The above-mentioned references show that most of the literature in the field of reinforcement corrosion refers to prestressing-steel sensitivity as such (ACI, 2001; McDougall and Barlett, 2002; see also the state-of-the art bulletin by FIP, 1980, on stress corrosion). In-situ environmental conditions of both cables and strands (that are embedded in the concrete), however, are different from those of the specimens subjected to accelerated corrosion. Consequently, the results obtained so far cannot be considered exhaustive, because corrosion effects should be studied making reference to the whole structure (concrete plus prestressing reinforcement), even more since corrosion phenomena in P/C members are very dangerous (ACI, 1992).

Corrosion in prestressing steel is rather underhand, because it does not produce rust in such amounts to cause concrete cracking, and the structural collapse may be sudden (Hoover, 1996). In particular, bond loss may reduce the prestressing force and steel mechanical degradation may cause a brittle failure.

Experimental evidence on the behavior of prestressed members is reported in Mircea et al. (1994) and in Valiente (2000). Numerical approaches for the safety assessment of post-tensioned beams exposed to an aggressive environment have been proposed by Coronelli et al. (2008), while probabilistic models for pitting corrosion have been formulated by Darmawan and Stewart (2007), to be used later in the numerical modeling of prestressed bridge girders.

In this paper, the effects that corrosion has on simple prestressed members have been investigated. Nine pretensioned beams (section size 200x300 mm; total length 3000 mm) have been subjected to four-point bending in the Laboratory of the University of Rome "Tor Vergata".

Three beams were kept in ordinary environmental conditions as a "reference", while the strands of the other six beams were artificially corroded, up to a mass loss of about 7%, 14% and 20%. Furthermore three different concrete grades were considered. The tests were displacement-controlled, and the load, the displacement in a number of points, the crack opening and the slip of the strands at the extremities (*pull-in*) were continuously monitored. The results clearly show the sizable influence that corrosion has on the structural behavior.

## 2. BEAM ELEMENTS AND CORROSION PROCESSES

Three groups of pretensioned beams (Series 1, 2 and 3), each consisting of 3 specimens, were tested in four-point bending (4PBT) up to failure.

All beams had the same geometry (section size 200 x 300 mm; total length 3000 mm; span during the tests 2700 mm). Prestressing was provided by three ½-inch – 7 wires strands, two placed at the bottom of the section and one at the top (Figure 1). The initial prestressing stress was 1300 MPa.

Some details of the geometry and of the reinforcement (4∅10 ordinary bars and ∅8 stirrups (spacing 100 or 200 mm), all epoxy coated against corrosion) are shown in Figure 1. The only difference among the three series is the grade of the concrete (see Table 1, where the average compression strength $f_{cc}$ measured on 150-mm cubes is reported as well).

The prestressing-induced precamber ($v_c$) is reported in Table 1, before and after the corrosion process, together with the corrosion levels.

In the six corroded beams, artificial corrosion was induced by a suitable direct current and was accelerated by means of a saline solution.

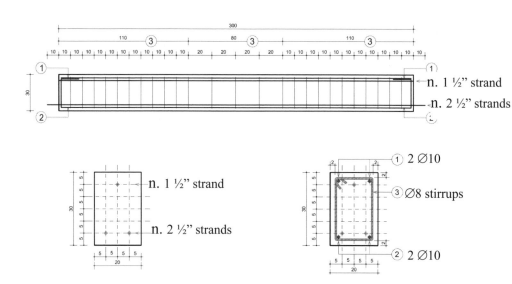

Figure 1 - Beam geometry and reinforcement.

Table 1. Test program, corrosion levels and precamber ($v_c$) of the specimens, prior and after being corroded.

| Series | 1 | | | 2 | | | 3 | | |
|---|---|---|---|---|---|---|---|---|---|
| $f_{cc}$ [MPa] | 34.0 | | | 41.5 | | | 47.4 | | |
| Beam No. | 7 | 8 | 9 | 2 | 3 | 1 | 4 | 6 | 5 |
| Corrosion level | 0% | 20% | 20% | 0% | 14% | 20% | 0% | 7% | 20% |
| $v_c$ before corr.[mm] | 1.6 | 3.0 | 1.3 | 3.1 | 3.4 | 4.4 | 0.7 | 1.1 | 2.1 |
| $v_c$ after corr.[mm] | - | 2.0 | 0.4 | - | 2.1 | 3.1 | - | 0.2 | 0.6 |

The corrosion is limited to the central zone of the beams (Figs. 2, 3), to avoid any corrosion-induced bond loss at the extremities of the strands. (Such loss may trigger a shear-type failure, while the objective of this research project is the bending-type failure of corroded beams).

Only the two bottom strands are subjected to accelerated corrosion, because these strands are in the tension zone during the loading process. During the corrosion process, however, the beam is turned upside down, in order to make the visual checks on concrete surface easier. (Crack formation and evolution can be monitored in a much better way looking downwards). Hence, the two strands subjected to corrosion appear at the top of the specimen during the corrosion process. The 5% NaCl saline solution fills specifically-handmade polystyrene containers (Fig. 3).

174

The layout of the system designed to accelerate the corrosion process is shown in Figure 2: the strands are the anode, while the steel bars dipped in the saline solution are the cathode.

Before starting the process of electrolytic corrosion, the central zone of each specimen was left for two days in the saline solution (*conditioning period*), in order to facilitate the corrosion process, by allowing the solution to permeate – by gravity – the concrete cover and to reach the strands.

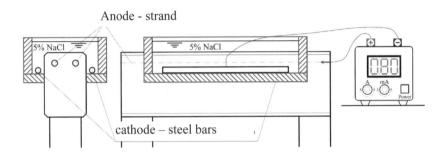

Figure 2 – Layout of the set-up designed to accelerate bar corrosion.

Figure 3 – (a) Polystyrene containers for the saline solution; and (b) beams subjected to the corrosion process.

The duration of the corrosion process, to reach the selected corrosion levels, was set according to Faraday's law, suitably corrected with a scale factor $\alpha \geq 1$, to account for the time lag of the corrosion process, because of the protection offered by the concrete cover. The expression of the Faraday's law is as follows:

$$time = \alpha \frac{m_{loss} \cdot n_{specimen} \cdot C_{Far}}{I_{corr} \cdot M_{specimen}} \quad (1)$$

where $M_{specimen}$ is the molar mass of the strands, $n_{specimen}$ is its valence, $C_{Far}$ is Faraday's constant (96480 C·mol⁻¹), $I_{corr}$ is the imposed current in ampères (A) and the time is expressed in seconds.

Of course, a preliminary calibration of the entire process was necessary. To this end, three specimens having the same cross section and reinforcement of the beams, but a length limited to 1000 mm and no prestressing strands, were subjected to accelerated corrosion (0.4 A).

All specimens showed that the desired corrosion level is reached in a period of time, that is twice as much that required by bare bars (only in this case does Faraday's law apply). Hence, a multiplier factor (= 2) was adopted in the evaluation of the time necessary to reach the desired level of corrosion, starting from the time evaluated by means of Faraday's law. Furthermore, preliminary corrosion tests showed the effectiveness of the process, because the strands were corroded as expected and corrosion was accompanied by the formation of longitudinal cracks in the concrete.

Looking at the beams after the corrosion process (duration close to 185 hours for a mass loss of 7%, and up to 528 hours for a mass loss of 20%), the following remarks can be made:

- with a current intensity of 0.4 A applied to a length of 60-70 cm, the first cracks appear roughly after 10 hours, for an expected mass loss of about 1%; in the following two days, cracks become visible along the whole surface subjected to corrosion; later, the cracks spread beyond the limits of the containers;

- at the end of the corrosion process, the beams exhibit a sizable reduction of the midspan precamber, due to the corrosion-induced prestressing loss.


## 3. TEST SET-UP

All specimens were subjected to displacement-controlled 4-point bending, and the tests were carried out by using an electromechanical jack of 1000 kN. The shear length was equal to one third of the total span length (900 mm, Fig. 4).

The instrumentation is shown in Figure 4: one 1000 kN load cell; 2 LVDTs to check strand slip at beam ends; 5 displacement transducers (Pot 1 to 5 in Fig. 4) to measure the vertical displacements; 2 displacement transducers (wire 1 and wire 2 in Figure 4) to detect any possible rotations in the midspan section due to a non uniform corrosion-induced behavior. A Witthemore deformometer was used for the evaluation of the strains, according to the 50x50-mm grid shown in Figure 4.

As indicated in Table 1, Series 1, 2 and 3 are characterized by an average concrete cubic strength ($f_{cc}$) of 34.0, 41.5 MPa and 47.4 MPa, respectively. In each series, one beam is kept in ordinary environmental conditions as a reference (Beams No. 7, 2 and 4).

The corrosion levels adopted in this study stand for low, mild and severe damage (7%, 14% and 20% by loss of steel mass).

It should be observed that two levels of corrosion were considered in Series 2 and 3 (14% and 20%, and 7% and 20%, respectively) and one level in Series 1 (20%, albeit repeated in two specimens). In this way, the tests gave some information about test repeatability (Beams No. 8 and 9 in Series 1), decay at the same maximum corrosion level (Beams No. 8, 9 in Series 1; Beam No. 1 in Series 2; and Beam No. 5 in Series 3), and decay at intermediate corrosion levels (Beam No. 3 in Series 2, and Beam No. 6 in Series 3).

Beam precamber was measured in each specimen before and after the corrosion process (Table 1). The reduction of the precamber (up to 70% for corrosion levels of 20%), is a clear indication of the prestressing loss ensuing from chemical attack.

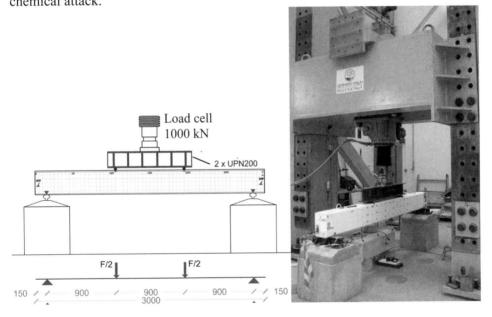

Figure 4a,b – Test set-up.

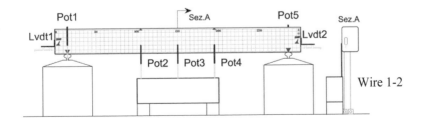

Figure 4c - Instrumentation.

# 4. EXPERIMENTAL RESULTS

## 4.1 Series 1

The results obtained by testing the first "reference" beam (No. 7) are shown in Figure 5. The load is plotted as a function of both midspan deflection (right-hand side) and strand slip (left-hand side, measured with LVDTs 1 and 2, Fig 4).

The first crack opens at about 70 kN (load level close to 43%), as shown by the Whittemore deformometer. Above 80 kN (load level close to 50%), the strand extremities start sliding, probably because of concrete low quality.

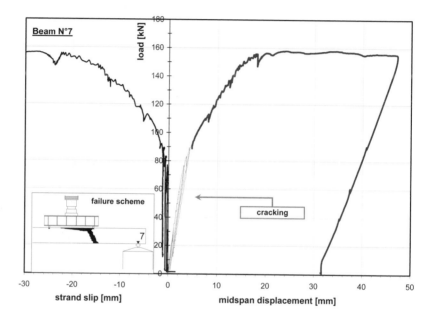

Figure 5 - Series 1, Beam No.7 (no corrosion): plots of the load as a function of midspan displacement and strand slip at beam extremities.

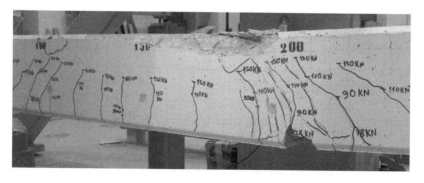

Figure 6 - Series 1, Beam No. 7 (no corrosion): crack pattern at failure.

178

At about 150 kN (load level close to 94%), the strand slip at the extremities is so large (about 30 mm), that practically no prestressing is left. The collapse occurs for a load level slightly lower than 160 kN; the crack pattern (Figure 6) shows clearly that the beam collapsed because of concrete crushing, with a sizable interaction between bending and shear (as demonstrated by the vertical cracks between the two point-loads and the inclined cracks close to the supports). The evolution of the cracks during the test is shown in Figure 7.

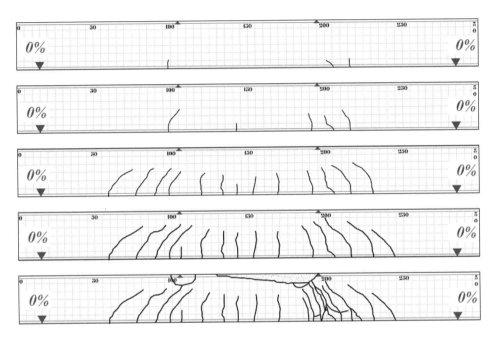

Figure 7 - Series 1, Beam No.7 (no corrosion): crack evolution (load levels = 47%, 56%, 72%, 94% and 100% = failure).

The collapse of the corroded beams of Series 1 is due to strand failure because of wire rupture. Both Beams No. 8 and 9 had the same corrosion level (close to 20%, extended to a length of 70 cm astride the midspan section). The expected value of the mass loss was confirmed, after demolishing the specimens and measuring the weight of the strands.

It is worth noting that - before the test - longitudinal cracks were already there close to the strands, because of previous corrosion.

The results obtained for Beam No. 8 are shown in Figure 8 (the plots have the same meaning as in Figure 5). In this case, however, the sudden rupture of a wire occurred at 45 kN (load level = 47%) and was accompanied by a sharp sound and a sudden decay of the stiffness.

Contrary to the reference Beam No.7, the crack pattern at failure exhibited only vertical cracks located between the point-loads, and no significant slip occurred at beam ends (Figures 9a,c).

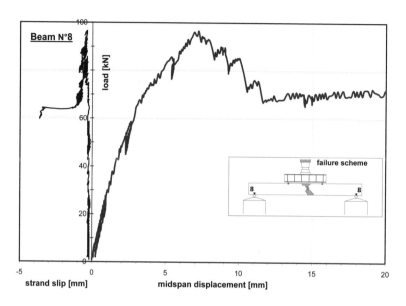

Figure 8 - Series 1, Beam No.8 (corrosion level 20%): plots of the load as a function of midspan displacement and strand slip at beam extremities.

After reaching the peak load (close to 95 kN), the external wires of the strand (composed of 7 wires) started breaking, and only the internal wire remained active. This aspect will be discussed in the final remarks. In Figure 9b the state of the prestressed strands and of an ordinary rebar is shown at failure.

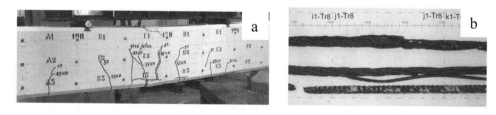

Figure 9 (a,b) – Series 1, Beam No.8 (corrosion level 20%): (a) crack pattern at failure; and (b) strands and ordinary rebars after failure;

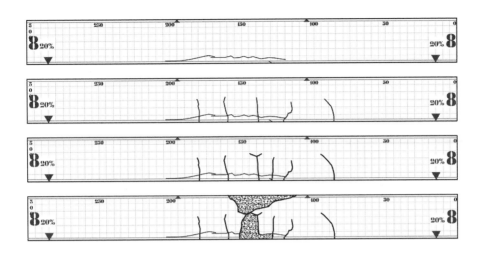

Figure 9 c – Series 1, Beam No. 8 (corrosion level 20%): crack evolution (load levels = 58%, 87%, 89% and 100% = failure). At 58 kN (load level close to 61%) flexural cracking started.

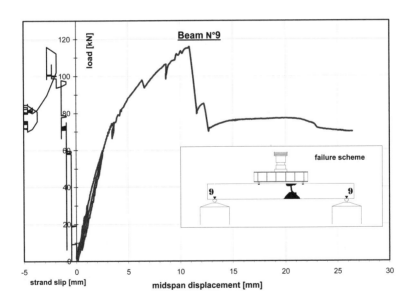

Figure 10 - Series 1, Beam No. 9 (corrosion level 20%): plots of the load as a function of midspan displacement and strand slip at beam extremities.

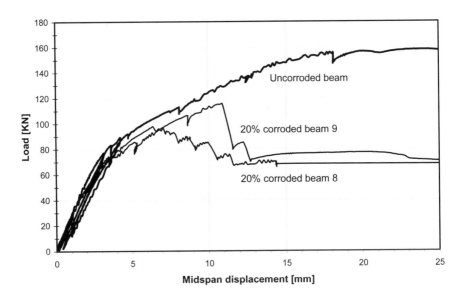

Figure 11 - Series 1 - Beams Nos. 7, 8 and 9 : plots of the load-midspan displacement curves.

Beam No.9, that is nominally identical to Beam No.8, shows similar results. The peak load, however, is 20% higher (close to 115 kN, Figure 10).

The load-displacement curves of the three beams of Series 1 are plotted in Figure 11. There is a sharp reduction of the peak load from Beam No.7 (reference beam = no corrosion) to both Beams Nos. 8 and 9 (high level of corrosion). The differences between Beams Nos.8 and 9 are due to the progressive break of the wires in the former case, and to the sudden break of the strands in the latter case.

Summing up, a rather severe corrosion (20% by mass loss in the prestressing reinforcement) brings in a bearing-capacity loss comprised between 28% and 41%, (reference Beam No.7, $P_{max}$ = 160 kN; Beam No.9, $P_{max}$ = 115 kN; Beam No.8, $P_{max}$ = 95 kN).

## 4.2 Series 2

The results obtained for the reference Beam No.2 are summarized in Figure 12 in the usual way. Similarly to Series 1, the collapse occurs due to concrete crushing accompanied by bending and shear interaction. The crack pattern (very similar to that of Beam No.7, Fig. 6) is characterized by vertical flexural cracks between the point-loads and by inclined cracks in the shear span. The maximum load is close to 190 kN. Prior to failure, the strand slip at beams ends is close to 4 mm (Fig. 12). The slip is smaller than that registered in Beam No.7 of Series 1, because of concrete better quality, that brings in a better bond quality as well, with favorable effects on concrete response in tension and less bending-shear interaction.

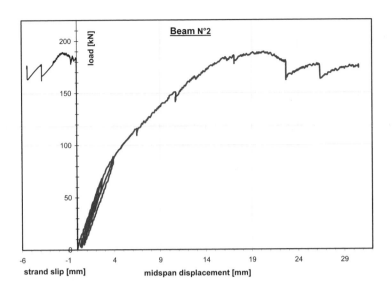

Figure 12 - Series 2, Reference Beam No. 2: plots of the load as a function of midspan displacement and strand slip at beam extremities.

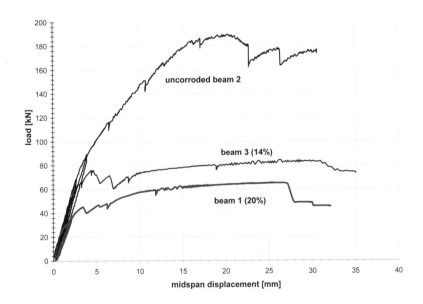

Figure 13 - Series 2 - Beams Nos. 2 (reference beam), 3 and 1: plots of the load-midspan displacement curves.

 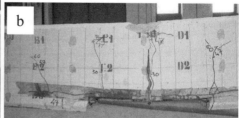

Figure 14 - Series 2 - Crack patterns at failure: (a) Beam No.3; and (b) Beam No.1, both corroded.

The crisis of the corroded beams (Beam No.3, corrosion level close to 14%; and Beam No.1, corrosion level close to 20%), is due to the rupture of the wires of the strands.

In both cases, the crack pattern at failure (Figure 14) is characterized by almost vertical multi-branched cracks.

The load-displacement curves of the three beams of Series 2 are plotted in Figure 13. Looking at Beam No.2 (reference beam = no corrosion), Beam No. 3 (intermediate level of corrosion) and Beam No.1 (high level of corrosion, there is a sharp reduction in terms of peak load, but none in terms of ductility. In both Beams Nos.3 and 1 the progressive break of the wires characterizes the post-peak behavior.

Summing up, intermediate and high levels of corrosion (14% and 20% by mass loss in the prestressing reinforcement) bring in bearing-capacity losses close to 55% and 65%, respectively (reference Beam No.2, $P_{max}$ = 190 kN; Beam No.3, $P_{max}$ = 85 kN; Beam No.1, $P_{max}$ = 66 kN). As for the ductility, the post-peak behavior exhibits either a moderate decrease or no decrease at all.

**4.3 Series 3**

The results obtained for the reference Beam No.4 are summarized in Figure 15 in the usual way. Up to 10-mm midspan displacement, the load-displacement curve is rather close to those of the companion reference Beams Nos.7 and 2 of Series 1 and 2.

Similarly to Series 1 and 2, the collapse occurs because of concrete crushing. The maximum load is 210 kN, this value being higher than in the two previous cases (Beams Nos.7 and 2), because of the higher concrete strength. The crack pattern is typical of the bending behavior (Figure 17).

Strand slip at beam ends starts at 150 kN (load level close to 71%) and reaches 3 mm prior to failure (Fig. 15). The slip is smaller than that registered in Beams Nos.7 and 2 of Series 1 and 2, because of concrete better quality.

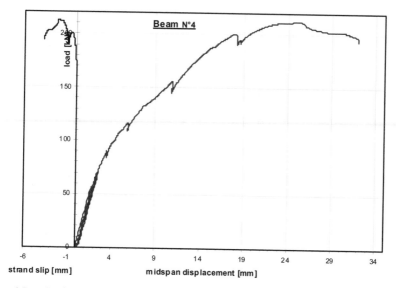

Figure 15 - Series 3, Beam 4 (no corrosion): plots of the load as a function of midspan displacement and strand slip at beam extremities.

Beam No.6 exhibits a rather peculiar behavior, because of its rather limited level of corrosion (7%), that makes this beam a sort of "transition case". The beam fails suddenly after the peak load, but until the peak load the behavior is very similar to that of the reference beams (the maximum load close to 200 kN is practically coincident with that of the reference Beam No.4 close to 210 kN).

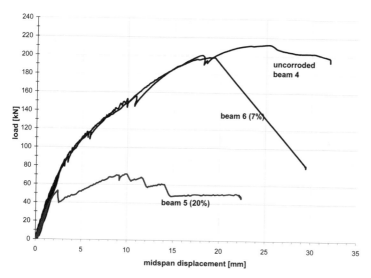

Figure 16 - Series 3 – Beams Nos.4, 6 and 5: plots of the load-midspan displacement curves.

185

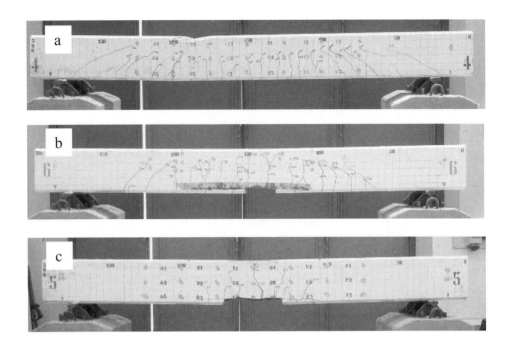

Figure 17 - Series 3 – Crack patterns at failure: (a) Beam No.4 (no corrosion); (b) No.6 (mild corrosion); and (c) Beam No.5 (high corrosion).


The failure is very abrupt, because of the simultaneous occurrence of concrete crushing and wire rupture in the strands.

The high corrosion level of Beam No.5 (close to 20%) makes its behavior rather similar to those of the other two highly-corroded beams (Beams Nos.8 and 1, Series 1 and 2, respectively): for instance, for a midspan displacement of 10 mm, the residual bearing capacity is close to 70 kN, more than in Beam No.1 (close to 60 kN) and less than in Beam No.8 (close to 80 kN). The failure is due to the rupture of strand wires. The crack pattern is shown in Figure 17.

Summing up, because of the good quality of concrete, rather low corrosion levels (7% by mass loss in the prestressing reinforcement) marginally reduce the peak load (by little more than 5%), while high corrosion levels (20%) induce a totally different behavior, with a sharp reduction of the peak load (-66%). In the reference Beam No.4, $P_{max}$ is close to 210 kN, and in Beam No.6, $P_{max}$ is close to 200 kN, while in Beam No.5, $P_{max}$ is down to 70 kN). As for the ductility, the largest corrosion level brings in an apparent ductility, but it is a questionable ductility, because the load-displacement curve becomes flat (50-80 kN) and very close to the bearing capacity of the beam having the ordinary reinforcement fully plasticized, and the pretensioning reinforcement partly broken and partly plasticized.

# 7. CONCLUDING REMARKS

To compare the behaviors of the nine beams tested in this project, the load-displacement curves are put together in Fig.18.

On the basis of the results, the following concluding remarks can be made:

- strand corrosion in simply-supported prestressed beams strongly affects their global behavior in bending, in terms of both bearing capacity and failure mode;

- contrary to the reference uncorroded beams, whose collapse is governed by concrete crushing, the collapse of corroded beams with mild and severe corrosion levels (14% and 20% mass loss, respectively) occurs because of the local rupture of strand wires;

- the only beam subjected to a low corrosion level (7%) shows a sharp ductility reduction and collapses abruptly for the simultaneous crisis of concrete and strands;

- the behavior of the uncorroded beams is strongly influenced by concrete quality, since a significant slip of the strands at their extremities, accompanied by a sizable prestressing loss, occurs in the case of low-grade concrete.

In order to better understand the experimental results, the ultimate capacity of the beams in question were worked out on the basis of the usual simplified sectional models, by introducing the stress-block for concrete and the elastic-perfectly plastic behavior for both ordinary and prestressed reinforcement. Obviously, the mean values of materials strengths were considered.

As an example, in Figure 19 the experimental results of Series 3 are shown again, together with the ultimate capacities analytically obtained for the following situations:

- ultimate capacity of uncorroded Beam 4 (full section; dotted line);

- ultimate capacity of Beam 6, evaluated by reducing the area of the pretensioned steel (by 7%; dashed line);

- ultimate capacity evaluated by considering only one wire active, plus the conventional reinforcement (each strand is composed of 7 wires; dash-dotted line);

- ultimate capacity evaluated by considering only the conventional rebars (the whole pretensioned reinforcement is gone, because of corrosion-induced rupture; dash-double dotted line).

Figure 19 clearly shows that the peak force of both the uncorroded and lightly corroded (7%) beams is well described by the analytical results.

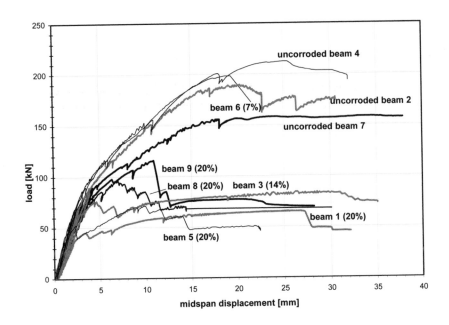

Figure 18 – Load - midspan displacement curves.

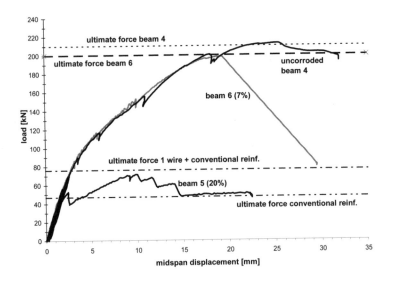

Figure 19 – Series 3: fitting of the peak loads with the design equations, under various assumptions concerning the effective reinforcement.

Because of wire rupture, the ultimate behavior of the severely-corroded beam (Beam 5) is comprised between the behaviors with only one active wire (dash-dotted line, including the conventional reinforcement) and with only the conventional reinforcement still active (dash-double dotted line). This result agrees with testing, which showed that often only the internal wire of the most-severely corroded strands (sectional reduction by 20%) was undamaged, while the external wires had failed.

It is also interesting to note that - after the collapse of all the wires - the beams tend to behave like R/C beams (no pretensioned reinforcement).

Similar results were found for the corroded beams of the Series 1 and 2, as shown in Figure 20.

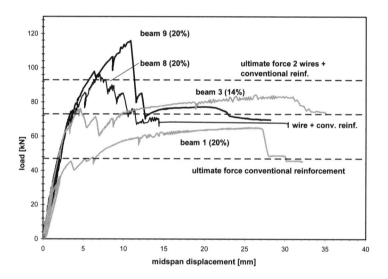

Figure 20 – Series 1 and 2: fitting of the peak loads with the design equations, under various assumptions concerning the effective reinforcement

## ACKNOWLEDGMENTS

The authors gratefully acknowledge the financial support by Autostrade S.p.A. Special thanks should be conveyed to MS. Eng. Livia Pardi of Autostrade S.p.A. for her valuable cooperation.

# REFERENCES

ACI-SP 151-2 (1992). *Corrosion of Prestressed Reinforcing Steel in Concrete Bridges: State-of-the-Art Report* by M. Nagi and D. Whiting.

ACI 222.2R-01 (2001). *Corrosion of Prestressing Steels* - ACI Committee 222.

Bergsma F., Boon J. W. and Etienne C. F. (1977). "Endurance Tests for Determining the Susceptibility of Prestressing Steel to Hydrogen Embrittlement". *HERON*, Vol. 22, No. 1, pp.46-71

Cairns J. (1998). "Assessment of the Effects of Reinforcement Corrosion on the Residual Strength of Deteriorating Concrete Structures". *Proc. First Int. Conf. on the Behaviour of Damaged Structures*, Rio de Janeiro, Federal University of Fluminense, Niteroi (Brazil), May, pp. 101-106.

Castel A., Francois R. and Arligue G. (2000). "Mechanical Behaviour of Corroded Reinforced-Concrete Beams - Part 1: Experimental Study of Corroded Beams". *Materials and Structures / Materiaux et Constructions*, Vol. 33 (233), November, pp. 539 – 544.

Coronelli D. and Gambarova P. G. (2001). "Structural Response of Corroded R/C Elements: Assessment by Numerical Analysis". *Proc. 9th Int. Conf. on Structural Faults and Repair (SFR2001 )*, London (UK), July (on CD).

Coronelli D. and Gambarova P.G. (2004). "Structural Assessment of Corroded Reinforced Concrete Beams: Modeling Guidelines". *ASCE - J. of Structural Engineering*, Vol.130, No.8, pp.1214-1224.

Coronelli D., Castel A., Vu N.A. and Francoise R. (2008). "Deterioration Modelling in Prestressed Structures: Corrosion Phenomena and Structural Effects". *Studies and Researchers – Politecnico di Milano*, pub. by Starrylink (Brescia, Italy), Vol. 28, pp. 39-78.

CUR (1977). *Cases of Damage Due to Corrosion of Prestressing Steel.* Report by Netherlands Committee for Concrete Research 49.

Darmawan S. M. and Stewart M. G. (2007). "Spatial Time-Dependent Reliability-Analysis of Corroding Pretentioned Prestressed Concrete Bridge-Girders". *Structural Safety,* Vol. 29, pp.16-31.

Fip Commission on Prestressing Steels and Systems (1980). *Prestressing Steel: Stress-Corrosion Cracking-Resistance Test for Prestressing Tendons.* Report by the Fédération Internationale de la Précontrainte, 56 pp. (ISBN 978-0-7210-1189-9).

Hoover K. C. (1996). "Special Problems in Evaluating the Safety of Concrete Bridges and Concrete-Bridge Components". *Construction and Building Materials,* Vol. 10 (1), pp. 39-43.

MacDougall C. and Bartlett F. M. (2002). "Tests of Corroded Unbonded Seven-Wire Strands with Broken Wires". *ACI Structural Journal,* Vol. 99 (6), November, pp. 803-810.

Mircea D., Ioani A., Filip M. and Pepenar I. (1994). "Long-term Durability of Reinforced and Prestressed Elements in Aggressive Environments". *ACI Material Journal,* March-April, pp. 132-140.

Nurnberger U. (2002). "Corrosion-Induced Failures of Prestressing Steel". *Otto-Graf Journal*, Vol. 12, pp. 9-25.

Rinaldi Z., Valente C. and Pardi L. (2007). "A Simplified Methodology for the Evaluation of the Residual Life of Corroded Elements". *Structure and Infrastructure Engineering*, Vol. 4 (2), Taylor & Francis Eds., pp. 139 – 152.

Rodriguez J., Ortega L., Casal J. and Diez J.M. (1996). "Assessing Structural Conditions of Concrete Structures with Corroded Reinforcement". *Proc. Int. Conf. on Concrete in the Service of Mankind*, Dundee, U.K, June, pp. 95-100.

U.S. Federal Highway Administration (2000). *Materials and Methods for Corrosion Control of Reinforced- and Prestressed-Concrete Structures in New Constructions.* Pub. No. 00-081, August, Washington D.C. (USA).

Valiente A. (2001). "Stress-Corrosion Failure of Large-Diameter Pressure Pipelines of Prestressed-Concrete". *Engineering Failure Analysis* (8), pp.245-261.

Vehovar L., Kuhar V. and Vehover A. (1998). "Hydrogen-Assisted Stress-Corrosion of Prestressing Wires in a Motorway Viaduct". *Engineering Failure Analysis,* Vol. 5 (1), Elsevier, pp. 21-27.

Whiting D., Stejskal B. and Nagi M. (1993). *Condition of Prestressed-Concrete Bridge-Components: Technology Review and Field Surveys.* Report No. FHWA-RD-93-037 by the Federal Highway Administration, Washington DC, USA.

STUDIES AND RESEARCHES – V.29, 2009
Graduate School in Concrete Structures – Fratelli Pesenti
Politecnico di Milano, Italy

# NOTCHED COLUMNS MADE OF QUASI-BRITTLE MATERIALS: STABILITY ANALYSIS BY MEANS OF R-CURVES

Luigi Fenu[1]

## ABSTRACT

The stability of columns made of quasi-brittle materials, subjected to an eccentric axial force, is investigated in this study, on the assumption that the base section is notched. As a matter of fact, looking at historical structures, there is a large number of columns made of quasi-brittle materials (stones and bricks), exhibiting cracks or indentations in their lowest regions, that are the most exposed to possible impacts or to various sources of damage. Moreover, since columns are often long, their stability may be a relevant issue, and methods for analysing simultaneously stability and fracture are necessary.

Stability analysis of notched long columns is studied here by means of an approximate analytical model, which is based on the use of $R$-curves and provides an intuitive understanding of the structural behaviour.

[1] Department of Structural Engineering, University of Cagliari, Cagliari, Italy

# 1. INTRODUCTION

The behaviour of axially-loaded columns is at the same time favoured and endangered by the use of high-grade materials, which bring in reduced resistant sections, but also exhibit a limited tensile strength (as it is well known in stone and concrete). As a matter of fact, reducing the sections may imply stability problems, while the limited tensile strength makes cracking very probable, should the axial force be accompanied by some bending (as it is unavoidably the case). Both occurrences prevent the compressive strength from being fully exploited.

The situation is even worse if the columns have a notch, since in such a case the failure envelope of the axial load versus the bending moment is reduced by the combination of buckling and fracture.

Since many columns, especially in historical buildings, are made of quasi-brittle materials (from limestone and granite, to concrete, just to cite a few examples of natural and artificial conglomerates), the finite length of the fracture process zone should be taken in due consideration in any advanced analysis of – for instance – the columns of ancient buildings, damaged by deep cracks or accidentally chipped by an impact.

In this paper, the case of a rectangular column exhibiting a horizontal edge-notch at its base and loaded at the top by an eccentric axial force is considered (Fig.1).

The analysis will be based on simplified methods for dealing with both structural stability and fracture, as concisely described in the following.

# 2. SIMPLIFIED METHODS FOR THE STABILITY ANALYSIS OF QUASI-BRITTLE NOTCHED COLUMNS

A general approach to structural stability of quasi-brittle columns has to take into account both the second-order effects and the mechanical non-linearity of the materials. Nonlinear Finite Element Analysis is usually required, with the use of rather complex numerical tools [1,2]. Nevertheless, the stability of columns can also be tackled with simplified methods, and often this approach is more than appropriate.

For instance, the so-called " Model-Column Method" yields sufficiently accurate results in many cases, like with steel and R/C columns, and – in general - whenever the moment-curvature diagrams are easily available.

Moreover, combining in a simplified analysis stability and fracture (as required in  notched columns made of quasi-brittle materials) is something challenging and  potentially useful.

Although columns are usually loaded in compression, an excessive eccentricity of the axial force may cause tensile stresses in the notch region.

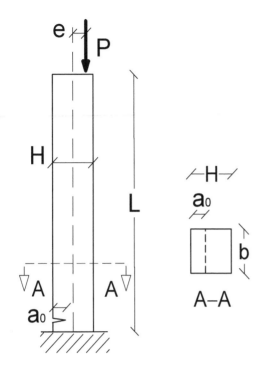

Fig. 1 - Sketch of a eccentrically-loaded column with an edge notch at its base.

Fracture can then propagate in spite of significant compressive forces transmitted to column base. Therefore, depending on both notch length and column slenderness, the failure envelope M–N is reduced not only because of structural buckling but also by fracture phenomena.

The fracture behaviour of quasi-brittle materials deviates significantly from linearity due to microcracks in the fracture process zone in front of the crack tip. Appropriate nonlinear theories have been developed to model this nonlinear behaviour. Suitable nonlinear crack models are - for example - the Fictitious Crack Model [3,4] and the Crack-Band Model [5-7].

Fracture in quasi-brittle structures can also be studied by means of R-curves, or resistance curves, see for instance the method based on Bazant's Size Effect law [8,9], with the R-curves put in parametric form [10]. Besides the tensile strength and elastic modulus, the construction of R-curves obtained from Bazant's Size Effect law requires two other material constants, that are intrinsic properties of the material, and have to be determined by testing.

By considering notched columns such as that of Fig.1, fracture propagation can be analysed for different compressive forces, as well as for different eccentricities and notch depths, through the R-curves.

For a given notch depth, the fracture propagates under combined compressive forces and eccentricities. As a result, column resistance is reduced, not just by 2nd -order effects, but also by fracture.

## 3. SECTIONS UNDER COMBINED AXIAL LOAD AND BENDING

Before evaluating the reduction of column bearing capacity because of buckling and fracture, it is first necessary to work out the ultimate axial load and bending moment for the given section, starting from the nonlinear mechanical behaviour

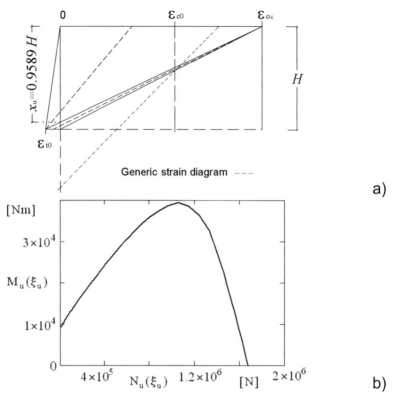

Fig. 2 – (a) Strain profiles for a quasi-brittle section subjected to combined bending moment and axial force; and (b) failure envelope.

of the quasi-brittle material under investigation.

The behaviour of concrete in compression is assumed to be represented by a parabolic stress-strain relationship up to the strain $\varepsilon_{c0}$. Beyond $\varepsilon_{c0}$, the strain increases up to the ultimate strain $\varepsilon_{cu}$, while the stress remains constant ($= 0.85\,f_c$, where $f_c$ is the cylindrical compressive strength). The parabolic part of the stress-strain diagram has been given the same analytical formulation found in the loading branch of Sargin's stress-strain diagram [11], see Appendix I.

The strains $\varepsilon_{c0}$, $\varepsilon_{cu}$, $\varepsilon_{t0}$ generally depend on the mechanical properties of the quasi-brittle material, and firstly on its compressive strength; in this paper the values $\varepsilon_{c0} = 0.002$, $\varepsilon_{cu} = 0.0035$ and $\varepsilon_{t0} = 0.00015$ were adopted, as suggested by various design codes.

Let us now consider a column characterised by a rectangular section (depth $H$ and width $b$), subjected to an eccentric axial load $P$; $x$ is the depth of the neutral axis (normalized value $\xi = x/H$, with $\xi_u = x_u/H$ at the ultimate limit state). By assuming that plane sections remain plane, failure can occur with the neutral axis intersecting the section or falling outside (Fig.2a). In the first case, failure occurs when either the maximum compressive strain is $\varepsilon_{cu}$, or the maximum tensile strain is $\varepsilon_{t0}$; these ultimate strains can also be reached simultaneously, for $\xi_u = 1/(1+|\varepsilon_{t0}/\varepsilon_{cu}|)$, that is for $\xi_u = 0.959$. In all these cases, the eccentricity is greater than $H/6$. Otherwise, when the eccentricity is smaller than $H/6$, failure occurs for $\xi_u > 1$, and, similarly to the well-known case of reinforced concrete sections, all the linear strain diagrams at ultimate pass through the point of Figure 2a, where the strain diagram for $\xi_u = 1$ intersects the line at constant strain $\varepsilon_{c0}$.

It is assumed that, at ultimate, for $\xi_u \leq 1$, $b\,0.85\,f_c\,\beta_{1c}x_u$ and $\beta_{2c}x_u$ are the resultant of the compressive stress-block and its distance from the compressed side (see Fig. 3); for $\xi_u > 1$, when the whole section is in compression, the previous parameters become $b\,0.85\,f_c$, $\beta_{1c}H$ and $\beta_{2c}H$. For $\xi_u \leq 1$, the resultant of the stress-block of the tensile stresses is $b\,f_t\,\beta_{1t}(H-x_u)$, and its distance from the side in tension is $\beta_{2t}(H-x_u)$, see Fig.3. Both $\beta_{1c}$ and $\beta_{2c}$, as well as $\beta_{1t}$ and $\beta_{2t}$, are functions of $\xi_u$, that are defined in Appendix II.

By algebraically summing the resultants of the compressive and tensile stresses in the direction of column axis, and calculating their moments with respect to the section centroid, the axial load $N_u(\xi_u)$ and the bending moment $M_u(\xi_u)$ at ultimate are obtained (Fig. 2b).

For values of $x_u$ lower than $H$, their expressions are:

$$N_u(\xi_u) = 0.85 f_c\, b\beta_{1c}(\xi_u)\, x_u - f_t\, b\, \beta_{1t}(1-\xi_u)\,(H-x_u) \tag{1a}$$

$$M_u(\xi_u) = 0.85 f_c\, b\beta_{1c}(\xi_u)\, x_u\,[H/2 - \beta_{2c}(\xi_u)\, x_u] + \tag{1b}$$

$$+ f_t\, b\, \beta_{1t}(1-\xi_u)\,(H-x_u)[H/2 - \beta_{2t}(1-\xi_u)\,(H-x_u)]$$

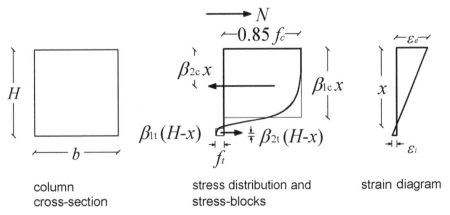

| column cross-section | stress distribution and stress-blocks | strain diagram |

Fig. 3 – Stress and strain profiles (subscripts: e = extrados, i = intrados).

while, for $x_u > H$, the following expressions hold:

$$N_u(\xi_u) = 0.85 f_c \, b\beta_{1c}(\xi_u) \, H \tag{2a}$$

$$M_u(\xi_u) = 0.85 f_c \, b\beta_{1c}(\xi_u) \, H \, [H/2 - \beta_{2c}(\xi_u) \, H] \tag{2b}$$

Therefore, by varying the position of the neutral axis, the failure envelope is obtained, where the values of the axial force $N_u(\xi_u)$ are plotted against the resisting moment $M_u(\xi_u)$ (Fig.2).

Unfortunately, the ultimate moment can be lower than $M_u(\xi_u)$, because of second-order effects and fracture, as shown in the following.

## 4. CONSTRUCTION OF R–CURVES

R-curves can be obtained through the so–called "effective crack model", by taking into account - in an approximate way - the nonlinear fracture behaviour of the quasi-brittle material under investigation. This approach allows to perform the fracture analysis of an actual quasi-brittle structure through an equivalent elastic structure with an effective crack suitably longer than that of the actual structure [12,13].

The R-curves can be obtained by applying Bazant's Size Effect law [5]. Bazant's studies on size effect in concrete structures lead to the following scaling law:

$$(\sigma_N)_u = \frac{B \, f_t}{\sqrt{1 + D / D_0}} \tag{3}$$

with $D$ = characteristic size, and:

$$B = \frac{1}{f_t} \left( \frac{G_f \, E_c}{D_0 \, g(\alpha_0)} \right)^{\frac{1}{2}} \qquad D_0 = c_f \frac{g'(\alpha_0)}{g(\alpha_0)} \tag{4}$$

where $\alpha_0 = a_0/D$ is the ratio between the crack length $a_0$ and the characteristic size $D$ of a pre-cracked member; $g(\alpha_0)$ is the value - calculated in $\alpha_0$ – of the function $g$ that, in general, depends on the specific geometry of the notched specimen (whose linear elastic fracture behaviour is well-known from analytical models or numerical FE analyses); $c_f$ and $G_f$ are the length of the equivalent elastic crack and the energy required for crack growth, respectively, for an infinitely large specimen, namely for $D \to +\infty$. (The asymptotic values $c_f$ and $G_f$ are material properties).

Consider then section depth $H$ as the characteristic size $D$. From the scaling law (3), the R-curves can be derived in parametric form according to Bazant and

Kazemi [10]. With reference to Bazant and Planas [13], being $K_{Ic} = \sigma_N \sqrt{H}\, k(\alpha)$, where $\sigma_N = P/(bH)$ is the nominal strength, we have:

$$K_{Ic}(\alpha)^2 = \frac{P^2}{H^2 b^2} H k(\alpha)^2 \qquad (5)$$

in which $k(\alpha)^2 = g(\alpha)$, and $\alpha = a/H$ is the normalized value of the length $a$ of the generic crack. Therefore, after the propagation of the original crack of length $a_0$, if $\Delta a$ is the equivalent crack extension, the crack length becomes $a = a_0 + \Delta a$ with $\alpha = \alpha_0 + \Delta a/H$.

The energy release-rate is then defined as $\mathcal{G}(\alpha) = \sigma_N^2 H g(\alpha)/E_c'$, where $E_c' = E_c$ in plane stresses and $E_c' = E_c/(1-v^2)$ in plane strains.

Introducing Bazant's Size Effect law (3), the energy release-rate at the peak load can be written as:

$$\mathcal{G}_u(\alpha) = \frac{1}{E_c'} \frac{(B f_t)^2}{1 + \dfrac{H}{D_0}} H g(\alpha) \qquad (6)$$

and by substituting $Bf_t$ as a function of $G_f$ through the first of (4):

$$\mathcal{G}_u(\alpha) = \frac{G_f}{g(\alpha_0)} \frac{H}{H + D_0} g(\alpha) \qquad (7)$$

Various $\mathcal{G}_u(\alpha)$ curves can be obtained for different sizes $H$, each of them for a different value of the peak load. The envelope of the curves $\mathcal{G}_u = \mathcal{G}_u(\alpha, H)$ is the R-curve, that is obtained by setting to zero the partial derivative of $\mathcal{G}_u$ with respect to $H$, and by successively solving for $H$. From $\partial \mathcal{G}_u/\partial H = 0$, that is

$$\frac{\partial \mathcal{G}_u}{\partial \alpha} \frac{d\alpha}{dH} = \frac{\partial \mathcal{G}_u}{\partial \alpha}\left(\frac{-\Delta a}{H^2}\right) = 0 \qquad (8)$$

substituting (7) into (8) we obtain $H/(H+D_0) = g'(\alpha)\, \Delta a/(g(\alpha) D_0)$. By expressing $D_0$ as a function of $c_f$ through the second of (4), substituting $H/(H+D_0)$ into expression (7) for $\mathcal{G}_u(\alpha)$ gives the equation for the R-curve:

$$R(\Delta a) = G_f \frac{g'(\alpha)}{g'(\alpha_0)} \frac{\Delta a}{c_f} \qquad (9)$$

in which

$$\Delta a = c_f \frac{g'(\alpha_0)}{g(\alpha_0)}\left[\frac{g(\alpha)}{g'(\alpha)} - (\alpha - \alpha_0)\right] \qquad (10)$$

is obtained eliminating $H$ between the left sides of (7) and (9) for $R(\Delta a) = \mathcal{G}_u(\alpha)$.

Being $\Delta a = (\alpha - \alpha_0) H$, both $\Delta a$ and $R$ are functions of $\alpha$, the latter through $\Delta a$ and $g$. Hence, equations (9) and (10) define the $R$-curve in a parametric form through the parameter $\alpha$.

By means of $R$-curves, the fracture analysis of an actual quasi-brittle structure can be performed, provided that the properties $c_f$ and $G_f$ of the material and the function $g(\alpha)$ are known.

## 5. COMBINED EFFECT OF FRACTURE AND SECOND-ORDER MOMENTS ON THE STABILITY OF NOTCHED COLUMNS

$R$-curves appear well suited for studying whether unstable fracture may occur in a quasi-brittle column, provided that the effects of second-order moments (including their increase caused by crack propagation) are taken into account. As a matter of fact, in order to obtain the total top displacement, the crack-induced contribution $\Delta_{IIb}$ must be added to the displacement $\Delta_{IIa}$ that would occur at the top of an identical but uncracked column subjected to the same load.

Hence, in the case of axial loads with sufficiently high eccentricities, besides first-order moments $M_I = Pe$, the contribution of second-order moments $M_{II} = P\Delta$ should be introduced, where $\Delta = \Delta_{IIa} + \Delta_{IIb}$ is the total displacement at the top of the notched column. The total moment $M_{I+II}$ is then: $Pe_t = P(e+\Delta)$, with $e_t = e+\Delta$.

### 5.1. Further developments in the construction of $R$-curves

To obtain the $R$-curves, it is first necessary to define the expression of the stress intensity factor for an eccentrically-loaded member with an edge crack at mid-length.

In general, from (5), the stress intensity factor $K_{Ic}$ can be expressed as a function of $\alpha$ through $g(\alpha)$, that is:

$$K_{Ic}(\alpha)^2 = \frac{P^2}{H^2 b^2} H\, g(\alpha) \tag{11}$$

It is then necessary to define the function $g(\alpha)$ for notched members under axial compression and bending. For both notched beams in four point bending (Fig.4) and edge-notched members in tension (Fig.5), function $g(\alpha)$ is easily available in some handbooks, see for instance [14]. For Four Point Bending beams (Fig. 4), the expression of the stress intensity factor is:

$$K_{Ic}(\alpha) = \frac{6M}{H^2 b} \sqrt{H} \sqrt{\pi\alpha}\, F_M(\alpha) \tag{12}$$

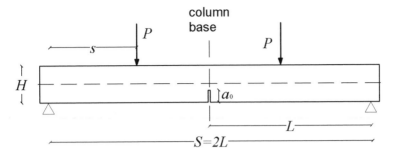

Fig. 4 – Beam in four-point bending with no axial force (moment $M = Ps$).

where the polynomial expression $F_M(\alpha) = 1.122 - 1.4\alpha + 7.33\alpha^2 - 13.08\alpha^3 + 14.0\alpha^4$, available in [14], can be used.

For span $S$ and distance $d$ between the force and the mid-span section, so that $s=S/2-d$ and $M=Ps$, by comparing (11) with (12), one obtains:

$$g(\alpha) = 36s^2 \pi \alpha F_M(\alpha)^2 / H^2 \qquad (13)$$

Similarly, for edge-notched members in tension (Fig. 5), we have:

$$K_{Ic}(\alpha) = \frac{P}{Hb}\sqrt{H}\sqrt{\pi\alpha}\, F_N(\alpha) \qquad (14)$$

with $F_N(\alpha) = 1.122 - 0.231\alpha + 10.55\alpha^2 - 21.71\alpha^3 + 30.382\alpha^4$ [14]. The comparison of (14) with (11) leads us to $g(\alpha) = \pi\alpha F_N(\alpha)^2$.

For beams in four-point bending subjected to an axial load, $g(\alpha)$ can be obtained from the $K$-superposition principle [15] (Fig.6). Hence, for edge-notched members subjected to an eccentric compressive force $P$, with $M = P(e+\Delta) = Pe_t$, where $e_t$ is the total eccentricity of $P$ (Fig.7), from (12) and (14) one obtains:

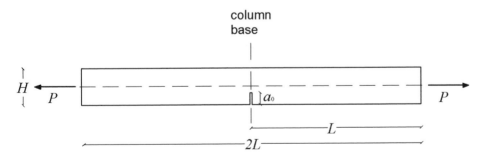

Fig. 5 – Edge-notched member subjected to a purely-axial force $P$.

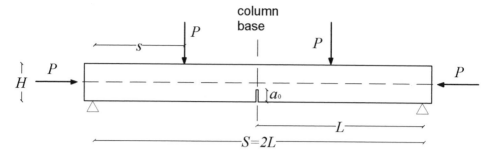

Fig. 6 – Beam in four-point bending subjected to bending (moment $M = Ps$) and compression (compressive force $P$).

$$K_{Ic}(\alpha) = \frac{P}{H b}\sqrt{H}\sqrt{\pi\alpha}\left(\frac{6e_t}{H}F_M(\alpha) - F_N(\alpha)\right) \qquad (15)$$

where the minus sign in brackets takes care of the fact that the column is subjected to compression, while in (14) $P$ is a tensile axial force. Therefore, the function $g(\alpha)$ becomes:

$$g(\alpha) = \pi\alpha\left(\frac{6e_t}{H}F_M(\alpha) - F_N(\alpha)\right)^2 \qquad (16)$$

Once $g(\alpha)$ and its first derivative $g'(\alpha)$ are known, together with the values of $c_f$ and $G_f$ of the material under investigation, the $R$-curve can be plotted.

Moreover, from (15), the energy release-rate $\mathscr{G}$ can be expressed as a function of $\alpha$:

$$\mathscr{G}(\alpha) = \frac{1}{E_c}\frac{P^2}{H^2 b^2}H\pi\alpha\left(\frac{6e_t}{H}F_M(\alpha) - F_N(\alpha)\right)^2 \qquad (17)$$

where $\alpha = \alpha_0 + \Delta a/H$.

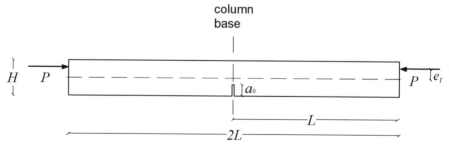

Fig. 7 - Edge-notched member subjected to an eccentric compressive force $P$.

## 5.2 *R*-curve approach

In a plane where the crack length $a$ is plotted along the $x$-axis and the energy release-rate $\mathscr{G}$ on the $y$-axis (Fig. 8), the function $\mathscr{G}(\alpha) = \mathscr{G}(a_0/H + \Delta a/H)$ starts from the point $(-a_0, 0)$ on the negative part of the horizontal axis and has positive first derivative, while the $R$-curve starts from the origin of the vertical axis and reaches its maximum value $G_f$ for the abscissa $\Delta a = c_f$. Since in perfectly-brittle materials no crack extension can occur, and therefore $\Delta a = c_f = 0$, then, in quasi-brittle materials, the higher the brittleness the smaller $c_f$. Thus, the lower the values of $c_f$, the steeper the $R$–curve, whose derivative tends to infinity for $c_f \rightarrow 0$.

$\mathscr{G}(\alpha)$ may – or may not - intersect the $R$-curve. If $\mathscr{G}$ is always above the $R$-curve with no intersection, an unstable fracture propagation from the notch with length $a_0$ occurs. On the contrary, if the $R$-curve is intersected, the crack is stable.

Hence, the abscissa $\Delta a$ of the point where the curve $\mathscr{G}(\alpha)$ and the $R$-curve are tangent represents the maximum stable crack-growth due to the application of the force $P$ with eccentricity $e$ at the column top.

To calculate the energy release-rate, the contribution of second-order moments to total moments is necessary. The crack-induced additional displacement $\Delta_{IIb}$ has to be taken into account, since, for any given value of the load $P$, the second-order moment is $M_{II}=P\Delta=P(\Delta_{IIa}+\Delta_{IIb})$, where $\Delta_{IIa}$ is the top displacement of the uncracked column in the same conditions as the cracked column.

It must also be noted that the crack-induced additional displacement $\Delta_{IIb}$ occurs only for sufficiently-high moments. As a matter of fact, if the eccentricity of the constant normal force $P$ is too low, the moment $P \cdot e$ is not able to induce a

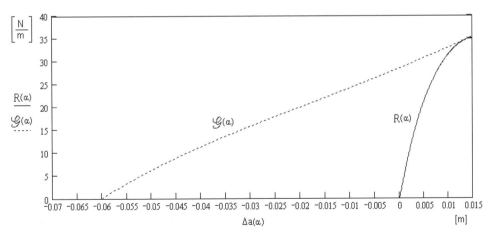

Fig. 8 – Plot of the energy release-rate (dotted line) $\mathscr{G}$ starting from the point on the abscissa axis with $-a_0 = -6$ cm and tangent to the $R$-curve (continuous line) for $\Delta a = 13$ mm.

sufficiently high additional rotation $\vartheta_M$ due to the crack, since it is proportional to $P \cdot e$. The crack-induced rotation $\vartheta_N$ -caused by the application of the constant axial force $P$, and with opposite sign with respect to $\vartheta_M$ - is instead proportional to only $P$, so that $\vartheta_N$ is independent of $e$. Hence, for low values of $e$, the total crack-induced additional rotation $\vartheta_{IIb}$ (which is the algebraic sum of $\vartheta_M$ and $\vartheta_N$) becomes low enough to make the additional displacement $\Delta_{IIb} = \vartheta_{IIb}L$ negligible.

In this latter case, second-order moments are caused only by the displacement $\Delta_{IIa}$, as if the column were uncracked.

On the contrary, in the former case, for higher moments $M$ the crack starts opening, with additional rotations and top displacements caused by the crack. Hence, a contribution to the second-order moments $P\Delta_{IIb}$ has to be added to $P\Delta_{IIa}$.

This means that, for smaller moments, second-order moments $M_{II}$ as a function of the curvature $\chi$ are first represented by a straight line, since $\Delta_{IIa}$ is assumed to be proportional to the curvature at the base of the uncracked column, in accordance, for instance, with the assumptions of the Model Column method. For higher moments, second-order moments are represented by a curve, obtained by increasing the ordinates of the straight line with the additional crack-induced contribution (Fig. 9).

While the second-order displacement $\Delta_{IIa}$ can be obtained through the curvature of the section at the base of the uncracked column by means of its moment-curvature diagram (see Appendix III), the displacement $\Delta_{IIb}$ can be calculated from the $R$-curve, as shown in the next section.

$R$-curves can be used only if $c_f$ and $G_f$ have been previously measured through Four- Point Bending tests on notched beams. For a number of sufficiently-homogeneous building stones (like - for example – granite and marble), the evaluation of $c_f$ and $G_f$ may be performed on the basis of the strength and elastic

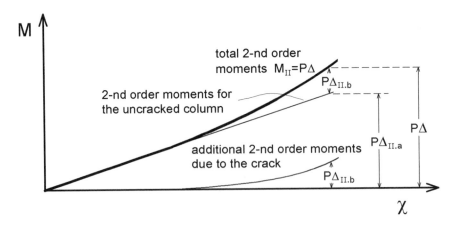

Fig. 9 – Second-order moment as a function of the curvature at column base.

modulus found in the literature.

The above *R*-curve approach to check fracture of columns made of quasi-brittle materials is easily applicable, since it only needs the simple calculations shown above. A numerical example is illustrated in the following.

Unfortunately, for quasi-brittle notched columns, the use of *R*-curves determined from the Size Effect law does not allow to achieve a solution in every case. It has been found that the equivalent crack extension $\Delta a$ increases from a lower bound value, when the axial load is zero (pure bending), to an upper value $\Delta a = c_f$ that can be achieved, for a certain axial load, when $\mathcal{G}(\alpha)$ is tangent to the *R*-curve at its upper point at the beginning of the plateau with constant $G_f$. Unfortunately, for higher axial loads, the *R*-curve determined from Size Effect vanishes.

Therefore, between the value of the eccentric axial load $P$ where collapse occurs with $\Delta a = c_f$, and the highest values of $P$ for which the column collapses by reaching the ultimate compressive strain or loosing its stability before, there is a range of axial loads where the crack extension reached at collapse cannot be identified through the *R*-curves based on Bazant's Size Effect law. In these latter cases, the *R*-curve approach is inapplicable to the study of notched columns stability.

## 5.3 Structural response from the *R*-curve

To calculate the second-order displacement $\Delta_{IIa}$ of an uncracked column, curvature $\chi_a$ can be taken directly from the moment-curvature diagram (obtained as shown in Appendix III) for a given value of *M*. Moreover, by using LEFM, in Appendix IV it is shown how to calculate in closed form the additional rotation $\vartheta_{IIb}$ of column sections at a distance *H* from the cracked section, as well as $\Delta_{IIb}$.

By using *R*-curves, the results achieved through LEFM can also be extended to columns made of quasi-brittle materials, in order to evaluate their structural response during a stable crack-growth $\Delta a$ [13].

The structural response of the column from the *R*-curve can be quantified by using an iterative procedure, since the additional crack-induced top displacement $\Delta_{IIb}$ and the maximum stable crack growth $\Delta a$, due to the application of the force *P* with the eccentricity *e* at the column top, are mutually related.

Therefore, for a given crack length $a_0$, in the first step one obtains $\Delta_{IIb}{}^{(1)}$ by means of LEFM from the expression (42) in Appendix IV. The second-order moment $M_{II}{}^{(1)} = P\Delta^{(1)} = P(\Delta_{IIa} + \Delta_{IIb}{}^{(1)})$ is then computed, together with the eccentricity *e* corresponding to the maximum stable crack-growth due to the application of the force *P* as determined by means of the *R*-curve.

The effect of the crack extension $\Delta a$ calculated on the *R*-curve is then taken into account, in order to quantify the structural response of the quasi-brittle cracked column.

The additional top displacement can be then updated as:

$$\Delta_{IIb}^{(2)} = \left\{ \frac{2}{E_c} \frac{P}{bH} \left[ \frac{6(e+\Delta^{(1)})}{H} S_M \left( \alpha_0 + \frac{\Delta a}{H} \right) - 2 \left( \alpha_0 + \frac{\Delta a}{H} \right) S_N \left( \alpha_0 + \frac{\Delta a}{H} \right) \right] \right\} L \quad (18)$$

together with the second order moments $P(\Delta_{IIa} + \Delta_{IIb}^{(2)})$.

The total moment $M = P[(\Delta_{IIa} + \Delta_{IIb}^{(2)}) + e]$ can now be calculated, where $e$ must be updated too, in order to obtain the moment for which $\mathcal{R}(\alpha)$ is tangent to the $R$-curve. Usually, only two or three steps are required to obtain $\Delta_{IIb}^{(j)} \cong \Delta_{IIb}^{(j-1)}$.

## 5.4   Numerical example

The $R$ and $\mathcal{G}$ curves shown in Figure 8 refer to a 3 m-tall column having a square section (side 24 cm), subjected to an eccentric axial load $P = 50$ kN and made of a quasi-brittle material ($c_f = 15$ mm and $G_f = 35$ N/m). The compressive and tensile strengths are $f_c = 35$ MPa and $f_t = 3$ MPa, respectively; the elastic modulus is $E_c = 30$ GPa.

Tangency occurs for $\Delta a = 13$ mm; since the initial notch depth is $a_0 = 60$ mm ($\alpha_0 = 0.25$), the total crack length after stable growth is $a = a_0 + \Delta a = 73$ mm. The total moment is $M_{I+II} = P(e+\Delta) = 7319$ Nm, where $M_I = Pe = 7146$ Nm with $e = 14.29$ cm, and $M_{II} = P\Delta = 172$ Nm with $\Delta = 3.44$ mm. $\Delta$ is the sum of $\Delta_{IIa} = 3.26$ mm and $\Delta_{IIb} = 0.18$ mm, the latter being due to the structural response of the column, and being determined by means of the $R$-curve through equation (18).

Although under an axial load of 50 kN the resisting moment of the section is $M_u = 11406$ Nm, the allowable moment is reduced to $Pe = 7146$ Nm by the combination of second-order moments and fracture determined through the $R$-curve approach.

## 6.   CONCLUSIONS

The stability analysis of quasi-brittle columns exhibiting a notch at their base and eccentrically loaded at the top by an axial force is described by means of an analytical model.

The proposed model is rather intuitive and leads to solutions that require a relatively limited computational effort even in problems that otherwise would imply a rather complex analysis by finite elements, because of geometric and mechanical nonlinearities, and fracture.

Some approximations have been introduced: the moment-curvature diagrams were obtained by using stress-blocks, and fracture analysis was carried out by means of $R$-curves, obtained from Bazant's Size Effect Law.

Once the curvature distribution and second-order displacements from the moment-curvature diagram are worked out, together with second-order moments, the R-curves allow a rather easy analysis of the stability of notched columns.

As for fracture and second-order moments, their combined effect has to do with the crack growth, that modifies the "effective" section and so the "effective" eccentricity of the axial load.

It must be noted, however, that working out the R-curves at high axial loads becomes increasingly difficult, since the fracture process continues to propagate until column collapse, but the R-curves are not able to identify the crack extension. In this case, other methods for stability analysis in cracked columns should be used.

## ACKNOWLEDGMENTS

This study was developed within a research project on the structural use of stone in Architecture and Building Engineering.

The financial and managerial supports by Sardegna Ricerche Consortium and by PROMEA Consortium, respectively, are gratefully acknowledged.

## REFERENCES

1.   Bazant Z.P. and Cedolin L. (2003). *Stability of structures. Elastic, Inelastic, Fracture, and Damage Theories.* 2$^{nd}$ ed. pub. by Dover Publishers, New York .

2.   Ferretti D., Iori I. and Morini M. (2002). *La stabilità delle strutture - Il caso delle costruzioni in cemento armato (Structural Stability – Reinforced-Concrete Constructions, in Italian).* Pub. by McGraw-Hill, Milan (Italy).

3.   Hillerborg A., Modéer M. and Petersson P.E. (1976). "Analysis of Crack Formation and Crack Growth in Concrete by means of Fracture Mechanics and Finite Elements". *Cement Concrete Research*, Vol.6, pp. 773-782.

4.   Nallathambi P. and Karihaloo B.L. (1986). "Determination of the Specimen-Size Independent Fracture Toughness of Plain Concrete". *Magazine of Concrete Research*, Vol. 38, No. 135, pp. 67-76.

5.   Bazant Z.P. (1976). "Instability, Ductility and Size Effect in Strain-Softening Concrete". *ASCE - Journal of Engineering Mechanics*, Vol. 102, pp. 331-344.

6.   Bazant Z.P. and Cedolin L. (1979). "Blunt Crack Band Propagation in Finite Element Analysis". *ASCE - Journal of Engineering Mechanics*, Vol. 105, pp. 297-315.

7.  Bazant Z.P. and Oh L. (1983). "Crack Band Theory for Fracture of Concrete". *Materials and Structures*, Vol.16, pp. 155-157.

8.  Bazant Z.P. (1984): "Size Effect in Blunt Fracture: Concrete, Rock, Metal". *ASCE - Journal of Engineering Mechanics*, Vol. 110, pp. 518-535.

9.  Bazant Z.P. (1989). "Fracture Energy of Heterogeneous Materials and Similitude". Proc. SEM/RILEM Int. Conf. on Fracture of Concrete and Rock, Houston (Texas), June 1987, ed. by S.P. Shah and S.E. Swartz, Springer-Verlagh, New York, pp. 229-241.

10. Bazant Z.P. and Kazemi M.T. (1990). "Determination of Fracture Energy, Process-Zone Length and Brittleness Number from Size Effect, with Application to Rock and Concrete". *International Journal of Fracture*, Vol. 44, pp. 111-131.

11. Sargin M. (1971). *Stress Strain Relationships for Concrete and the Analysis of Structural Concrete Sections*. University of Waterloo, Department of Civil Engineering, Solid Mechanics Division, S.M. Study No.4.

12. Karihaloo B.L. (1995). *Fracture Mechanics and Structural Concrete*, pub. by Longman Scientific & Technical, Burnt Mills (UK).

13. Bazant Z.P. and Planas J. (1998). *Fracture and Size Effect in Concrete and Other Quasibrittle Materials*, pub. by CRC Press, Boca Raton, Florida (USA).

14. Tada H., Paris P.C. and Irwin G.R. (2000). *The Stress Analysis of Cracks Handbook*, pub. by ASME Press, New York.

15. Smith R. N. L. (1991). *BASIC Fracture Mechanics*, pub. by Butterworth-Heinemann, Oxford (UK).

16. Biasioli F., Debernardi P.G. and Marro P. (1993). *Eurocodice 2 - Esempi di calcolo (Eurocode 2 – Worked Examples, in Italian)*, pub. by Edizioni Keope Srl, Turin (Italy).

## APPENDIX I – CONSTITUTIVE LAW

Sargin's law [11] has been adopted for $\varepsilon_c < \varepsilon_{c0}$ :

$$\sigma_c(\varepsilon_c) = \frac{\dfrac{E_{ci}}{E_{c0}}\dfrac{\varepsilon_c}{\varepsilon_{c0}} + (D-1)\left(\dfrac{\varepsilon_c}{\varepsilon_{c0}}\right)^2}{1 + \left(\dfrac{E_{ci}}{E_{c0}} - 2\right)\dfrac{\varepsilon_c}{\varepsilon_{c0}} + D\left(\dfrac{\varepsilon_c}{\varepsilon_{c0}}\right)^2} f_c \tag{25}$$

with the assumption of $E_{ci}/E_{c0} = 2$ and $D = 0$. $E_{ci}$ and $E_{c0}$ are the initial elastic modulus and the secant elastic modulus at failure, respectively. For any given strain diagram of Figure 2a, the related stress distribution is then known.

In tension too the stress-strain diagram is assumed to be parabolic up to a certain value $\varepsilon_{t0}$ (= collapse) of the strain.

Integrating the actual stress profiles (for any given position of the neutral axis), makes it possible to evaluate the parameters $\beta_{1c}$, $\beta_{2c}$, $\beta_{1t}$, $\beta_{2t}$ (Appendix II), which are instrumental in working out the stress-blocks in compression and in tension, together with the position of their resultants.

## APPENDIX II – CONSTRUCTION OF FAILURE ENVELOPES AND MOMENT-CURVATURE DIAGRAMS

The construction of the failure envelopes (Fig. 2b) and moment-curvature diagrams (Fig. 12) is made easier once the parametersw $\beta_{1c}$, $\beta_{2c}$, $\beta_{1t}$, $\beta_{2t}$ have been evaluated.

### Use of stress-blocks to plot failure envelopes

It is initially shown how to determine the stress-blocks through the functions $\beta_{1c}$, $\beta_{2c}$, $\beta_{1t}$, $\beta_{2t}$ for ultimate stress and strain distributions.

Consider first the ultimate strain diagrams for $x_u < H$, and therefore $\xi_u < 1$. Let us assume that the compressive stress blocks are limited to $0.85 f_c$. Since, at ultimate, each $\xi_u$ corresponds to a specific strain $\varepsilon_e$ of the edge in compression, $\beta_{1c}(\xi_u)x_u$ is assumed to be the other side of the stress-block, where $\beta_{1c}(\xi_u)$ is a function of $\xi_u$. Each value of this function is obtained by integrating the distribution of the compressive stresses for every failure strain diagram.

Therefore, the depth of the stress-block can also be written as $\beta_{1c}(\varepsilon_e)x_u$. From the previous integration, by evaluating the centroid of the compressive stress distribution, the position of the stress resultant at ultimate is also obtained, that is its distance $\beta_{2c}(\xi_u)x_u$ from the edge in compression, as well as its distance $d_c(\xi_u)=H/2-\beta_{2c}(\xi_u)x_u$ from the section centroid. Also $\beta_{2c}(\xi_u)$ is a function of $\xi_u$, and, similarly to the case of function $\beta_{1c}$, it can be assumed that $d_c(\varepsilon_e) = H/2 - \beta_{2c}(\varepsilon_e)x_u$.

The stress-block of the tensile stresses can be described analogously. Let us assume that also for tensile stresses, the parabolic stress-strain relationship follows Sargin's law, and that the value of the ultimate tensile stress is $f_t$. The depth is assumed to be $\beta_{1t}(1-\xi_u)\cdot(H-x_u)$, with $\beta_{1t}$ as a function of $\xi_u$. The depth is obtained by integrating the relationship between strain and tensile stresses, and by imposing that its integral at ultimate is $R_{tu}(\xi_u) = f_t b \beta_{1t}(1-\xi_u)\cdot(H-x_u)$.

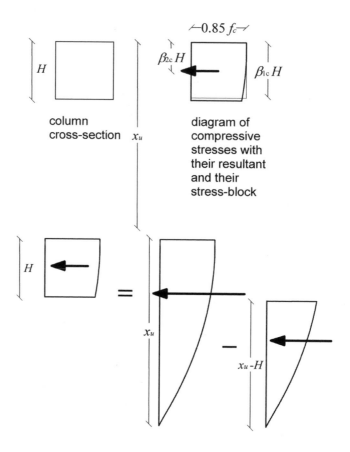

Fig. 10 – Diagram of the compressive stresses for $x_u > H$, and their stress-block.

To evaluate the position of $R_{tu}$, the distances from the edge in tension and from section centroid are assumed to be $\beta_{2t}(1-\xi_u)\cdot(H-x_u)$ and $d_t(\xi_u)=H/2-\beta_{2t}(\xi_u)\cdot(H-x_u)$, respectively, with $\beta_{2t}(\xi_u)$ being a function of $\xi_u$. Similarly to the case of compressive strains, $R_{tu}$ and $d_t(\xi_u)$ can be defined as $f_{ct}\cdot\beta_{1t}(\varepsilon_i)\cdot(H-x_u)$ and $H/2-\beta_{2t}(\varepsilon_i)\cdot(H-x_u)$, respectively.

Consider then the ultimate strain diagrams of Figure 2a for $x_u > H$, and therefore $\xi_u > 1$. The whole section is compressed and – by referring to Figure 10 - if the strain of the most compressed edge is $\varepsilon_e$ and that of the less compressed one is $\varepsilon_i$ ($e$ = extrados, $i$ = intrados), we have [16]:

$$\beta_{1c}(\xi_u)=\beta_{1c}(\varepsilon_e)\cdot\xi_u - \beta_{1c}(\varepsilon_i)\cdot(\xi_u-1) \qquad (26a)$$

210

$$\beta_{2c}(\xi_u) = \frac{[\beta_{2c}(\varepsilon_e) \cdot \xi_u][\beta_{1c}(\varepsilon_e) \cdot \xi_u]}{\beta_{1c}(\xi_u)} - \frac{[\beta_{2c}(\varepsilon_i) \cdot (\xi_u - 1) + 1][\beta_{1c}(\varepsilon_i) \cdot (\xi_u - 1)]}{\beta_{1c}(\xi_u)}$$

$$(26b)$$

with $\varepsilon_i = \varepsilon_e \cdot (\xi_u - 1)/\xi_u$. Therefore, the compressive stress resultant and its position with respect to the section centroid are $R_{cu}(\xi_u) = 0.85\, f_c\, b \beta_{1c}(\xi_u)\, H$ and $d_c(\xi_u) = H/2 - \beta_{2c}(\xi_u)\, H$, respectively. At ultimate, for a given position of the neutral axis $\xi_u$, the knowledge of the values assumed by the functions $\beta_{1c}(\xi_u)$, $\beta_{2c}(\xi_u)$, $\beta_{1t}(\xi_u)$, $\beta_{2t}(\xi_u)$ allows to identify each point $[N_u(\xi_u), M_u(\xi_u)]$ of the failure envelope (Fig. 2b) through equations (1) and (2).

### Use of stress-blocks to plot moment-curvature diagrams

Each point $[N_u(\xi_u), M_u(\xi_u)]$ of the failure envelope corresponds to a moment-curvature diagram plotted for a given axial load $P = N_u(\xi_u)$, and therefore for a given value of $\xi_u$. All the points of the moment-curvature diagram are then obtained for $\xi_u \le \xi \le +\infty$, and therefore $M_u(\xi_u) \ge M \ge 0$.

Considering a short column, no second-order displacements occur when the axial load $P$ is applied. Then, by constructing the moment-curvature diagram, if $\xi_u > 1$, all the points of the moment-curvature diagram are calculated for $\xi > 1$, while, if $\xi_u < 1$, there is a certain moment $M$ for which $\xi$ becomes lower than 1.

In the former case, for small values of the eccentricity $e$, and therefore of moment $P \cdot e$ and curvature $\chi$, high values of $\xi$ occur, tending to infinity for $e=0$.

By increasing the eccentricity $e$, the bending moment $M = P \cdot e$ increases with $e$ while $\xi$ decreases until the former reaches $M_u$ and the latter $\xi_u$. Since for all the points of the moment-curvature diagram $\xi > 1$, the equilibrium equation in the column axis direction becomes $P = 0.85 f_c b \beta_{1c} H$. By solving for $\beta_{1c}$, one obtains $\beta_{1c} = P/(0.85 f_c b H)$. All the terms of the previous equation are constant except $\beta_{1c}$. Since the edge strains $\varepsilon_e$ and $\varepsilon_i$ are mutually related by the linear strain distribution, $\beta_{1c}$ is a function of both $\xi$ and one of the edge strains, for instance $\varepsilon_e$. Besides, since the moment equilibrium yields $M = 0.85 f_c b \beta_{1c} H\, (H/2 - \beta_{2c} H)$, also $\beta_{2c}$ is a function of both $\xi$ and $\varepsilon_e$. By referring to Figure 10, for $\xi > 1$, the functions $\beta_{1c}(\xi, \varepsilon_e)$ and $\beta_{2c}(\xi, \varepsilon_e)$ have the following formulation:

$$\beta_{1c}(\xi, \varepsilon_e) = \beta_{1c}(\varepsilon_e) \cdot \xi - \beta_{1c}\left(\varepsilon_e \frac{\xi - 1}{\xi}\right) \cdot (\xi - 1) \qquad (27a)$$

$$\beta_{2c}(\xi, \varepsilon_e) = \frac{(\beta_{2c}(\varepsilon_e) \cdot \xi) \cdot (\beta_{1c}(\varepsilon_e) \cdot \xi)}{\beta_{1c}(\xi, \varepsilon_e)} -$$

$$+ \frac{\left[ \beta_{2c} \left( \varepsilon_e \frac{\xi-1}{\xi} \right) \cdot (\xi-1) + 1 \right] \cdot \left[ \beta_{1c} \left( \varepsilon_e \frac{\xi-1}{\xi} \right) \cdot (\xi-1) \right]}{\beta_{1c}(\xi,\varepsilon_e)}$$

(27b)

Hence, for any point of the moment-curvature diagram with $\xi > 1$, once $\xi$ has been assigned and $\beta_{1c}=P/(0.85 f_c b H)$ has been calculated, $\varepsilon_e$ can be easily obtained by solving equation (27a), where the function $\beta_{1c}$ is pre-calculated in advance (see also Figure 11). Once the values of $\beta_{1c}$ and $\varepsilon_e$ are known, the curvature $\chi = (\varepsilon_e + \varepsilon_i)/H$ is obtained from $\xi$ and $\varepsilon_e$. By calculating the value of $\beta_{2c}$ from the equation (27b), the moment $M = 0.85 f_c b \beta_{1c} H (H/2 - \beta_{2c} H)$ is also obtained.

In the case of moment-curvature diagrams where - for sufficiently high values of $M$ - the parameter $\xi$ becomes lower than 1, the equilibrium equation in the axial direction becomes $P = 0.85 f_c b \beta_{1c} \xi H - f_t b \beta_{1t}(1-\xi H)$.

Since both compressive and tensile resultants depend on the strains $\varepsilon_e$ and $\varepsilon_i$

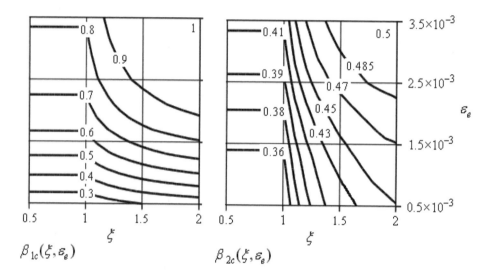

Fig. 11 – Plots of functions $\beta_{1c}(\xi,\varepsilon_e)$ and $\beta_{2c}(\xi,\varepsilon_e)$.

on the edge in compression and in tension respectively – mutually related by the linear strain distribution – $\varepsilon_e$ and $\xi$ are not independent, and both functions $\beta_{1c}$ and $\beta_{1t}$ should depend only on one of the edge strains, for instance $\varepsilon_e$. Therefore, it can be assumed that $\beta_{1c}=\beta_{1c}(\varepsilon_e)$ and $\beta_{1t}=\beta_{1t}(\varepsilon_i)$, with $\varepsilon_i=\varepsilon_e \cdot (1-\xi)/\xi$.

Consequently, also $\beta_{1t}$ depends on $\varepsilon_e$. Besides, moment equilibrium brings in $\beta_{2c}=\beta_{2c}(\varepsilon_e)$ and $\beta_{2t}=\beta_{2t}(\varepsilon_i)$. Therefore, taking into account that $\varepsilon_i=\varepsilon_e \cdot (1-\xi)/\xi$, for $\xi \leq 1$ one obtains:

$$\beta_{1c}(\xi, \varepsilon_e) = \beta_{1c}(\varepsilon_e) \qquad\qquad \beta_{2c}(\xi, \varepsilon_e) = \beta_{2c}(\varepsilon_e) \qquad (28)$$

$$\beta_{1t}(\xi, \varepsilon_e) = \beta_{1t}(\varepsilon_e) \qquad\qquad \beta_{2t}(\xi, \varepsilon_e) = \beta_{2t}(\varepsilon_e) \qquad (29)$$

Hence, for moment-curvature diagrams with $\xi_u \le 1$, functions (28) and (29) are used, while for moment-curvature diagrams with $\xi_u > 1$, functions (28) are coupled with functions (27), and, for $\xi < 1$, the same functions are used together with functions (29). The plots of functions $\beta_{1c}(\xi, \varepsilon_e)$ and $\beta_{2c}(\xi, \varepsilon_e)$ in Figure 11 were obtained by plotting together functions (28) and functions (27).

## APPENDIX III – CONSTRUCTION OF MOMENT-CURVATURE DIAGRAMS OF ECCENTRICALLY LOADED SECTIONS

Moment-curvature diagrams under a constant normal force $P = N_u(\xi_u)$ to reach the ultimate moment $M_u$ are now considered. Each point of the diagrams is obtained for $\xi \ge \xi_u$, but two main cases can be distinguished, for $\xi_u \ge 1$ and for $\xi_u < 1$.

For a given constant value $P = N_u(\xi_u)$ of the axial load, the equilibrium equation in the longitudinal direction can be written as follows:

$$N_u(\xi_u) = R_c(\xi, \varepsilon_e) - R_t(\xi, \varepsilon_e) \qquad (30)$$

with

$$R_c(\xi, \varepsilon_e) = 0.85 f_c \, b \beta_{1c}\left(\xi, \varepsilon_e\right) \cdot \xi H \qquad (31a)$$

$$R_t(\xi, \varepsilon_e) = f_t \, b \beta_{1t}\left(1 - \xi, \varepsilon_e \frac{\xi - 1}{\xi}\right) \cdot (H - \xi H) \qquad (31b)$$

where, for $\xi < 1$, both $R_c(\xi, \varepsilon_e) \ne 0$ and $R_t(\xi, \varepsilon_e) \ne 0$, while, for $\xi \ge 1$, $R_t(\xi, \varepsilon_e) = 0$. Let us plot the moment-curvature diagram with $n$ points. Once the functions $\beta_{1c}$ and $\beta_{1t}$ are known, it is easy to solve equation (30) by trial-and-error, and to find $\varepsilon_e$ for given values of the neutral axis $\xi_j$, $j = 1, \ldots n$.

Solving equation (30) is even easier for $\xi_j > 1$, since $R_t$ becomes zero, and $\beta_{1c} = P/(0.85 f_c b \xi_j H)$ can be immediately obtained from (30), so that $\varepsilon_{ej}$ is then obtained through function $\beta_{1c}(\xi, \varepsilon_e)$, see for instance the plots in Figure 11 (Appendix II).

Therefore, by solving equation (30) $n$ times, for $n$ assigned values $\xi_j$, $n$ values $\varepsilon_{ej}$ are obtained. Because of the linear strain distribution, $\varepsilon_{ij} = \varepsilon_{ej}(\xi_j - 1)/\xi_j$ is known, and the $j$-th value $1/r_j = \chi_j = (\varepsilon_{ej} - \varepsilon_{ij})/H$ of the curvature is obtained. It must be plotted together with the $j$-th value $M_j$ of the moment, that has to be calculated $n$ times from the moment equation

$$M = R_c(\xi,\varepsilon_e)d_c(\xi,\varepsilon_e) + R_t(\xi,\varepsilon_i)d_t(\xi,\varepsilon_i) \qquad (32)$$

where $R_c$ and $R_t$ are the compressive and tensile resultants, respectively, with $R_t = 0$ for $\xi > 1$, and where $d_c$ and $d_t$ are their lever arms with respect to section centroid.

Figure 12 shows the moment-curvature diagram of the section at the base of a 24 cm × 24 cm column, for an eccentric axial load $P = 1250$ kN, corresponding to $N_u(\xi_u = 0.951)$. The compressive and tensile strengths are $f_c = 35$ MPa and $f_t = 3$ MPa, respectively, and the elastic modulus is $E_c = 30$ GPa.

The diagram is plotted with 11 points, including the origin $(0,0)$ for $j = 1$ and the ultimate point $(\chi_u, M_u)$ for $j = 11$.

Consider first a point for which $\xi < 1$. For instance, $\chi_9$ and $M_9$ have been calculated by first assigning $\xi_9 = 0.980$, and by solving equation (30) by trial-and-error to obtain the unknown compressive strain $\varepsilon_{e9} = 2.64\cdot10^{-3}$. The tensile strain is $\varepsilon_{i9} = 5.4\cdot10^{-5}$, and the corresponding curvature is $\chi_9 = 11.22\cdot10^{-3}$ m$^{-1}$.

From (32) the related moment is $M_9 = 34080$ Nm. For the 4-th point, a neutral axis with $\xi > 1$ has been assigned, i.e. $\xi_4 = 1.3$. Since $R_t$ is zero, from (30) we obtain $\beta_{1c} = P/(0.85f_cb\xi_4H) = 0.730$ and, from the plots of Figure 11 in Appendix II, $\varepsilon_{e4} = 1.67\cdot10^{-3}$. For the linear strain distribution along the section, the compressive strain on the opposite edge $\varepsilon_{i4} = 3.87\cdot10^{-4}$ is calculated, together with the curvature $\chi_4 = 5.37\cdot10^{-3}$ m$^{-1}$. Finally, from (32), the moment $M_4 = 20990$ Nm can be worked out.

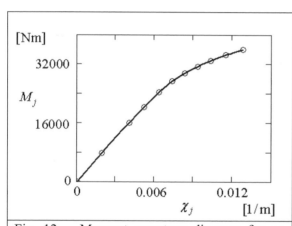

[Nm]

$M_j$

32000

16000

0

0    0.006    0.012

$\chi_j$    [1/m]

Fig. 12 – Moment-curvature diagram for an eccentrically-compressed square section (side = 24 cm), loaded by the axial force $P = 1250$ kN.

## APPENDIX IV – CRACK-INDUCED ADDITIONAL ROTATIONS IN SPECIMENS SUBJECTED TO COMBINED AXIAL LOAD/BENDING

The already mentioned LEFM handbook [14] gives, as a function of $\alpha$, crack-induced additional rotation $\vartheta$ and crack opening $w$ for different test specimens.

In four-point bending tests we have:

$$w_M(\alpha) = \frac{4}{E_c} \frac{6M}{bH^2} \alpha H V_M(\alpha) \tag{33}$$

where $V_M(\alpha) = 0.8\text{-}1.7\,\alpha + 2.4\,\alpha^2 + 0.66/(1\text{-}\alpha)^2$, and

$$\vartheta_M(\alpha) = \frac{1}{2} \frac{4}{E_c} \frac{6M}{bH^2} S_M(\alpha) \tag{34}$$

with:

$$S_M(\alpha) = \left(\frac{\alpha}{1-\alpha}\right)^2 \left(5.93 - 19.69\alpha + 37.14\alpha^2 - 35.84\,\alpha^3 + 13.12\,\alpha^4\right) \tag{35}$$

In the case of edge-cracked specimens in tension (Fig.13), the expression of the crack opening is also available:

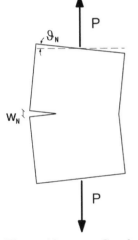

$$w_N(\alpha) = \frac{4}{E_c} \frac{P}{bH} \alpha H V_N(\alpha) \tag{36}$$

with:

$$V_N(\alpha) = \frac{1.46 + 3.42\left[1 - \cos\left(\frac{\pi}{2}\alpha\right)\right]}{\left[\cos\left(\frac{\pi}{2}\alpha\right)\right]^2} \tag{37}$$

Fig. 13 – Crack-induced additional rotation of edge-cracked specimens subjected to the axial force $P$.

For the additional rotation $\vartheta_N$ (Fig.13), an appropriate expression has been obtained by interpolating the results provided by the FE modelling of an edge-cracked specimen in tension:

$$\vartheta_N(\alpha) = \frac{4}{E_c} \frac{P}{bH} \alpha\, S_N(\alpha) \tag{38}$$

with:

$$S_N(\alpha) = \frac{1.816 + 1.499 \cdot 10^7 \left[ 1 - \cos\left(\frac{\pi}{2}\alpha\right)^{6.333} \right]}{\left[ \cos\left(\frac{\pi}{2}\alpha\right) \right]^{-22.253}} \tag{39}$$

For $0.2 \leq \alpha \leq 0.6$, this expression has been shown to fit rather well FEM results, with errors of the same order of magnitude found in the interpolation of both crack opening and centerline displacement, whose accuracy in the same interval is 0.5% [14].

By applying the superposition principle, the expressions for crack opening and additional rotation are:

$$w(\alpha) = \frac{4}{E_c} \frac{6M}{bH^2} \alpha H V_M(\alpha) - \frac{4}{E_c} \frac{P}{bH} \alpha H V_N(\alpha) \tag{40}$$

$$\vartheta_{IIb}(\alpha) = \frac{2}{E_c} \frac{6M}{bH^2} S_M(\alpha) - \frac{4}{E_c} \frac{P}{bH} \alpha S_N(\alpha) \tag{41}$$

Therefore, with reference to a cracked specimen subjected to combined axial load and bending, an additional rotation $\vartheta_{IIb}$ occurs at the section located at distance $H$ from the cracked section. Hence, the additional curvature $\chi_{IIb} = \vartheta_{IIb}/L$ at the column base can be obtained.

The total rotation $\vartheta$ is the sum of the rotation $\vartheta_{IIa}$ of the uncracked specimen plus the additional crack-induced rotation $\vartheta_{IIb}$, so that the total rotation at the column base is $\vartheta = \vartheta_{IIa} + \vartheta_{IIb}$.

The additional rotation gives rise to the additional top displacement $\Delta_{IIb} = \vartheta_{IIb}L$, that, from (41), has the following expression (for any given value of $\alpha$):

$$\Delta_{IIb} = \left( \frac{2}{E_c} \frac{6M}{bH^2} S_M(\alpha) - \frac{4}{E_c} \frac{P}{bH} \alpha S_N(\alpha) \right) L \tag{42}$$

The rotation at the base and the displacement at the top $\Delta_{IIa}$ of the uncracked column are mutually related through the curvature $\chi_{IIa}$. According to the Model Column Method, $\Delta_{IIa} = 4\chi_{IIa}L^2/\pi^2$, where the curvature $\chi_{IIa}$ at the base of the uncracked column is calculated as $\chi_{IIa} = (\varepsilon_e - \varepsilon_i)/H$. The total curvature at the column base is then $\chi = \chi_{IIa} + \chi_{IIb}$.

STUDIES AND RESEARCHES – V.29, 2009
Graduate School in Concrete Structures – Fratelli Pesenti
Politecnico di Milano, Italy

# SEISMIC ASSESSMENT AND RETROFITTING OF A PLAN-WISE IRREGULAR R/C STRUCTURE DESIGNED FOR GRAVITY LOADS

Marco Valente[1]

## ABSTRACT

The seismic performance of an under-designed plan-wise irregular R/C structure tested at the Joint Research Centre – JRC (Ispra, Italy) and the effectiveness of a seismic retrofitting intervention based on both FRP wrapping and R/C jacketing applied to a number of critical columns are presented and discussed in this paper.

The retrofitting strategy was selected on the basis of the structural deficiencies, that were highlighted by both numerical analysis and testing. Retrofitting was mostly aimed at reducing the torsional component of the seismic response and at improving the global ductility of the structure.

Nonlinear dynamic time-history analyses were performed and bidirectional damage indexes were worked out to assess the seismic response of the structure in the original and retrofitted configurations.

Simplified procedures based on nonlinear static pushover analyses taking into account the effect of torsion were used in the seismic assessment of the plan-wise irregular structure and in the selection of the retrofitting strategy.

The simplified procedures adopted in this study (a) provide results, that are consistent with the experimental evidence and with nonlinear dynamic time-history analyses, and (b) allow to identify the most critical columns affecting the seismic performance of the structure.

The numerical results show the effectiveness of the retrofitting strategy based on R/C jacketing of selected columns, with specific reference to the decrease of the torsional effects, but the enhancement of the column ductility provided by FRP wrapping is instrumental in improving the seismic behaviour of the under-designed structure, in case of high-level seismic excitation.

---

[1] Assistant Professor, Dept. of Structural Eng., Politecnico di Milano, Milan, Italy.

# 1. INTRODUCTION

The main purposes of this study are (1) to evaluate the effectiveness of a "mixed" retrofitting intervention, by using both FRP wrapping and R/C jacketing on selected columns, and (2) to check the consistency of simplified procedures for the seismic assessment and retrofitting strategy in the case of existing plan-wise irregular R/C structures.

Based on the results of some tests carried out at the Elsa Laboratory of the Joint Research Centre – JRC (Ispra, Italy), numerical models were developed in order to properly describe the seismic response of a plan-asymmetric R/C structure designed only for gravity loads.

The design criteria for structural retrofitting, aimed at improving the global response of the torsionally-unbalanced R/C structure under seismic excitation, were suggested by the deficiencies indicated by the numerical analyses supported by the test results. The design strategy was based on the basic concept of reducing the torsional component of the seismic response of the bare structure, by reducing the eccentricity between the centre of strength (CP) and the centre of stiffness (CR), with respect to the centre of mass (CM). The strength and stiffness relocation was achieved by using the traditional technique of R/C jacketing, limited to selected members.

Moreover, the local deformation capacity of the critical columns was increased by applying fibre-reinforced polymer (FRP) jackets, which improved confinement of column extremities. In this way, the overall stiffness of the structural system was unaffected, and the ensuing rather small strength increase could be neglected. FRP retrofitting of columns increased the ductility capacity of the structure, without modifying the location of both the centre of stiffness (CR) and the centre of strength (CP).

Numerical results showed the effectiveness of the proposed strength-and-stiffness relocation strategy based on R/C jacketing of selected columns, but the local ductility increase based on FRP wrapping was necessary for improving the global seismic performance of the under-designed irregular R/C building in case of high-level seismic excitation.

Nonlinear dynamic time-history analyses and a simplified assessment procedure, named N2 method and based on nonlinear static pushover analyses, were used in this study. Because of the asymmetry of the structure, the N2 method was extended to take into account the effect of torsion, in order to accurately evaluate the seismic performance of the plan-wise irregular structure, and - more specifically - to identify the critical columns affecting the overall seismic behaviour of the structure.

The comparison with the results obtained by means of nonlinear dynamic time-history analyses shows that the simplified procedures based on pushover analyses are a simple and effective tool in the assessment of the global structural behaviour under seismic excitation and in the identification of the best retrofit strategy.

## 2. TEST STRUCTURE

Within the SPEAR Research Project, a series of experimental tests on a torsionally unbalanced three-storey R/C frame structure was carried out at the JRC ELSA Laboratory at Ispra (Negro, 2004). The plan view of the building and three typical beam/column sections are shown in Fig. 1. The structure represents - with some simplifications - typical old constructions in Southern Europe, that are characterized by (a) irregular plan layout, (b) slender columns with scanty stirrups, (c) smooth reinforcing bars, and (d) lack of shear reinforcement in beam-to-column joints. The full-scale R/C structure was subjected to bidirectional pseudo-dynamic tests under the Montenegro Herceg-Novi record scaled to two different values of the peak ground acceleration (PGA), i.e. 0.15g and 0.2g.

The damaged structure was rehabilitated by means of two retrofitting techniques, using FRP laminates and R/C jacketing, respectively. Then, the structure was subjected to a second series of tests with the same input accelerograms scaled to PGA values of 0.2g and 0.3g. In the retrofit by means of R/C jackets, the aim of the rehabilitation strategy was to increase both the strength and the stiffness of the structure, by jacketing a number of selected columns, in order to minimize the torsional effects due to the doubly-asymmetric plan layout of the structure. (In so doing, the displacement demand on the external columns was reduced). The original cross-section of Columns C1 and C4 was increased from 250x250 mm to 400x400 mm, Fig. 2 (thickness of the jacket = 75 mm). The reinforcement of the jacketed columns was: (a) three 16 mm-diameter bars for each side of the column, and (b) 8 mm-stirrups, spaced by 100 mm at the top/bottom of each column, and by 150 mm at mid height. More details on the structure can be found in Mola and Negro (2005).

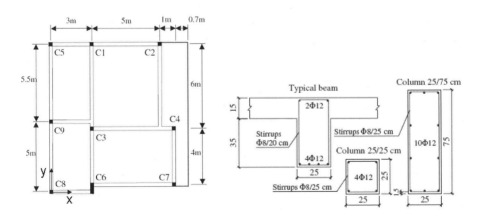

Figure 1 - Plan view and typical beam/column sections of the SPEAR structure. (Project "SPEAR" = Standing Patrol for Emergency Assessment and Response).

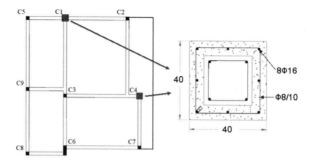

Figure 2 - Plan of the retrofitted structure tested at the JRC ELSA Laboratory and R/C jacketing applied to Columns C1 and C4.

## 3. NUMERICAL MODELS

The full-scale R/C structure was numerically modelled by using the SeismoStruct Code, in order to investigate the seismic response of the structure in the different configurations. The spread of the inelastic behaviour along the length of any member and within its cross-section was described by means of a fibre model, that made it possible to accurately evaluate the damage distribution. The sectional stress-strain state of inelastic frame elements was obtained via the integration of the nonlinear uniaxial stress-strain response of the individual fibres into which the section was subdivided. The discretisation of a typical R/C section is illustrated in Fig. 3.

The idealization of the structure was based on frames placed in the mean planes of the members and connected at the nodes. Each member (column or beam) was subdivided into a number of elements (from 4 to 6), whose length was critical to effectively capture the expected inelastic behaviour of the dissipative zones of the structure.

The storey height was 2.75 m for the first storey and 3 m for the remaining two storeys. The contribution of the slab to both beam stiffness and strength was included by using the effective flange-width for the beams framing into the columns. A reinforced concrete T-section was utilized for modelling the beam and the effective flange, the width of the latter being assumed as 7% of beam clear span, on either side of the beam, as proposed by Fardis (1994). Rigid elements were used to connect the geometric axes of the misaligned Beams B5 and B6 to Column C6, in order to account for the size of column section (Fig. 4). In order to model in-plane slab stiffness, the opposite corners of the slabs were diagonally connected by axially-stiff rods. The size and reinforcement of the connecting rods were determined in such a way that their contribution to the horizontal stiffness was large, while the contribution to the vertical stiffness was negligible, because slab contribution to beam flexural stiffness was already modelled via the effective width. Viscous damping was not included in the analytical model, because the pseudo-dynamic tests were performed by assuming zero damping.

The above assumptions markedly contributed to the very satisfactory fitting of the test results, this being a confirmation of the validity of the proposed numerical model.

Concrete was modelled by using a uniaxial constant-confinement model based on the constitutive relationship proposed by Mander et al. (1988), and later modified by Martinez-Rueda and Elnashai (1997), to cope with some problems concerning numerical stability under large displacements. Confinement effects, provided by the transverse reinforcement, were taken into account through the rules proposed by Mander, whereby a constant confining pressure was assumed in the entire stress-strain range.

The model required the introduction of four parameters: the compressive and tensile strengths of the unconfined concrete, the crushing strain and the confinement factor (defined as the ratio between the confined and unconfined compressive strength of the concrete).

In the case investigated here, the amount of transverse reinforcement of all members was very small to produce any effective confinement on the concrete. Because of the insufficiency of the stirrups, the confinement factor K was assumed to be close to 1 for all members in the analytical model. Fig. 5 shows the stress-strain curves for the unloading and reloading branches according to Mander's model (Mander et al., 1988) and to Martinez-Elnashai's model (Martinez-Rueda and Elnashai, 1997).

The constitutive model proposed by Menegotto and Pinto (1973), coupled with the isotropic hardening rules introduced by Filippou et al. (1983), was used for the longitudinal reinforcement.

The actual materials properties measured during the tests (Mola, 2007) were implemented.

The R/C-jacketed rectangular section available in SeismoStruct library was used for modelling the square columns retrofitted by means of R/C jacketing. Different confinement levels for the internal (pre-existing) and the external (new) concrete materials were defined.

The properties of the retrofitted elements were evaluated on the basis of the following assumptions (Eurocode 8):

- the jacketed column behaves monolithically with full composite action between the old and new concrete;

- the properties of the concrete used for the jacket apply over the full section of the element; and

- the axial load is assumed to be acting on the full composite section.

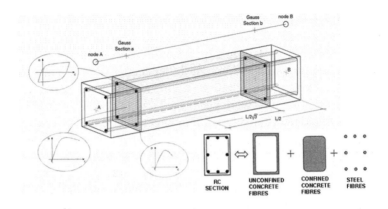

Figure 3 – Location of the Gauss sections and discretisation of a R/C section by means of fibres.

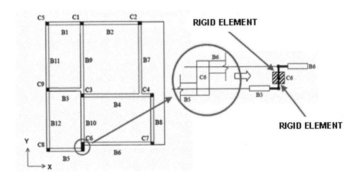

Figure 4 - Rigid "arms" for modelling the connection of Beams B5 and B6 to Column C6.

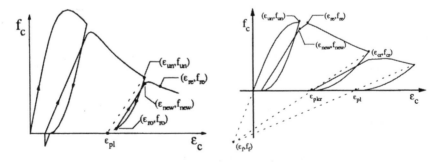

Figure 5. Stress-strain curves including the unloading and reloading branches, according to Mander's model (Mander et al., 1988) and to Martinez-Elnashai model's (Martinez-Rueda and Elnashai, 1997).

# 4. SEISMIC ASSESSMENT OF THE BARE STRUCTURE

## 4.1 Nonlinear bidirectional dynamic analyses

Nonlinear dynamic time-history simulations of the pseudo-dynamic tests carried out at the JRC Elsa Laboratory were performed and the Montenegro Herceg-Novi records for longitudinal and transverse components scaled to different PGA values (0.15g and 0.2g) were adopted.

In Fig. 6, with reference to CM, the experimental and numerical profiles of the maximum inter-storey drift and inter-storey rotation are shown under bidirectional 0.2g PGA earthquake. The comparison of the inter-storey drift shows that the stiffness of the structure was larger in the Y than in the X direction, this result being consistent with the arrangement of the large Column C6 placed with its strong axis in the Y direction.

The magnitude of the second storey drift at CM was slightly underestimated by the numerical model compared to experimental results, whereas the predicted drifts in the first storey were slightly overestimated. The model was able to correctly predict the largest drift occurred at the second storey both in the X and Y direction. The maximum value of the inter-storey rotation was about 9 mrad (second level, Fig. 6).

The assessment of the seismic response and damage of the structure resulting from the application of the bidirectional excitation was performed by using the Inter-storey Drift Ratio (IDR) and the ductility Demand-to-Capacity Ratio (DCR). Considering the test results, the possibility of a shear failure was ruled out.

The Inter-storey Drift Ratio is defined as follows:

$$IDR = \frac{\Delta_i - \Delta_{i-1}}{h_i} \tag{1}$$

where $\Delta_i - \Delta_{i-1}$ is the relative displacement between two successive storeys and $h_i$ is the storey height.

The values of the Inter-storey Drift Ratio for the columns of all the storeys are reported in Fig. 7. The highest IDR values were observed at the second storey and the columns of the flexible sides exhibited very large drift demands in the two transverse directions. The maximum values of the storey drifts at the mass centre CM of the second storey were about 55 and 45 mm in the X and Y directions, respectively.

Because of the torsion of the building, the drifts at the flexible edges (Columns C1, C2 and C5 in the X direction, and Columns C4 and C7 in the Y direction) increased to about 70 mm in both directions. (Editors' note: "flexible/stiff edge" or "flexible/stiff side" = edge/side of the plan configuration of the building, whose columns are the farthest from/closest to the centre of stiffness - CR).

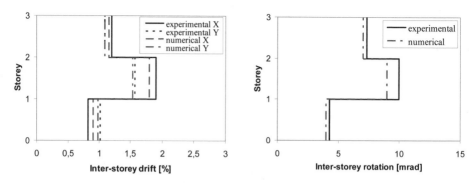

Figure 6 – Profiles of the maximum inter-storey drift and inter-storey rotation of the bare structure under 0.2 PGA earthquake.

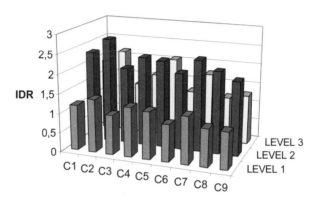

Figure 7 – Values of the maximum Inter-storey Drift Ratio (IDR) for the columns of the bare structure under 0.2 PGA earthquake.

In order to accurately evaluate the damage induced in the most critical columns, the bidirectional Demand-to-Capacity Ratio (DCR) was used and calculated by the following expression:

$$DCR = \sqrt{\left(\frac{\theta_x}{\theta_{u,x}}\right)^2 + \left(\frac{\theta_y}{\theta_{u,y}}\right)^2} \qquad (2)$$

where $\theta_x$ and $\theta_y$ are the chord-rotation demands of the columns in the X and Y directions, respectively, and $\theta_{u,x}$ and $\theta_{u,y}$ are the ultimate chord-rotation capacities.

The chord-rotation demand may be taken equal to the element drift-ratio, that is the deflection at the end of the shear span with respect to the tangent to the axis at the yielding end, divided by the shear span. In the columns belonging to a structure under seismic action, the lateral drifts at shear-span ends are generally much larger than the nodal rotations at the ends of the columns. The nodal rotations of the columns can be neglected in any structures designed without capacity-design procedures, where the flexural stiffness of the beams is much larger than that of the columns. Fig. 8 shows the simplified computation of the chord-rotation demand on columns assuming the shear span $L_V$ be equal to half the member length.

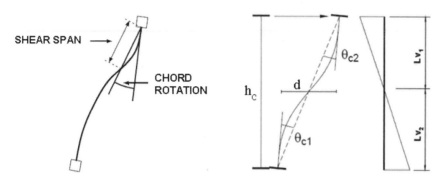

Figure 8 - Definition of the shear span and of the chord rotation (left), and simplified computation of the chord-rotation demand on columns, assuming for $L_V$ a value equal to half the column length (right).

The deformation capacity of the structural members is evaluated in terms of chord rotation. An empirical conservative expression, implemented in Eurocode 8, was used for evaluating the member deformation capacity. This expression was obtained through a regression procedure applied to the results of over 1000 monotonic or cyclic tests carried out up to the bending-controlled failure of beam, column or wall specimens (Panagiotakos and Fardis, 2001).

The value of the total ultimate chord-rotation capacity, $\theta_u$, of concrete members under cyclic loading at the Limit State of Near Collapse may be calculated by means of the following expression (see EC8-Part 3):

$$\theta_u = \frac{1}{\gamma_{el}} \cdot 0.016 \cdot \left(0.3^v\right) \cdot \left[\frac{\max(0.01;\omega')}{\max(0.01;\omega)} \cdot f_c\right]^{0.225} \cdot \left(\frac{L_V}{h}\right)^{0.35} \cdot 25^{\left(\alpha \cdot \rho_{sx} \frac{f_{yw}}{f_c}\right)} \cdot (1.25^{100 \cdot \rho_d}) \qquad (3)$$

where $\gamma_{el}$ = factor for primary seismic elements; $v$ = normalised axial force; $\omega$, $\omega'$ = mechanical reinforcement ratio of the tension (compression) longitudinal reinforcement; $f_c$ = concrete compressive strength; $\alpha$ = confinement effectiveness factor; $\rho_{sx}$ = steel ratio of the transverse reinforcement; $f_{yw}$ = yield strength of the transverse reinforcement.

The values of the total chord-rotation capacity given by expression (3) should be multiplied by 0.825 in those members whose design did not take into account any seismic provisions, and multiplied by 0.575 in those members which were reinforced with continuous smooth (plain) longitudinal bars in the end regions, where steel yielding is expected.

The aforementioned expression indicates that chord rotation capacity depends (a) on both geometrical and mechanical characteristics, and (b) on the seismic demand. In fact chord rotation capacity is affected by the axial load and by the shear span, the latter being defined as the ratio of moment demand to shear demand at the end sections. Consequently, the same member may exhibit different capacities because of the variation of the axial load and shear span due to the seismic action.

In Fig. 9, on the assumption that the axial load be due only to the gravity loads pertaining to the seismic-load combination, the values of chord-rotation capacity are reported for the columns at each storey. In the analysis carried out in this study, the values of chord-rotation capacity were computed as a function of the seismic demand, considering the values of the axial load at each time step.

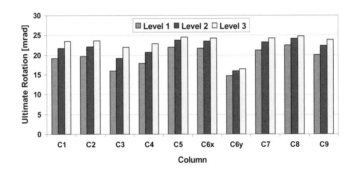

Figure 9 – Chord-rotation capacity of the columns of the bare structure under gravity loads.


The numerical results confirmed that the damage was concentrated mainly in the columns. Fig. 10 shows the DCR values calculated for the columns of the bare structure under bidirectional 0.2g PGA earthquake. The columns at the flexible sides sustained very large drift demands because of torsion, and presented higher DCR values than the columns at the stiff edges. Critical columns were Columns C1, C2 and C4, located at the flexible edges and with relatively large axial loads, and Column C3, with the largest axial load, these results being consistent with the experimental evidence. Significant damage was detected especially in correspondence of column end sections at the second storey of the flexible edges and Column C3 exhibited a significant level of spalling and cracking. Poor local structural detailing limited the rotational capacity of the columns, especially under high axial loads.

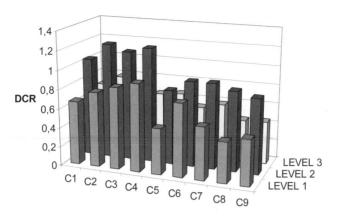

Figure 10 - Maximum DCR values for the columns of the bare structure under 0.2g PGA earthquake.

## 4.2 Simplified procedure assessment

A simplified assessment procedure, named N2 method, was also adopted for the seismic verification of the global structural behaviour of the R/C structure. The N2 method was developed at the University of Ljubljana by Fajfar (1996) and is based on pushover analyses and on inelastic demand spectra. This simplified method is an effective technique for the seismic assessment of existing structures and combines pushover analysis of a multi-degree-of-freedom (MDOF) model with the response spectrum analysis of an equivalent single-degree-of-freedom (SDOF) model. The method is formulated in the acceleration-displacement (AD) format, which enables the visual interpretation of the results. By means of a graphical procedure, the seismic demand is compared with the capacity of a structure for different limit states. For further details about the N2 method, see Fajfar (2000).

According to the requirements of Eurocode 8 Part 3, the level of damage in the structure was evaluated with reference to three Limit States (LS): Damage Limitation (DL), Significant Damage (SD) and Near Collapse (NC).

In the structural model, each limit state is achieved once a specific chord rotation is attained in one of the members of the structure: the LSDL, the LSSD and the LSNC correspond to the first attainment of $\theta_y$, $0.75 \cdot \theta_u$ and $\theta_u$, respectively. According to Eurocode 8, in this study the most critical column was conservatively assumed to control the behaviour of the structure.

The nonlinear static pushover analyses were numerically performed in each of the two horizontal directions, under positive or negative loading. The distribution of the horizontal forces along the height of the building was determined using the fundamental mode which is critical for each particular direction. Thus the distributions in the X and Y directions were determined from the first and second mode of vibration, respectively. The bilinear idealization of the pushover curve with zero post-yield stiffness was defined on the basis of the "equal-energy" concept (the areas underneath the actual and idealized bilinear curves are approximately the same, within the range of interest). The period of the equivalent SDOF system amounted to 0.95 s and 0.92 s in the X and Y directions, respectively.

The seismic demand was evaluated with reference to Eurocode 8 response spectrum (Type 1, Subsoil Class C) with $a_g$ = 0.25g, as the record used in the experimental tests was Eurocode 8 spectrum compatible. The elastic and inelastic demand spectra, and the capacity diagrams (for equivalent SDOF systems) for the bare structure in the X and Y directions at the LSSD are shown in Fig. 11. The seismic assessment of the structure is performed by comparing seismic demand and capacity. The target displacement at the LSSD is computed as the intersection between the bilinear capacity curve and the inelastic demand spectrum characterized by the relevant ductility. The inelastic displacement demand is equal to the elastic displacement demand according to the equal-displacement rule, because the period of the equivalent SDOF system is larger than the characteristic period $T_C$ = 0.6 s.

Due to the asymmetry of the investigated structure, the extension of the N2 Method to plan-asymmetric building structures was used in order to take into account the effect of torsion, as proposed by Fajfar (2005). The results obtained by pushover analysis were combined with the results of a linear dynamic (spectral) analysis. The target displacements and the distribution of deformations along the height of the building were determined by means of N2 Method, which is based on pushover analysis, whereas the torsional amplifications were determined by linear dynamic analysis in terms of correction factors to be applied to the results of pushover analyses. The correction factor is defined as the ratio between the normalized roof displacements (the roof displacement at an arbitrary location divided by the roof displacement at CM) obtained by linear dynamic analysis and by pushover analysis. Displacement reductions due to torsion were neglected. Torsional amplifications were taken into account for the columns of the flexible sides of the structure.

Fig. 11 shows that the bare structure was unable to satisfy the demand in both directions at a peak ground acceleration $Sa_g$ = 0.29g ($S$ = soil factor) at the Limit State of Significant Damage. The displacement demand and capacity in Fig. 11 refer to the equivalent SDOF system. The displacement demand and capacity of the MDOF system were obtained by multiplying the SDOF system demand by the transformation factor. The difference between the seismic demand and the displacement capacity was 0.044 m (0.127 m *vs* 0.083 m) in the X direction and 0.019 m (0.126 m *vs* 0.107 m) in the Y direction. The comparison of the bilinear idealized capacity curves of the structure in the X and Y directions shows an increase of the strength in the Y direction.

The simplified assessment procedure confirmed that the critical columns were the central Column C3 (with the highest axial load) and the corner Columns C1,

C2, C4, C7 (belonging to the flexible edges with the highest torsional amplifications). In particular, the Limit State of Significant Damage was reached in Column C4 at the second floor, where significant damage was observed in the tests and the highest DCR value was registered during the nonlinear dynamic analysis.

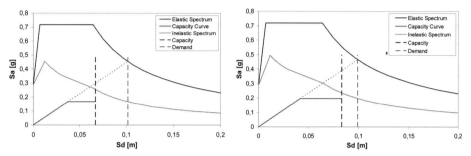

Figure 11 - Demand spectra and capacity curves in AD format at LSSD for the bare structure in the X (left) and Y direction (right) for $Sa_g = 0.29g$.

## 5. SEISMIC ASSESSMENT OF THE STRUCTURE RETROFITTED BY R/C JACKETING (R1)

### 5.1 Nonlinear bidirectional dynamic analyses

The retrofitted structure - previously tested at the JRC Elsa Laboratory and indicated in the following with "R1" - was analysed under 0.2g PGA with the input accelerograms used in the bare structure. In Fig. 12, the numerical and experimental inter-storey drifts and rotations of the retrofitted structure are reported. As in the case of the bare structure, there is a good agreement with the experimental results. The maximum values of the inter-storey drift and rotation were registered at the second level.

The retrofitting scheme modified the stiffness of the structure, and reduced the maximum top displacement and the inter-storey drift at all levels, especially in the X direction, which was originally significantly weaker than the Y direction (hence more sensitive to the increase of the cross-section of the two retrofitted columns).

As expected, retrofitting selected columns by means of a strategy based on stiffness-and-strength centre relocation was effective in reducing the torsional effects with respect to the original configuration. A significant decrease of the inter-storey rotation at the second level was observed in the R/C jacketed structure. The maximum inter-storey rotation was about 4 mrad in the retrofitted structure R1, compared to about 9 mrad in the original structure.

Fig. 13 shows the maximum IDR values for all the columns of the retrofitted structure R1; furthermore, a significant decrease of the IDR values was observed

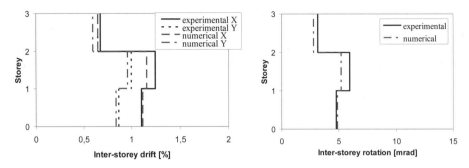

Figure 12 – Profiles of the maximum inter-storey drift and inter-storey rotation in the retrofitted structure R1 under 0.2g PGA earthquake.

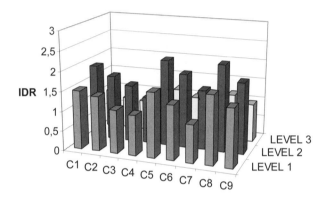

Figure 13 - Maximum inter-storey drift ratio (IDR) for the columns of the retrofitted structure R1 under 0.2g PGA earthquake.

in the columns of the second storey, especially in Columns C1, C2, C4 and C7, whereas only limited reduction was registered in Columns C5 and C8.

The reduction of the torsional effects was confirmed by the sizable decrease of DCR values in the columns of the flexible edges, Fig. 14. Furthermore, reducing stiffness-and-strength eccentricity brought in a reduction of the rotational component of the response, but the lack of ductility in the columns was not reduced. Consequently, the maximum DCR value was registered in Column C3 (in the bare structure, the maximum DCR value was observed in Column C4). Columns C5, C8, C9 presented high DCR values at the second storey too.

By increasing the seismic intensity level up to a PGA value of 0.3g, the maximum displacement recorded on the retrofitted structure R1 significantly increased, especially in the X direction, and the structure showed a considerable level of damage. In Fig. 15 the DCR values for all the columns of the structure subjected to 0.3g PGA ground motion are indicated. Columns were again the most damaged members of the structure, where the highest DCR values were registered at the first storey. The numerically-computed DCR values reproduced quite well the behaviour observed during the tests. The maximum DCR values were registered in Columns C3 and C9 at the first storey, this fact being consistent with the test, that was stopped because of the severe damage observed in Columns C3 and C9 at the first storey (heavy spalling of concrete cover and buckling of the longitudinal rebars). The analysis showed that retrofitting reduced the rotational component of the response, as intended in the design phase, but this was not enough to allow the structure to withstand high-intensity seismic excitations (0.3g PGA). The lack of ductility due to poor structural detailing of the un-retrofitted columns (where the axial load was high and the rotational capacity limited) was only partially overcome by the retrofitting process, and high DCR values were registered for Columns C2, C3 and C9.

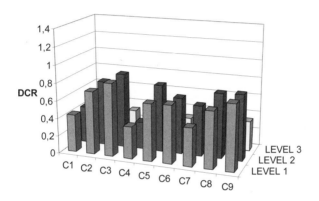

Figure 14 - Maximum DCR values for the columns of the retrofitted structure R1 under 0.2g PGA earthquake.

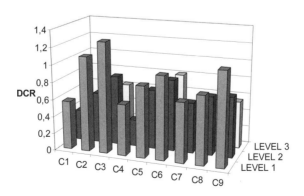

Figure 15 - Maximum DCR values for the columns of the retrofitted structure R1 under 0.3g PGA earthquake.

## 5.2 Assessment by simplified procedures

The seismic assessment of the retrofitted structure R1 was also carried out using the simplified procedure based on the N2 Method at different PGA levels ($Sa_g$=0.2g and $Sa_g$=0.29g). As the retrofitting reduced the irregularities of the structure, its global response could be more accurately described by the N2 method.

The capacity curves and the demand spectra of the equivalent SDOF system are presented in Fig. 16. The results are reported only for X direction, which proved to be the critical direction of the structure.

In the case of $Sa_g$ = 0.2g, the retrofitted structure was able to satisfy the requirements of the Limit State of Significant Damage - LSSD. The seismic demand in terms of displacements, transformed into the given MDOF system, was reduced to 0.076 m (0.088 m in the bare structure), while the capacity of the structure in terms of top displacement was increased up to 0.1 m (0.084 m in the bare structure). The retrofitted structure fully complied with LSSD requirements, contrary to the original structure, where this limit state was reached.

In the case of $Sa_g$ = 0.29g, the LSSD verification was not satisfied and a gap in terms of maximum top displacement was observed; the difference between the seismic demand and the displacement capacity in terms of top displacement amounted to 0.01 m (0.11 m *vs* 0.1 m). According to the nonlinear pushover analyses, LSSD was firstly reached in correspondence of Column C3 at the first floor. These results agree with those coming from nonlinear dynamic analyses and with post-test damage assessment.

Summing up, the deformation capacity of the structure at LSSD was large enough to accommodate the demand for $Sa_g$ = 0.2g; the demand, however, exceeded the deformation capacity for $Sa_g$ = 0.29g. The numerical results suggested to improve the global ductility of the building in order to withstand larger seismic actions.

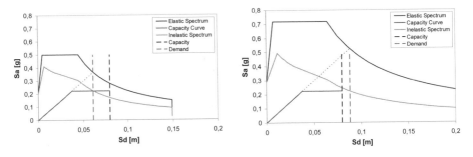

Figure 16 - Demand spectra and capacity curves (X direction) in AD format at LSSD for the retrofitted structure R1, for $Sa_g$ = 0.2g (left) and $Sa_g$ = 0.29g (right).

# 6. ALTERNATIVE APPROACH TO RETROFITING

An alternative retrofitting approach using both R/C jacketing and glass-fibre-reinforced polymer (GFRP) laminates was considered in order to allow the structure to withstand 0.3g PGA seismic actions. A schematic view of the proposed retrofitted structure, hereafter named "R2", is shown in Fig. 17. Columns C2 and C4 at the flexible edges, and the central Column C3 were strengthened at all storeys with 75 mm-thick jackets, longitudinally reinforced with 8∅14 bars.

The ductility of these columns was improved by adding ∅8 stirrups, spaced by 100 mm. At all storeys, the square columns other than C2, C4 and C3 were confined at the top and at the bottom by means of a single GFRP uniaxial laminate (= one ply; thickness = 0.48 mm/ply; modulus of elasticity = 65.7 GPa; tensile strength = 1314 MPa; ultimate strain = 0.02) in order to improve structural ductility. In the retrofitted columns, the ultimate chord rotation increased by about 100% with respect to the original columns. Quadriaxial GFRP laminates (thickness = 0.11 mm/ply; modulus of elasticity = 65.7 GPa; tensile strength = 986 MPa; ultimate strain = 0.015) were used for the large Column C6, wrapped for the entire height at all storeys, in order to increase its shear capacity.

The combination of two retrofitting approaches (FRP wrapping and R/C jacketing) applied to selected columns was aimed at optimizing the seismic performance of the structure, by increasing its strength, stiffness and ductility. The selection of the columns to be retrofitted was based on the deficiencies underlined by the tests and confirmed by the numerical analyses performed on both the bare structure and R1 structure. Retrofitting had two main objectives: (1) relocating both the centre of strength (CP) and the centre of stiffness (CR) in order to reduce the torsional component of the response, and to increase the structural strength and stiffness; and (2) increasing the local deformation capacity of the columns and thus the global deformation capacity of the structure. The first objective was achieved by applying R/C jackets to selected columns (their strength and stiffness were increased because of the added concrete layers and longitudinal reinforcement, and their ductility was increased as well, because of the added confining stirrups). The second objective was achieved by applying fibre-reinforced polymer (FRP) jackets to existing columns, to increase concrete confinement. (In this way, the overall structural stiffness is not modified and the strength is only marginally increased, something that is neglected in the following). FRP retrofitting, however, increased the ductility capacity, without modifying the location of both CR and CP.

To be effective, this alternative retrofitting procedure requires the identification of the structural members that mostly affect the behaviour of the building. In the case of structure R1, although the strength of the column C1 and C4 was increased, the resulting behaviour under 0.3g PGA level was not as expected, since the members that were not strengthened turned out to control the structural behaviour. The critical members were identified during the assessment procedure as those undergoing the highest DCR values. These members were Columns C2 and C4 located at the flexible edge and the central Column C3. Moreover, the choice of the columns to be retrofitted was performed in order to relocate CP and CR of the plan-wise irregular structure to reduce the torsional component of the response. The centre of strength (also called plastic centre) is the location of the resultant of the yield moments of the columns at each floor. In the inelastic range, torsional effects are mainly governed by strength eccentricity, rather than stiffness eccentricity. With reference to the coordinate system of Fig. 1, the coordinates of CM, CR and CP are reported in Table 1 for a typical storey, according to three configurations (bare structure; R1 with some R/C –jacketed columns; and R2 with some R/C jacketed and some GFRP-wrapped columns). For the bare structure, the eccentricities between CM and CR amount to 1.04 m and 1.31 m (about 10% and 14% of the plan dimensions) in the X and Y directions, respectively, while the eccentricities between CM and CP are close to 0.76 m and 0.45 m in the X and Y directions, respectively.

The eccentricity of CP and CR with respect to CM was significantly reduced by increasing the sections of Columns C1 and C4, compared to the bare structure. A further decrease was obtained in the retrofitted structure R2 (R/C jacketing of Columns C2, C3 and C4), and CP eccentricities with respect to CM became 0.03 m and 0.07 m in the X and Y directions, respectively. Such a retrofitting turned out to be very effective, since a sizable reduction of the torsional response was achieved in a rather simple way (only three columns were involved).

The local ductility of the selected columns was gradually increased and analyses were performed in order to confirm whether the retrofitted structure would meet the specified demands. The results indicated that upgrading the structural members in question above a certain limit would bring in no further benefits in the overall structural behaviour, since the non-retrofitted members would become critical for the structural behaviour (their limited deformation capacity would be exceeded). Hence, it was decided to increase the ductility of the other columns. Such an objective was pursued by confining these columns with GFRP laminates.

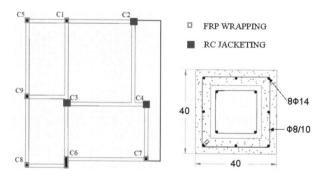

Figure 17 - Plan of the retrofitted structure R2 and cross-section increase.

Table 1. Coordinates of the of centre of mass (CM), centre of stiffness (CR) and centre of strength (CP) of the structures examined in this study.

|  | Bare structure | | Structure R1 | | Structure R2 | |
|---|---|---|---|---|---|---|
|  | X [m] | Y [m] | X [m] | Y [m] | X [m] | Y [m] |
| C.M. | 4.54 | 5.29 | 4.57 | 5.34 | 4.56 | 5.34 |
| C.R. | 3.23 | 4.25 | 3.90 | 5.88 | 4.34 | 5.61 |
| C.P. | 3.78 | 4.84 | 4.39 | 5.77 | 4.59 | 5.41 |

Since the deformation capacity of the square columns was similar, upgrading all the remaining columns was considered as a reasonable approach. Thus, applying the above technique to the columns, their local ductility was gradually increased until the building was able to meet the specified demands.

## 7. SEISMIC ASSESSMENT OF THE STRUCTURE RETROFITTED BY USING GFRP LAMINATES IN ADDITION TO R/C JACKETING (R2)

### 7.1 Simplified procedure assessment

A numerical model of the retrofitted structure R2 was developed. The nonlinear variable-confinement model including the constitutive relationship and cyclic rules proposed by Mander (1988) in compression, and by Yankelevsky and Reinhardt (1989) in tension, was adopted to model R/C sections retrofitted by FRP. The confinement effect introduced by the FRP wrapping was modelled according to Spoelstra and Monti (1999). The model is based on Mander's model (Mander, 1988), but the peak stress and the corresponding strain of the confined concrete are a function of the confinement pressure. A constant lateral pressure, depending on steel yielding stress, is introduced for steel confinement, whereas confinement pressure is assumed to be a linear function of concrete lateral dilation in the case of FRP wrapping. An iterative procedure is adopted to obtain the axial stress $\sigma_c$ corresponding to any given value of the axial strain $\varepsilon_c$, taking into account the confinement effect, according to Spoelstra and Monti (1999). For the model used to represent the sections retrofitted by R/C jacketing, see Section 3.

For the verification of the ductile mechanisms, the enhancement of the deformation capacity $\theta_u$ of the member was determined by adding a term (due to FRP wrapping) to that describing the confinement provided by transverse reinforcement. The total chord rotation capacity was calculated from expression (3) with the exponent of the confinement-related term increased by $(\alpha^* \rho_f\, f_{f,e} / f_c)$:

- $\alpha^* = 1 - \dfrac{(b - 2 \cdot R)^2 + (h - 2 \cdot R)^2}{3 \cdot b \cdot h}$ = confinement effectiveness factor, with:

  R = 20 mm (radius of the rounded corners) and b,h = section sides;

- $\rho_f = \dfrac{2 \cdot t_f}{b}$ = FRP ratio parallel to the loading direction, where $t_f$ = thickness of FRP;

- $f_{f,e} = \min(f_{u,f}; \varepsilon_{u,f} \cdot E_f) \cdot \left(1 - 0{,}7 \cdot \min(f_{u,f}; \varepsilon_{u,f} \cdot E_f) \cdot \dfrac{\rho_f}{f_c}\right)$ = effective stress, where $f_{u,f}$ and $E_f$ are FRP strength and the elastic modulus, and $\varepsilon_{u,f}$ is the ultimate strain.

Nonlinear static pushover analyses were performed on the retrofitted structure R2 in order to assess the effectiveness of the applied retrofitting technique. Retrofitting slightly increased structural stiffness and strength, but considerably increased structural ductility. The numerical results pointed out that the retrofitted structure R2 was able to withstand the displacement demand due to the increased seismic actions ($Sa_g$=0.29g) and to satisfy the LSSD, as shown in Fig. 18. The seismic demand (in terms of displacement), transformed into the given MDOF system, was reduced to 0.103 m (0.127 m for the bare structure and 0.11 m for the retrofitted structure R1), while the capacity of the structure was increased up to 0.12 m (0.083 m for the bare structure and 0.1 m for the retrofitted structure R1).

The combination of the two retrofitting techniques (FRP wrapping, aimed at overcoming the shortcomings of the columns in term of ductility, and R/C jacketing, aimed at decreasing the ductility demand through the reduction of the rotational component of the structural response) results in the fulfilment of LSSD requirements, compared to the response of the original and R/C jacketed R1 structures, where a failure condition was reached. In particular, column confinement generated by the application of FRP wrapping gave the structure a significantly-enhanced ductility and allowed the structure to meet the seismic demand by increasing the plastic branch of the base shear - top displacement curve, see Fig. 18. According to the nonlinear pushover analyses, Columns C3 and C1 at the first floor were identified as the most critical columns.

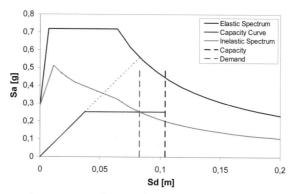

Figure 18 - Demand spectra and capacity curves (X direction) in AD format at LSSD for the retrofitted structure R2 ($Sa_g$=0.29g).

## 7.2 Nonlinear bidirectional dynamic analyses

The retrofitted structure R2 was analyzed under the same input ground motion as the bare structure and R1 structure at different PGA levels (0.2g and 0.3g) to allow a comparison with the previous time-history analyses. Note that the bare structure was analyzed only under 0.2g PGA level. A comparison of the inter-storey drifts and rotations for all three storeys of the different configurations of the structure is shown in Fig. 19. The alternative retrofitting procedure increased the stiffness of the structure and reduced the maximum inter-storey drift at all levels with respect to the bare structure. Inter-storey drifts similar to those of the bare structure subjected to lower seismic action (PGA=0.2g) were observed in the case of the structure R2 under 0.3g PGA earthquake.

A reduction of the inter-storey rotation at all levels, in particular at the second level, was observed compared to both the bare and R1 structures. The retrofitting procedure on selected columns of the structure R2 with R/C jacketing was effective in reducing the effects of torsion in the development of the failure mechanism at the second floor. In so doing, the global behaviour of the structure was improved as well.

In Fig. 20 the DCR values for the columns of all levels in the retrofitted structure R2, provided by the dynamic analysis with 0.3g PGA, are indicated. Large values of deformation demand were registered for the columns due to the high seismic excitation, but in this case the columns had a large ductility because of the high level of confinement provided by FRP wrapping. Consequently, a significant reduction of the DCR values can be observed for all the columns of the three storeys, especially at the first storey, compared to structure R1. In particular, the increase in deformation capacity of Columns C3 and C9 gave the structure a sufficient ductility to withstand the 0.3g PGA level without attaining high DCR values. The maximum DCR values were registered for Columns C3 and C1.

Comparing the results under 0.3g PGA level, the overall effect of R/C jacketing (structure R1) was not as effective as that of the combination of R/C jacketing and FRP wrapping (structure R2). In structure R1, the drift reduction was not enough when the 0.3g intensity level was reached, because structure R1 did not have the necessary ductility. In the case of structure R2, a considerable improvement in deformation capacity was obtained by using FRP and a significant decrease of the DCR values was observed as well.

## 8. COMPARISON OF THE SEISMIC CAPACITIES

The N2 Method was used for the evaluation of the seismic capacities of the previous structures, with reference to the largest ground motion that the structures can withstand. Given the capacity in terms of drift, it was possible to determine the demand spectrum at which the seismic demand was equal to the capacity.

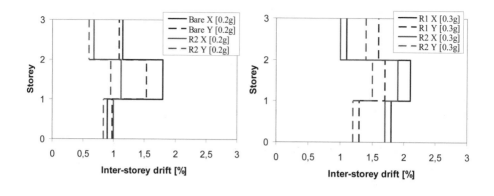

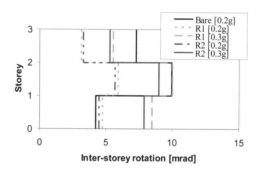

Figure 19 - Maximum inter-storey drift and inter-storey rotation for the structures investigated in this study.

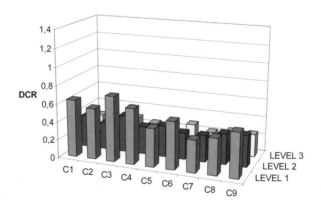

Figure 20 - Maximum DCR values for the columns of the retrofitted structure R2 (R/C jacketing + FRP laminates) under 0.3g PGA earthquake.

The seismic capacities of the structures are summarized in Fig. 21. The seismic capacity in terms of effective peak ground acceleration $Sa_g$ amounts to 0.19g (which corresponds to a peak ground acceleration $a_g = 0.165g$ on rock) for the original structure and 0.26g (which corresponds to $a_g = 0.23g$ on rock) for the retrofitted structure R1. In the retrofitted structure R2, the SD limit state is reached at $Sa_g = 0.36g$ ($a_g = 0.31g$ on rock). The seismic capacity of the structure R2 is about twice as much greater than the capacity of the bare structure. The structure R2 can survive stronger ground motions than both the bare and R1 structures, because of the increased ductility of R2 provided by the application of GFRP, and the strength/stiffness enhancement provided by R/C jacketing of selected columns. It should be observed that the assessment of the seismic capacity of the structure was on the safe side compared to the experimental results, because of the safety factors implemented in the standards and of the assumption that the most critical column controls the state of the structure.

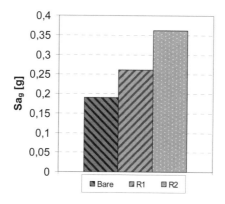

Figure 21 - Seismic capacity in terms of effective peak ground acceleration $Sa_g$ at LSSD for the different structures investigated in this study.


## 9. CONCLUSIONS

Detailed numerical models of a gravity-load-designed plan-wise irregular R/C building tested in the original and retrofitted configurations at the JRC ELSA Laboratory were developed and validated on the basis of experimental results. The effectiveness of using R/C jacketing as a global retrofitting technique for the seismic rehabilitation of under-designed plan-asymmetric R/C buildings was confirmed. The retrofitting design strategy was based on the decrease of the torsional component exhibited by the seismic response of the original structure. Such a decrease was obtained by reducing the eccentricity of the centre of strength (CP) and stiffness (CR) with respect to the centre of mass (CM).

In the original configuration, high values were registered for the Demand-to-Capacity Ratio (DCR) in the columns located at the flexible edges (higher demands) and for the columns with higher axial loads (lower rotational capacity). A considerable reduction of DCR values at the critical columns of the flexible edges was observed under 0.2g PGA ground motion for the retrofitted structure R1. However, the lack of ductility of the critical columns (where the axial load was high and the rotational capacity was rather small) was only partially overcome by the retrofitting, and high DCR values were registered for larger seismic intensity levels (PGA = 0.3g).

Non-retrofitted columns became critical as their limited deformation capacity was not improved and the rotation capacity corresponding to the LSSD was achieved. Consequently, it was necessary to increase the local deformation capacity of the remaining columns by applying FRP laminates resulting in better confinement. In this way, the ductility capacity of the structure was increased without modifying the location of both CR and CP (structure R2).

Numerical results suggest that the retrofitting strategy based on strength and stiffness relocation obtained by R/C jacketing of selected columns requires an accurate knowledge of the response of the structure, that is sensitive to the members to be retrofitted. This retrofitting strategy is effective under rather low seismic actions. For high seismic-intensity levels, the torsional effects generally decrease under increasing plastic deformations and smaller amplification of displacements due to torsion occurs on the flexible side.

Since increasing column ductility is decisive for improving the seismic behaviour of under-designed structures, any retrofitting strategy should take it into account, even more since the poor structural detailing typical of many existing R/C structures may contribute negatively to the structural ductility prior to retrofitting.

The adequacy of simplified procedures, based on nonlinear static pushover analyses, for the seismic assessment of existing R/C structures was investigated too. In order to take into account the effect of torsion in asymmetric structures, the extended N2 Method was used in order to accurately evaluate the seismic performance of the plan-wise irregular structure under examination. The simplified method provided many results consistent with experimental evidence and with nonlinear dynamic time-history analyses, and allowed to identify the critical columns affecting the overall seismic performance of the structure. In other terms, the simplified procedure made it possible to easily identify the structural deficiencies that should be properly taken care of in any retrofitting process and to select a suitable retrofitting strategy.

## ACKNOWLEDGEMENTS

The author is grateful to Dr. Paolo Negro (JRC ELSA Laboratory) and Prof. Alberto Castellani (Politecnico di Milano) for their valuable suggestions and continuous technical/scientific support.

# REFERENCES

CEN (2004). *European Standard EN 1998-1. Eurocode 8: Design of Structures for Earthquake Resistance. Part 1: General Rules, Seismic Action and Rules for Buildings.* European Committee for Standardization, Brussels.

CEN (2005). *European Standard EN 1998-3. Eurocode 8: Design of Structures for Earthquake Resistance. Part 3: Assessment and Retrofitting of Buildings.* European Committee for Standardization, Brussels.

OPCM 3431 (2005). *Modifications and Integrations to the Decree 3274 Issued by the First Minister [of the Italian Government], Containing Some Basic Indications on the General Criteria to be Adopted in the Seismic Ranking of the National Territory, and on the Design Provisions for the Constructions in Seismic Areas (in Italian).* Italian Ministry of Public Works.

CNR-DT 200/2004 (2004). *Guidelines for the Design, Construction and Inspection of Structural Repairing and Strengthening Actions by means of Fiber-Reinforced Cementitious Composites (in Italian).* Italian Nat. Council for Research – CNR.

Bousias S., Spathis A.-L. and Fardis M.N. (2006). "Concrete or FRP Jacketing of Columns with Lap Splices for Seismic Rehabilitation". *Journal of Advanced Concrete Technology*, 4(3), pp. 431-444.

Di Ludovico M., Prota A., Manfredi G. and Cosenza E. (2008). "Seismic Strengthening of an Under-Designed RC Structure with FRP". *Earthquake Engineering and Structural Dynamics* (37), pp. 141-162.

Fajfar P. (2000). "A Nonlinear Analysis Method for Performance-Based Seismic Design". *Earthquake Spectra*, 16, pp. 573-592.

Fajfar P. and Gaspersic P. (1996). "The N2 Method for the Seismic Damage Analysis of RC Buildings". *Earthquake Engineering and Structural Dynamics* 1996(25), pp. 31-46.

Fajfar P., Marušić D. and Peruš I. (2005). "Torsional Effects in the Pushover-Based Seismic Analysis of Buildings. *Journal of Earthquake Engineering,* 9(6), pp. 831-854.

Fardis M. N. (1994). *Analyses and Design of Reinforced Concrete Buildings according to Eurocodes 2 and 8. Configuration 3, 5 and 6*, Reports on Prenormative Research in Support of Eurocode 8.

Ferracuti B.and Savoia M. (2005). "Cyclic Behaviour of FRP-Wrapped Columns under Axial and Flexural Loadings". *Proceedings of the International Conference on Fracture,* Torino, Italy.

Filippou F.C., Popov E.P. and Bertero V.V. (1983). "Modelling of R/C Joints under Cyclic Excitations". *ASCE-J. of Struc. Eng.*, 109(11), pp. 2666-2684.

Jeong S.-H. and Elnashai A.S. (2005). "Analytical Assessment of an Irregular RC Frame for Full-Scale 3D Pseudo-Dynamic Testing - Part I: Analytical Model Verification". *Journal of Earthquake Engineering*, 9(1), pp. 95-128.

Mander J.B., Priestley M.J.N. and Park R. (1988). "Theoretical Stress-Strain Model for Confined Concrete". *ASCE-Journal of Structural Engineering*, 114(8), pp. 1804-1826.

Martinez-Rueda J.E. and Elnashai A.S. (1997). "Confined Concrete Model under Cyclic Load". *Materials and Structures*, 30(197), pp. 139-147.

Menegotto M. and Pinto P.E. (1973). "Method of Analysis for Cyclically Loaded R.C. Plane Frames Including Changes in Geometry and Non-Elastic Behavior of Elements under Combined Normal Force and Bending". *Preliminary Report, IABSE*, Zurich, 13, pp. 15-22.

Mola E. and Negro P. (2005). "Full-Scale PsD Testing of the Torsionally Unbalanced SPEAR Structure in the "as-Built" and Retrofitted Configurations". *Proc. Int. Workshop SPEAR*, Ispra, Italy.

Negro P., Mola E., Molina J. and Magonette G. (2004). "Full-Scale Bi-Directional PSD Testing of a Torsionally Unbalanced Three-Storey Non-Seismic RC Frame". *Proc. 13th World Conference on Earthquake Engineering*, Vancouver, Canada.

Panagiotakos T. B. and Fardis M. N. (2001). "Deformations of Reinforced Concrete Members at Yielding and Ultimate". *ACI-Structural Journal*, 98(2), pp. 135-148.

Priestley M. J. N. (1997). "Displacement-Based Seismic Assessment of Reinforced Concrete Buildings". *Journal of Earthquake Engineering*, 1(1), pp. 157–192.

Rozman M. and Fajfar P. (2009). "Seismic Response of a RC Frame Building Designed according to Old and Modern Practices". *Bulletin of Earthquake Engineering*, 7, pp. 779-799.

SeismoSoft (2007). *SeismoStruct – A Computer Program for Static and Dynamic Nonlinear Analysis of Framed Structures*.

Spoelstra M. and Monti G. (1999). "FRP-Confined Concrete Model". Journal of Composites for Construction, ASCE, 3, pp. 143-150.

Valente M. (2008). "Seismic Assessment and Selective Retrofitting of an Under-Designed R/C frame". *Studies and Researches, Politecnico di Milano*, V.28, pub. by Starrylink (Brescia, Italy), pp. 211-243.

Yankelevsky D.Z. and Reinhardt H.W. (1989). "Uniaxial Behavior of Concrete in Cyclic Tension". *ASCE-Journal of Structural Engineering*, 115(1), pp. 166-182.

**MAJOR SYMBOLS AND ACRONYMS** (from the Editors)

$a_g$     = peak ground acceleration;

AD     = acceleration-displacement (format);

CM     = centre of mass;

CP     = centre of strength;

CR     = centre of stiffness;

DCR     = demand-to-capacity ratio;

DL     = damage limitation;

FRP     = fibre-reinforced polymer;

GFRP     = glass fibre-reinforced polymer;

IDR     = inter-storey drift ratio;

LS     = limit state;

MDOF     = multi-degree-of-freedom (system);

NC     = near collapse;

PGA     = peak ground acceleration;

$Sa_g$     = effective peak ground acceleration;

SD     = significant damage;

SPEAR = (Project) Standing Patrol for Emergency Assessment and Response.

STUDIES AND RESEARCHES – V.29, 2009
Graduate School in Concrete Structures – Fratelli Pesenti
Politecnico di Milano, Italy

# ASSESSMENT OF CONCRETE STRUCTURES AFFECTED BY COVER DELAMINATION PART 1 – EFFECT OF BOND LOSS

Paul E. Regan [1] , Iain L. Kennedy Reid [2]

## Abstract

The behaviour of bars in concrete with corrosion-induced delamination has been investigated  by testing specimens in which bars were either flush with the concrete surface or exposed to mid-barrel. The results of pull-out tests, and tests of development lengths and lap splices in beams are used to derive proposals for limiting bond stresses.

The effect of cover delamination on shearcracking is investigated and a proposal is made for a reduction of the normal calculated resistance. The effects of complete loss of bond by the main steel along all or a part of a span are also studied, and methods are given for treating arching action and the effects at the ends of debonded lengths.

Applications of limiting bond stresses in truss models of more complex beams are described and validated in a companion paper.

[1] Professor, formerly Head of the Architecture and Engineering Dept. at the University of Westminster, London, UK.
[2] Atkins Highways and Transportation, London, UK.

# 1. INTRODUCTION

Delamination of concrete cover is a common result of corrosion of reinforcement. It can occur while the loss of area of reinforcement is insignificant in terms of strength, and the resulting reduction in bond resistance can well be the first major problem to result from corrosion of main reinforcement. Longitudinal cracking along deformed bars does not cause a great loss of bond unless it is associated with either delamination or very large losses of bar area.

Research carried out at the University of Westminster in collaboration with WS Atkins Consultants is shown in two companion papers, investigating the effects of delamination on bond resistance and the effects of reductions of bond on the behaviour of structural members. This first paper treats the evaluation of bond resistance, on the basis of pull-out tests and beam tests involving development lengths and splices. It also treats the influence of reduced bond on resistance to shear cracking and the behaviour of beams affected by complete loss of bond in parts of their lengths. The second paper (Regan and Kennedy Reid, 2010) addresses the more complex situations arising from interactions of bond and shear in cases where main bars, in different situations in terms of bond, act together.

The experimental work was almost entirely conducted on specimens cast without cover to the main bars, which were either flush with the concrete surface or exposed to mid-barrel. There were two reasons for this approach. One was that any much more precise definition of the state of delamination in an actual structure is unlikely to be practicable. The other was that this approach appeared to be the only one able to give results for well-defined and predetermined degrees of deterioration.

The use of specimens without actual corrosion has the disadvantage of not representing the effects of rusting of the bar surfaces, but corrosion normally begins at the outer face of a bar and has to be very far advanced for the deformations in contact with the core concrete to be much reduced or for the rust to lift the bar from the concrete below mid-barrel level.

The corrosion of stirrups, which is often severe at their bends and can cause loss of anchorage, is not treated here but is the subject of a separate paper (Regan and Kennedy Reid, 2004).

## 2. BOND OF BARS WITH DELAMINATED COVER

Experimental data on the bond of delaminated Type 2 deformed bars in tension ($\phi = 20$ mm in most cases) were obtained by tests of pull-out specimens (Fig 1) and flexural members. The latter type of specimens included beams with lap splices in regions of constant moment (Fig 2), and both beams and slabs in which development lengths were tested (Fig 3). The test results are summarised in Tables 1 and 2.

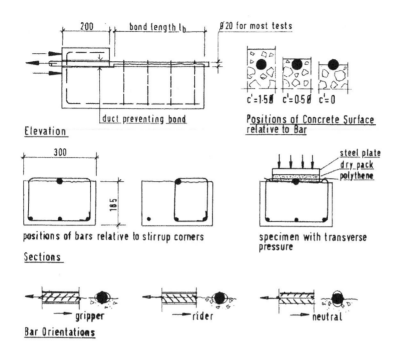

Figure 1 – Pull-out specimens.

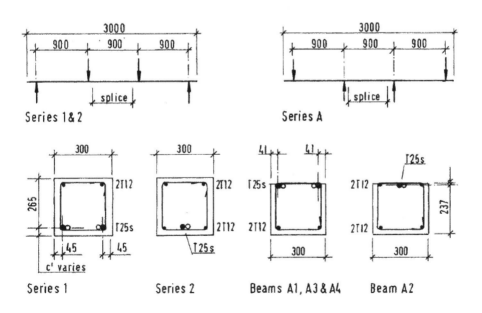

Figure 2 – Beam specimens for splice tests.

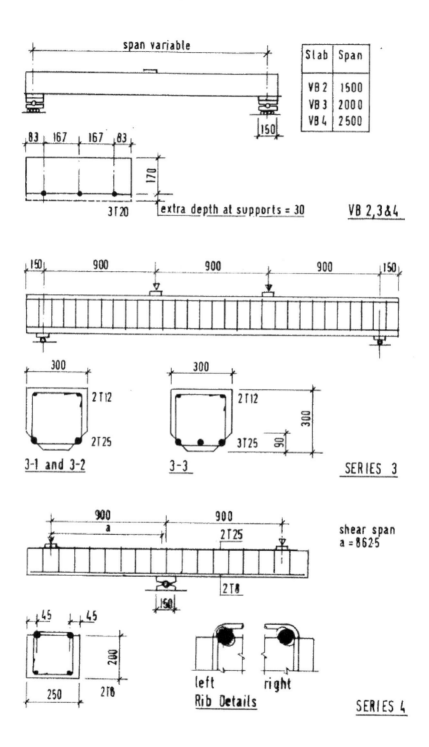

Figure 3 – Slab and beam specimens for development length tests.

For the splice tests, average ultimate bond stresses were calculated as $N_u/\pi\phi l_b$, where $l_b$ is the splice length and $N_u$ is the bar force at the ultimate load. Bar forces were determined from strains measured at the ends of splices, or - where strain measurements were not available - from the load-strain relationships of specimens with similar reinforcement.

For the development lengths in beams, the average ultimate bond stresses were determined as $V_u /z\sum u$. Strain measurements were used to check the values for $z$, and that forces were similar in individual bars. Any influence from shear cracking was minor, as - where any such cracking did occur - the short distances beyond the sections of zero moment were approximately equal to the shift of the main tension. For the slab tests, the stage at which bond broke down over the length between the end anchorages was determined by measurements of strains at sections just before the bars entered the end blocks.

The major factors determining the bond strength of bars in concrete affected by delamination are as follows:

Bar type

The results given here apply only to Type 2 deformed bars (projected rib factor > 0.056 for sizes above 12 mm). A few tests of plain round bars resulted in very low bond strengths.

Position of surface of delamination

Fig 4 shows ultimate bond stresses from pull-out tests and it can be seen that where bars had normal top cover the stresses were above the $0.7\sqrt{f_{cu}}$ characteristic resistance of British codes, in spite of being top cast. Their bond was probably helped by the large side cover. Bond strength increased linearly with cover.

Where the bars were flush with the concrete surface, the strengths were only a little below those obtained if the bond strength-cover relationship were extrapolated to cover = $0$. They were systematically dependent on the stirrups' restraining the main bars. With mid-barrel exposure bond resistance was much lower and in relative terms much more dependent on the stirrups.

Restraint by stirrups

Where a bar is exposed to mid-barrel, the mechanism of bond slip is the formation of a narrow furrow in the concrete surface and the bar lifting from the sound concrete to free the lower parts of its ribs. Where stirrups pin a bar to the concrete and resist the lifting, both the ultimate bond strength and the bond at large slip values are increased.

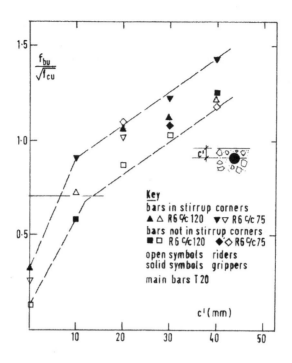

Figure 4 – Pull-out test results : Influence of cover on bond strength.

With flush exposure there is generally inclined cracking of the concrete surface originating from the ribs. This is followed by fractures of the concrete in a small width, and a tendency to lift, although this is somewhat restrained by the concrete adjacent to the bar. The influence of stirrups on the maximum bond stress is lower than for mid-barrel exposure, but remains the same in terms of resistance at large slip values.

The function $A_{ss}/s\phi$ is used to express the stirrup restraint, where $A_{ss}$ is the effective stirrup area, $s$ is the spacing of the stirrups along the main bar and $\phi$ is the diameter of the main bar.

$A_{ss}/s\phi$ was adopted as being the simplest dimensionless form to give reasonable correlation with test data. It can, very loosely, be related to the performance of a bent cantilever of stirrup providing restraint to the movement of the bar, and anchored elastically in the sound concrete The function was derived from the performance of specimens in which the main bars were either in the corners of stirrups ($A_{ss} = A_b$ where $A_b$ is the area of a stirrup leg) or well away from them $A_{ss} = 0$. Its extensions to other cases, see Fig 5, are justified to a greater or lesser extent by the results of other tests.

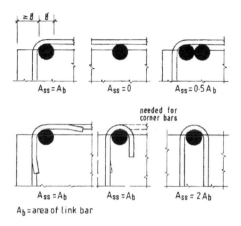

Figure 5 – Restraint provided by links : definitions of the effective stirrup area $A_{ss}$ for different reinforcement arrangements.

For spliced bars (and horizontal pairs of bars) the justification is the splice tests. For stirrups with anchorages at a main bar, the principal justification is that the bends at the remote ends of the exposed horizontal legs of stirrups probably have little effect in tests. The performances of beam C4 with 90° anchorages and beams C1-C3 with hooked anchorages also support this view (Regan and Kennedy Reid, 2010). For sausage links, with both legs well anchored in sound concrete, the use of $A_{ss} = 2A_b$ seems logical and is given some support by earlier pull-out tests on multiple bars, although these did not allow bar forces to be determined individually.

The horizontal legs of stirrups indicated in the figure are necessary for edge bars with limited side cover and in cases where forces are to be transferred horizontally between parallel main bars.

Figs 6 and 7 show all the relevant results for ultimate bond stresses for beams and slabs, and the results from pull-out tests of 20 mm bars, with the rider orientation of Fig 1, which gave results lower than those for other orientations. The test strengths in terms of $f_{bu}/\sqrt{f_{cu}}$ are plotted against $A_{ss}/s\phi$.

For mid-barrel exposure, there is a clear difference between the beam and pull-out results, and this is believed to be the result of the curvature developed in flexural members helping to hold the bars to the core concrete. There is no such difference in the strengths of bars flush with the concrete surface.

The expressions proposed for bond resistance are shown in the figures and require some explanation. They are intended to provide values of bond resistance which can in most cases be treated as "plastic". Thus for mid-barrel exposure the equation is a lower bound to all the beam and slab data and very much so for small values of $A_{ss}/s\phi$, for which resistance at large slip values is lower relative to the maximum.

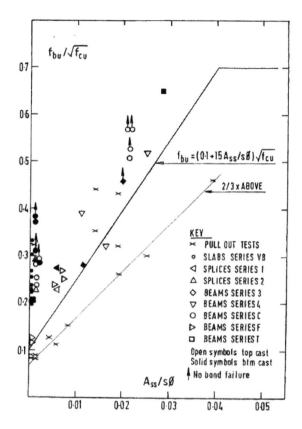

Figure 6 – Influence of stirrup restraint on bond strength of bars exposed to mid barrel.

For flush exposure, the expression is a reasonable near-lower bound. It is distinctly conservative in relation to the pull-out results for $A_{ss}/s\phi = 0$, because of the poor post-peak resistance in such cases. The conservatism is somewhat less for the beam specimens with $A_{ss}/s\phi = 0$ as the longer bond lengths involved mean that the experimental strengths involve a degree of averaging of resistance over a considerable range of slip.

The exception to the calculated strengths being able to be treated as plastic values arises for midbarrel exposure of bars not restrained by stirrups. In the extreme case of a slab without stirrups, such bars may become completely detached from the sound concrete and even in beams the residual resistance is negligible. For flush exposure the situation for beams in which there are stirrups should be covered adequately by the conservatism of the expression as $A_{ss}/s\phi$ tends to zero. For slabs there is perhaps a problem if complete cover delamination is possible.

252

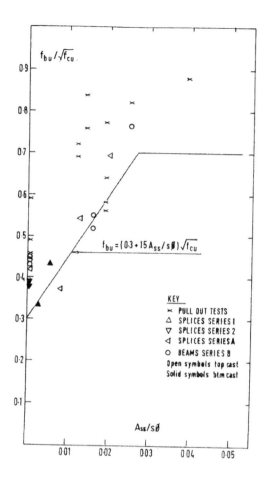

Figure 7 – Influence of stirrup restraint on bond strength of bars flush with the concrete.

## Restraint by transverse pressure

Pull-out tests were made with transverse (vertical) pressure applied by a load-maintaining jack acting on a steel plate bedded on dry-pack mortar separated from the concrete and bars by a sheet of heavy-duty polythene (see Fig 1). The ultimate bond strengths are related to the transverse pressure $p$ (= vertical load/plate area of 230 x 200 mm) in Fig 8.

The tests with mid-barrel exposure were all of bars away from stirrups. For the flush bars, the stirrup factor was deducted from the values of $f_{bu} < \sqrt{f_{cu}}$ as this reduces the scatter of the data.

The expressions shown in this figure represent the results well, so long as there is any significant transverse pressure, but overestimate bond strength for very low values of $p$. It is thus proposed that they be applied only when $p > 0.05 \sqrt{f_{cu}}$. It is also proposed that the effects of stirrups and transverse pressure should not be combined, as there is no relevant data for mid-barrel exposure and that for flush bars is limited to low values of $A_{ss}/s\phi$.

Ductility is not an important matter for end anchorages, as a member's ultimate load is reached when the end anchorages of its main bars reach their peak resistance. Behaviour is in fact not too brittle, as the resistance dependent on p is maintained at large slip values.

Transverse pressure also increases the bond resistance of bars with cover and this is of considerable significance in relation to end anchorages particularly in short spans. For the present no change is proposed to the current UK approach which neglects this effect but the tests made on the end anchorages of slabs are of interest in relation to the treatment of bars in delaminated concrete.

The anchorages were 150 mm long and the bottom-cast bars had 20 mm cover below them (see Fig 3). The cross-sections including the patterns of cracking at failure are shown in Fig 9 along with the test results given in terms of $f_{bu}/\sqrt{f_{cu}}$ as there were no stirrups. The test data are given in Table 3. End forces were determined from strain gauge measurements.

All of the bars of slabs VB5, 6 and 7 with full-width steel supports behaved similarly. With reduced plate widths in slabs VB9 and 10 the maximum bond stresses were related to the pressures calculated separately for the individual bars, with the bond of the centre of bar of VB9 declining before the stresses of the outer bars reached their maximum. In VB8, where the bearing was of hard rubber on top of steel and provided no lateral restraint, the outer bars failed first at a relatively low bond stress and then the inner bar developed a maximum bond similar to that obtained with a steel bearing.

### Concrete strength

Most of the concretes used in the pull-out tests had cube strengths between 40 and 50 N/mm$^2$, with a few specimens having strengths down to 25 N/mm$^2$. In the beams, the range of cube strengths was from 30 to 60 N/mm$^2$. The bond strength results would relate somewhat better to a power of $\sqrt{f_{cu}}$ greater than the square root, but the results obtained using $\sqrt{f_{cu}}$ are adequate. The dependence on $\sqrt{f_{cu}}$ has been introduced as it is currently used in all UK codes, and the relationship between cube strength and the properties of the top few millimetres of a pour is rather uncertain.

### Other factors

The numbers of tests made with bottom-cast bars were small. Although bottom cast and vertical bars very probably do have higher bond strengths than top cast bars even after delamination, the effect has been ignored for simplicity.

Bond lengths were varied from 20 to $32\phi$ in the splice tests and from $11.5\phi$ to $36.5\phi$ in pull-out tests with no clear effect on ultimate bond stresses. The longer development lengths in some of the beam tests are not relevant in most cases as the bond rate was controlled by the beam action to be $V/z\sum u$. In some of the more complex arrangements of reinforcement this was not the case for individual bars. For these, the rules proposed give safe results.

Tests were made with both plain round and deformed stirrups and for equal stirrup areas and spacings the steel type appeared to have little or no effect.

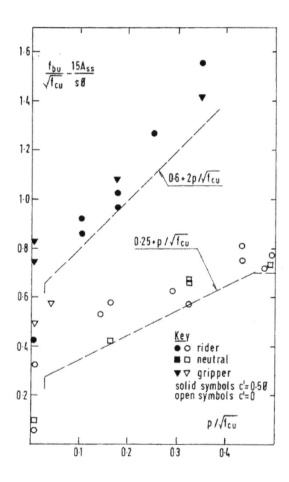

Figure 8 – Influence of transverse pressure on bond strength of bars flush with the concrete or exposed to mid barrel.

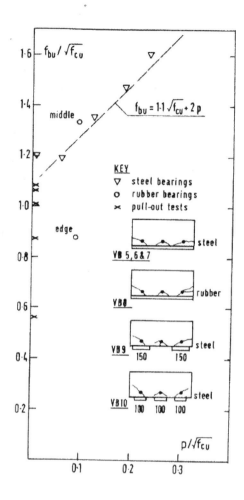

Figure 9 - Influence of transverse pressure on bond strength of bars with cover.

Some pull-out specimens were made in an attempt to define a transition between a main bar's being in stirrup corners and remote from them. The results were inconclusive, but it appears that any bar that could rationally be viewed as being in stirrup corners can be treated as such. The two bars of a horizontal splice can each be treated as having a restraint equal to half the value for a single bar. Interior bars not too far from corner bars can also experience some restraint. This accounts for some of the high bond strengths at $A_s/s_v\phi = 0$ in Fig 6, but it seems impractical to take account of the effect.

Bar size and the projected rib area factor may have some influence. In the beams, bar sizes varied from 16 to 25 mm without apparent effect, but a few pull-out tests with 12 mm bars did give rather low results for mid-barrel exposure. A few tests made with 20 mm Swedish Ks60 bars, which had annular ribs and a projected rib factor about 50% higher than UK bars, gave results similar to those for UK bars tested as "grippers" (Fig 1).

Provided that a normal side-cover is present, its size should not have much influence on the behaviour of bars in delaminated concrete, as the widths of their failure zones are narrow.

<u>Expressions proposed for bond resistance</u>

In view of the limits of the test data available and the limited detail in which the conditions of existing structures can be defined, it seems best to restrict expressions for bond strength to relatively simple forms taking account of only those influences found to be of major importance.

Irrespective of how much of a bar is embedded in sound concrete, in all the expressions given in the following $f_b$ is the nominal bond stress = change of bar force per unit length/$\pi\phi$.

For bars with sound cover greater than or equal to $\phi$ :

$$f_{b1} = 0.7\sqrt{f_{cu}} \tag{1}$$

For bars flush with the surface of sound concrete :

$$f_{b2} = (0.3 + 15A_{ss}/s\phi)\sqrt{f_{cu}} \quad \leq 0.7\sqrt{f_{cu}} \tag{2}$$

$$\text{or} \quad f_{b3} = 0.6\sqrt{f_{cu}} + 2p \quad \leq 0.7\sqrt{f_{cu}} \tag{3}$$

For bars in concrete with delamination at mid-barrel level :

$$f_{b4} = (0.1 + 15A_{ss}/s\phi)\sqrt{f_{cu}} \quad \leq 0.7\sqrt{f_{cu}} \tag{4}$$

$$\text{or} \quad f_{b5} = 0.25\sqrt{f_{cu}} + p \quad \leq 0.7\sqrt{f_{cu}} \tag{5}$$

These expressions should be subjected to the following restrictions:

(1) Equations (3) and (5) apply only if $p > 0.05\sqrt{f_{cu}}$ . The upper limit of equation (3) is not justified by test results (see Fig 8) but is included to be consistent with BD 44/95's treatment of bars with cover.

(2) If $A_{ss}/s\phi = 0$, equation (4) is applicable only if all bars contributing to the

257

main steel's resistance are treated as having a limiting bond stress of $0,1\sqrt{f_{cu}}$. As an alternative the bar lengths with $A_{ss}/s\phi$ may be treated as having zero bond resistance and the relevant values from equations (1) to (5) may then be used for the other bar lengths. The latter option allows account to be taken of the resistance from equation (5) if the bars with mid-barrel exposure and $A_{ss} = 0$ are restrained by transverse pressure.

Where the delamination is at a depth greater than mid-barrel the bond resistance of a bar should be treated as unreliable.

The bond stresses of equations (1) to (5) cannot really be defined as characteristic values. This would remain the case, even if the equations could be improved and more data were available, as there is no simple experimental definition of a bond resistance which is treated as "plastic". It is however the intention that their use in the analysis of beams and slabs should lead to predictions of ultimate loads, which can reasonably be regarded as at a characteristic level, provided that the models in which they are used are in equilibrium and respect other relevant stress limits.

## 3. SHEAR CRACKING/SHEAR RESISTANCE OF MEMBERS WITHOUT STIRRUPS

The flexure-shear cracking commonly found in reinforced concrete is caused by the action of bond forces on the teeth of concrete between flexural cracks. Such cracking does not occur if there is no bond, although web shear cracking remains possible. The question then arises as to whether a reduction, but not an elimination of bond, can reduce shear cracking resistance by widening flexural cracks and reducing the transfer of shear by aggregate interlock.

Kani et al. (1979) tested beams without stirrups in which the main bars were cast inside prisms of weak vermiculite concrete except at their ends. The encased bars were then cast in ordinary-concrete beams and the bond between the bars and the ordinary concrete was regulated by the strength of the vermiculite material, as shown in Fig 10. When the bond strength was very low, the beams functioned as arches, there was no shear cracking and the ultimate loads were above the calculated shear cracking resistance. When the bond strength was high, failure was caused by shear cracking and the loads were well predicted by usual methods. There were, however, some results for intermediate bond strengths in which the beams failed by shear cracking, but did so at loads below the predicted values.

There is thus a risk of shear cracking at a reduced load if the bond resistance is lowered by delamination, but not to an extent where shear cracking cannot occur. The lowest resistance found in Kani's tests was 85% of the characteristic strength according to BD44/95 (Highways Agency, 1995).

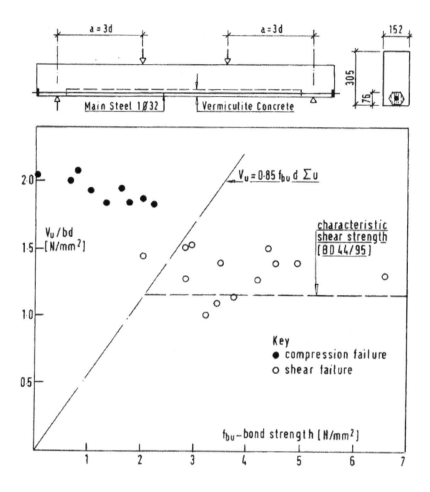

Figure 10 – Tests by Kani et al. (1979): influence of bond strength on ultimate loads of beams without stirrups.

The five beams detailed in Fig 11 were tested to get an idea of how great the reduction in shear resistance could be. Their crack patterns are shown in Fig 12 and the test results are given in table 4. The characteristic shear resistances of beams without delamination, calculated by BD44/95 would be:

$$V_{BD} = 0.24 \left[ \frac{100A_s}{b_v d} \cdot f_{cu} \right]^{1/3} \left[ \frac{500}{d} \right]^{1/4} b_v d \qquad (6)$$

The shear cracking loads ranged from 0.82 to 1.02 $V_{BD}$. Taking these results together with Kani's, it is suggested that a smaller value be used for the characteristic resistance:

$$V_{BD} = 0.19 \left[ \frac{100A_s}{b_v d} \cdot f_{cu} \right]^{1/3} \left[ \frac{500}{d} \right]^{1/4} b_v d \qquad (7)$$

where delamination has occurred, but the remaining bond strength $\Sigma f_b \pi \phi$ is greater than $V_{k,red}/z$.

If $\Sigma f_b \pi \phi \leq V_{k,red}/z$, flexure-shear cracking is unlikely.

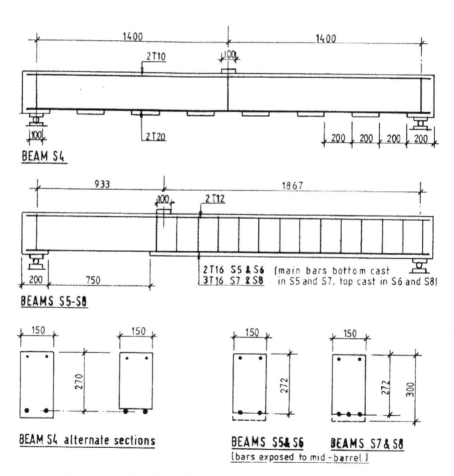

Figure 11 - Details of beams S4-S8 with delaminated covers.

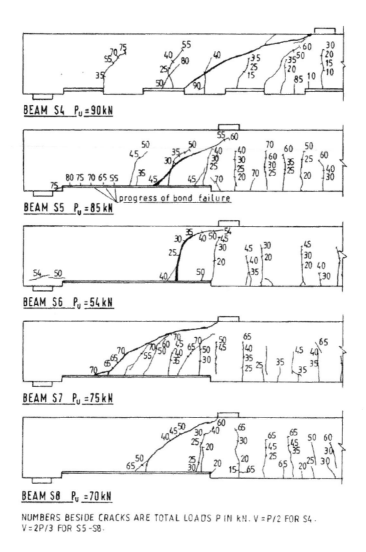

BEAM S4  $P_u = 90 kN$

BEAM S5  $P_u = 85 kN$

BEAM S6  $P_u = 54 kN$

BEAM S7  $P_u = 75 kN$

BEAM S8  $P_u = 70 kN$

NUMBERS BESIDE CRACKS ARE TOTAL LOADS P IN kN. V = P/2 FOR S4.
V = 2P/3 FOR S5-S8.

Figure 12 – Beams S4-S8 with delaminated covers: crack patterns and ultimate loads.

## 4. EFFECTS OF TOTAL DEBONDING OF MAIN BARS

If bond is completely lost along the length between the end anchorages of a simple span, but some or all of the main bars are continuous and anchored at both ends, a beam or slab is able to resist the loads by an arch action in the concrete, with the anchored main steel acting as a tie.

Tests were made on beams of the type shown in Fig 13, with reinforcement unbonded by being placed in steel duct tubes. With the exception of beam U1, they all behaved in much the same way developing only one or two flexural cracks and undergoing large local rotations at one of them. Failures were by crushing of the concrete adjacent to loading plates and, with one exception, without yield of the main bars. The results, which are given in Table 5, are not predicted well by either Pannell (1969) and Tam & Pannell (1976) - whose approach is used in BS8110 and BS5400 for unbonded prestressed members - or by Lorentsen (1964).

Pannell's approach assumes the deformation of the concrete to be concentrated over a length equal to 10 times the neutral axis depth and to be uniform over this length. It greatly overestimates the influence of the span-depth ratio. Lorentsen obtains concrete deformations by integration over the whole span. Where there is a region of constant moment, this overestimates its significance.

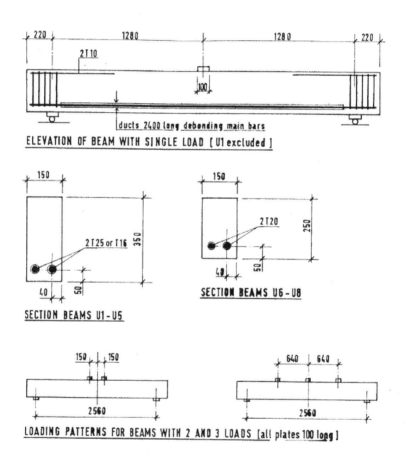

Figure 13 – Details of beams of series U with total debonding of main bars.

More satisfactory predictions of ultimate strength were obtained by Regan (1969), who empirically modified expressions previously used in relation to shear-compression failures, which share the essential characteristic of failure being by crushing of the concrete in a compression zone, the area of which is reduced by an increase in the extension of the main steel and a reduction of the overall shortening of the compression zone, as compared with normal flexural behaviour

$$M_{calc} = 0.6f_{cu}bx_u \left( d - \frac{x_u}{2} \right) \leq M_{flex} \tag{8}$$

$$\left( \frac{x_u}{d} \right) = \left( \frac{x_o}{d} \right) \left[ \frac{x_o/d}{(0.5a_o/a)+(x_o/d)} \right] \tag{9}$$

$$\frac{x_o}{d} = \frac{K}{2} \left[ \sqrt{1+\frac{4}{K}} - 1 \right] \tag{10}$$

where: $M_{flex}$ = flexural capacity corresponding to yield of main steel;

$x_u$ = ultimate neutral axis depth;

$x_o$ = ultimate neutral axis depth corresponding to crushing of the concrete obtained from normal flexural theory if it is assumed that the main steel stress is not limited by $f_y$.;

$K = 1167 \, \rho_l/f_{cu}$;

$a_o$ = unbonded part of the overall length a from a section of maximum moment to the support beyond $a_o$.

Fig 14 compares the predictions obtained from these equations with the present test results and others from Cairns and Zhao (1993), and Lorentsen (1964). In the beams of Cairns and Zhao there were gaps between the underside of the concrete and the tops of the main bars in the unbonded lengths. The effect of this has been allowed for by subtracting the gap heights from d. The correlation of the experimental and calculated strengths seems satisfactory.

A few other beams and slabs tested developed arching actions. Their failures were in the end anchorages, but - where the anchorages were relatively good (slab VB-5 and beam MV2) - the ultimate loads were 90% of the values predicted by equations (8) to (10).

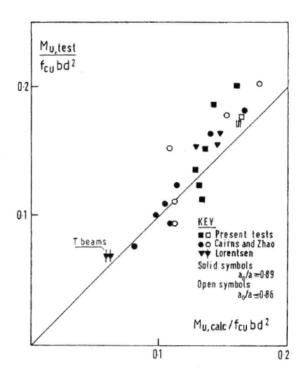

Figure 14 – Comparison of ultimate moments of debonded beams with predictions from equations (8) to (10).

Two cautionary comments should be made here. One is that - where the arch thrust in the concrete approaches the main steel - there is tension at what would normally be the extreme fibre in compression. In the absence of top steel, if this tension causes cracking, the result can be a compression failure at the bottom. This is particularly a risk if the bottom cover has delaminated.

The other point concerns the behaviour of spans in which bond is absent over only a part of the length. Even though Fig 14 shows that equation (9) can give reasonable predictions with M taken as the moment at the end of the exposed length, less satisfactory behaviour is possible.

In beam U1 the failure occurred following the development of bond cracks in the region where the bars entered the zone of full cover. The failure was extremely violent with one of the bond cracks extending upward toward the load and an explosive compression failure occurring adjacent to the load. The reason for the violence of the failure is probably that the load already being carried when the bond cracks developed was greater than the capacity predicted for full-length debonding.

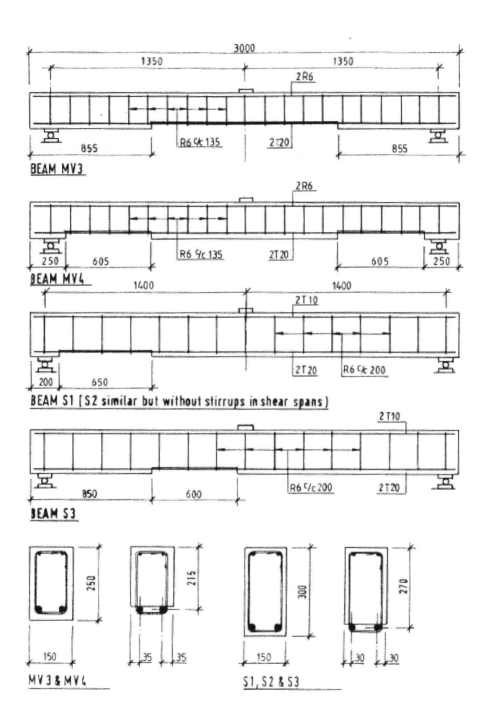

Figure 15 – Details of beams with part-length debonding of main steel.

Further tests were made to investigate the effects of part-length debonding and the specimens used are shown in Fig 15. The test results are given in Tables 4 and 6, and the crack patterns of beams Sl to S3 are drawn in Fig 16. In beams MV3 and S3, which lacked bond in regions close to loads, there was practically no cracking in the unbonded lengths and cracking occurred in the bonded zones only at high loads. Measurement of strains on the main bars showed that main-steel stresses were low at the supports and bond stresses were high near the high-moment ends of the bonded lengths.

At high loads these bond stresses caused inclined cracking in the tension zone of the type that caused the failure of Ul. In MV3 and S3 the stirrups prevented this sort of failure. MV3 failed in the compression zone adjacent to the load. The main steel did not yield and the ultimate moment was a little under the normal flexural capacity. The arching-action capacity calculated from equations (8) to (10) is equal to the test load if $a_o$ is taken to be the exposed length plus $d/2$ to allow for the disturbance of beam action where the bars entered the concrete. S3 failed in flexure with the main bars yielding. Measurements of strains on its stirrups showed that significant forces were developed in the stirrups closest to the unbonded region.

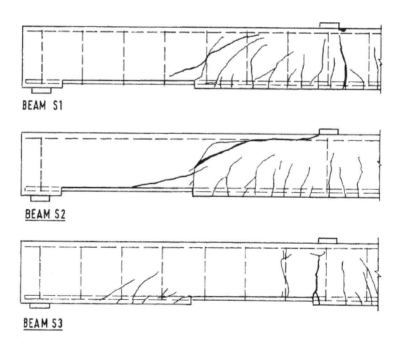

Figure 16 – Crack patterns in beams S1-S3.

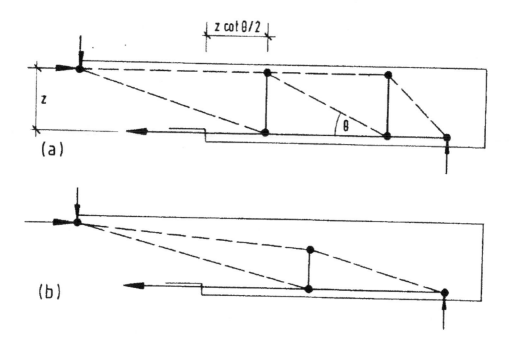

Figure 17 – Models of the behaviour of beams debonded near loads.

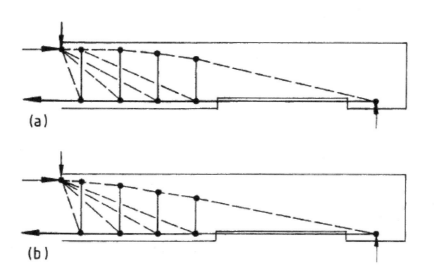

Fig.18 – Models of the behaviour of beams debonded near supports.

Fig 17 shows models for the behaviour of these beams. For model (a) to be applicable, if EC2's limit of $cot\theta \sim\, < 2.5$ is applied, the stirrups in a length $2.5z$ must be able to resist the full shear. In model (b) a deterioration to overall arching is being accepted and the extension of $a_o$ beyond the unbonded length might well be greater than the $d/2$ used above. Nonetheless the presence of stirrups still has a useful effect on the main steel force that has to be anchored at the support.

In beams S1, S2 and MV3 the unbonded zones were near supports. Flexural cracking was practically confined to the bonded lengths, and the cracks that formed early at the transitions between the bonded and unbonded regions rose high. In beam S2, without stirrups, this crack turned and ran toward the load, but there was no immediate failure, and it was obvious that a shear force was being transferred across the crack. Failure occurred at a flatter straighter crack which intersected the original one. In S1 and MV3 with stirrups, the initial cracks at the bonded/unbonded interface developed less far. The flatter crack which caused the failure of S2 was formed, but in the presence of stirrups the failures were by flexure at the loaded sections.

The ultimate load of S2 was exactly equal to that predicted by equation (7). A simple conservative model for the beams with stirrups is shown in Fig 18. In the model of Fig 18a, the compression chord becomes horizontal before the load is reached. This requires that the stirrups in the bonded length before the load should be able to resist the full shear and should do so within a length $2.5\,d$. The model in Fig 18b accepts an arching action over the whole shear span. In both cases the ultimate moment at the end of the arching length should be checked by equations (8) to (1 0).

For beam MV4 the arching length, calculated assuming arching to continue "$V_u$/stirrup force per metre" beyond the end of the debonding, was 1140 mm and the load calculated by equations (8) to (10) was 91% of the actual ultimate load. For S1 the arching extended up to the load and the calculated arch resistance was 12% above the test load but failure was by yield of the main bars.

## 5. CONCLUSIONS

The bond strength of deformed bars in concrete affected by delamination depends primarily on the following factors: (a) depth of the surface of delamination relative to the bars; (b) restraint to the movement of the bars provided by links; (c) any transverse pressure, e.g. from supports, which may hold the bars to sound concrete; and (d) concrete strength. Expressions quantifying these effects are given in equations (1) to (5).

A reduction of bond strength can reduce resistance to inclined cracking, presumably due to an increase in the widths of flexural cracks. An estimate of 20% as the maximum likely reduction appears reasonable. If the residual bond strength is very low, flexure-shear cracking is improbable.

If the bond resistance in a span is very low, or if it is lost in bond failure, but the main bars are continuous and well anchored at supports, a beam or slab can function as an arch. Expressions for the ultimate strength corresponding to the compression failure of such an arch are given in equations (8) to (10).

Where the loss of bond affects only part of a span, conditions at the meeting of the bonded and debonded regions need special consideration. Quite small amounts of stirrups, however, can be shown to be sufficient to provide for the development of satisfactory strut-and-tie systems.

## ACKNOWLEDGEMENTS

The work reported here was part of a research programme carried out by W.S. Atkins under contract to the Highways Agency and supervised by the Agency's Technical Director for Bridge Design, Sibdas Chakrabarti OBE. The authors are grateful to the Agency and to Mr Chakrabarti for permission to publish this paper.

Any views expressed are those of the  authors and not necessarily those of the Highways Agency.

## REFERENCES

BD44/95 (1995). *The Assessment of Concrete Highway Bridges and Structures,* pub. by Highways Agency, London, UK.

Cairns J. and Zhao Z. (1993). "Behaviour of Concrete Beams with Exposed Reinforcement". *Proc. Inst. Civil Engineers, Structures and Buildings*, 99, pp. l-154.

Kani M.W., Huggins M.W. and Wittkop R.R (1979). *Kani on Shear in Reinforced Concrete*, pub. by Dept of Civil Engineering, University of Toronto, Toronto (CN).

Lorentsen M. (1964). *Shear and Bond in Prestressed-Concrete Beams without Shear Reinforcement*, Transactions No. 47, Statens Rad for Byggnadsforskning, Stockholm, Sweden, 195 pp.

Panell F.N. (1969). "The Ultimate Moment Resistance of Unbonded P0restressed-Concrete Beams". *Magazine of Concrete Research*, V. 21, No 66, pp. 43 -53.

Regan P.E. (1969). "Shear in Reinforced-Concrete Beams". *Magazine of Concrete Research*, V. 21, No 66, pp. 31-42.

Regan P.E. and Kennedy Reid LL. (2004). "Shear Strengths of R.C. Beams with Defective Stirrup Anchorages. *Magazine of Concrete Research*, V. 56, No. 3, pp. 159–166.

Regan P. E. and Kennedy Reid I.L. (2010). "Assessment of Concrete Structures Affected by Cover Delamination - Part 2: Bond-Shear Interaction", *Studies and Researches – Annual Review of Structural Concrete.* Politecnico di Milano, pub. by Starrylink (Brescia, Italy) V. 30 (in press).

Tam A. and Pannell F.N. (1976). "The Ultimate Moment Resistance of Unbonded Partially-Prestressed Concrete Beams". *Magazine of Concrete Research*, V. 28, No. 97, pp. 203-208.

## NOTATION

| | |
|---|---|
| $A_b$ | area of a bar and area of one leg of a link |
| $A_s$ | area of a main bar |
| $A_{ss}$ | effective area of a link restraining a main bar |
| $M_{flex}$ | flexural capacity corresponding to yield of main steel and crushing of concrete |
| $M_u$ | ultimate moment |
| $V_{BD}$ | characteristic shear force at shear cracking according to BD44/95 |
| $V_{k,red}$ | resistance to shear cracking as reduced by delamination of reinforcement |
| $V_u$ | ultimate shear force |
| $a$ | shear span or distance from support to critical section for bending |
| $a_o$ | part of $a$ along which main bars are debonded |
| $b_v$ | web breadth of a beam |
| $c'$ | concrete cover measured from the centre of a bar |
| $d$ | effective depth of a beam |
| $f_b$ | bond stress |
| $f_{bu}$ | ultimate bond strength (experimental) |
| $f_{b1}...f_{b5}$ | limiting bond stresses for ULS analysis |
| $f_{cu}$ | cube crushing strength of concrete |
| $l_b$ | bonded length (development length or splice length) |
| $p$ | pressure transverse to a plane of delamination or other concrete surface |
| $s$ | spacing of links along a main bar |
| $u$ | perimeter of a reinforcing bar $(u = \pi\phi)$ |
| $x_o$ | reference neutral axis depth (see equation 10) |
| $x_u$ | neutral axis depth at failure |
| $z$ | internal lever arm |
| $\phi$ | diameter of a main bar |
| $\theta$ | angle between web compression and main steel in a truss model |

## TECHNICAL TERMS (from the Editors)

- Bar flush with concrete surface : any bar whose net concrete cover is zero.
- Gripper (bar) : any bar whose bonded slanted lugs tend to push against concrete core under the effect of a pull-out force (Fig.1, bottom left: bond is enhanced).
- Mid-barrel exposure : any situation with the bar partially embedded in the concrete, so that only half of its surface is bonded to the concrete (the bar is like a floating barrel, partly emerging from the water and partly submerged).
- Neutral bar : any bar whose bonded slanted lugs neither push against concrete core nor tend to uplift the bar – and the cover (if any) – but push laterally and symmetrically against concrete embedment under the effect of a pull-out force (Fig.1, bottom center).
- Rider (bar) : any bar whose bonded slanted lugs tend to uplift the bar and to remove it from concrete embedment under the effect of a pull-out force (Fig.1, bottom right: bond is impaired).
- Sausage link : any tie or link that encircles a bar without overlapping (Fig. 5, bottom right).
- Unbonded (bar), debonded (bar) : any situation where bond is intentionally zeroed or unintentionally decreased.

## Table 1 – Results of lap-splice tests

General data

All mains bars T25

For series 1 and 2  $f_y$ (main bars) = 490 N/mm$^2$  $f_y$ (stirrups) = 260 N/mm$^2$

For A-1 and A2    $f_y$ (main bars) = 520 N/mm$^2$  $f_y$ (stirrups) = 531 N/mm$^2$

For A3 and A4 $f_y$ (main bars) = 550 N/mm$^2$  $f_y$ (stirrups) = 480 N/mm$^2$

| Beam No | $f_{cu}$ (MPa) | $\dfrac{c'}{\phi}$ | $\dfrac{l_b}{\phi}$ | Stirrups | top or bottom cast | $V_u$ (kN) | $f_{bu}$ (MPa) | $\dfrac{f_{bu}}{\sqrt{f_{cu}}}$ | Notes |
|---|---|---|---|---|---|---|---|---|---|
| 1-1 | 55.0 | 1.8 | 30 | R6@100 | btm | 128 | 4.44 | 0.60 | |
| 1-2 | 46.3 | 0 | 30 | R6@100 | top | 45 | 1.56 | 0.23 | |
| 1-3 | 54.0 | 0 | 30 | R6@100 | btm | 58 | 2.01 | 0.27 | |
| 1-4 | 48.8 | 1.8 | 30 | R6@100 | btm | 90 | 3.12 | 0.45 | corroded |
| 1-5 | 45.7 | 0.5 | 30 | R6@100 | btm | 84 | 2.92 | 0.43 | |
| 1-6 | 44.8 | 1.8 | 30 | R6@100 | btm | 105 | 3.65 | 0.55 | |
| 1-7 | 53.6 | 0.5 | 30 | R6@100 | btm | 70 | 2.43 | 0.33 | |
| 2-1 | 51.7 | 1.8 | 30 | (R6@100) | btm | 100 | 4.10 | 0.57 | |
| 2-2 | 49.2 | 0 | 30 | (R6@100) | top | 36 | 1.62 | 0.23 | |
| 2-3 | 57.4 | 0 | 30 | (R6@100) | btm | 50 | 2.25 | 0.30 | |
| 2-4 | 51.6 | 1.8 | 30 | (R6@100) | btm | 75 | 3.38 | 0.47 | corroded |
| 2-5 | 47.7 | 0.5 | 30 | (R6@100) | btm | 58 | 2.61 | 0.38 | |
| 2-6 | 46.1 | 1.8 | 30 | (R6@100) | btm | 87 | 3.92 | 0.58 | |
| 2-7 | 56.5 | 0.5 | 30 | (R6@200) | btm | 65 | 2.93 | 0.39 | |
| A-1 | 29.7 | 0.5 | 20 | T8@125 | top | 42 | 2.03 | 0.37 | |
| A-2 | 29.7 | 0.5 | 20 | (T8@125) | top | 26.5 | 2.31 | 0.42 | |
| A-3 | 38.8 | 0.5 | 32 | T10@125 | top | 105 | 3.36 | 0.55 | |
| A-4 | 38.8 | 0.5 | 32 | T10@80 | top | (133) | (4.29) | (0.70) | No bond failure |

Note: lapped bars were away from stirrup corners, where stirrup details are in parentheses.

# Table 2 – Results of development length tests

General data

Mains bars $f_y = 510$ N/mm$^2$

Stirrups R6 $f_y = 260$ N/mm$^2$

Stirrups R8 $f_y = 350$ N/mm$^2$

| Spec No | $f_{cu}$ (MPa) | $\dfrac{c'}{\phi}$ | Stirrups | top or bottom cast | $V_u$ (kN) | $f_{bu}$ (MPa) | $\dfrac{f_{bu}}{\sqrt{f_{cu}}}$ | Notes |
|---|---|---|---|---|---|---|---|---|
| VB-2 | 41.7 | 0 | none | btm | (95) | 1.59 to 2.12 | 0.24 to 0.33 | |
| VB-3 | 47.8 | 0 | none | btm | (60) | 1.59 to 2.12 | 0.21 to 0.26 | |
| VB-4 | 50.9 | 0 | none | btm | (50) | 1.59 to 2.12 | 0.20 to 0.22 | |
| 3-1 | 53.3 | 0 | R6@100 | btm | 75 | 2.06 | 0.28 | |
| 3-2 | 50.0 | 0 | R8@100 | btm | 118 | (3.27) | (0.46) | (*) |
| 3-3 | 58.9 | 0 | R8@100 | btm | 190 | (3.59) | (0.47) | (*) |
| 4-1 | 42.2 | 0 | R6@200 | top | 69 | 2.51 | 0.39 | |
| 4-2 | 42.2 | 0 | R8@120 | top | 56 | 2.04 | 0.32 | |
| 4-3 | 42.2 | 0 | R8@80 | top | 92 | 3.35 | 0.52 | |

(*) No bond failure

Note:     (1) For series VB failure did not occur at the breakdown of bond, as the slabs thereafter functioned as arches. $f_{bu}$ values given relate to the breakdown of bond, which was recorded for individual bars.

**Table 3 – Results of tests of end anchorages in slabs**

| Slabs No | a (mm) | $f_{cu}$ (MPa) | V (kN) | p (MPa) | Fs [1] (KN) | $f_b$ (MPa) | $\dfrac{P}{\sqrt{f_{cu}}}$ | $\dfrac{f_b}{\sqrt{f_{cu}}}$ |
|---|---|---|---|---|---|---|---|---|
| VB5[2] | 900 | 51.2 | 72.5 | 0.97 | 136 | - | - | - |
| VB6 | 650 | 47.4 | 62.5 | 0.83 | 88 | 9.33 | 0.121 | 1.355 |
| VB7 | 1150 | 46.9 | 32.0 | 0.43 | 84 | 8.17 | 0.063 | 1.096 |
| VB8 | 650 | 50.4 | 45.0 | 0.60 | 64e | 6.24 | 0.085 | 0.879 |
|  |  |  |  | 0.60 | 70c | 6.82 | 0.085 | 0.355 |
| VB8 |  |  | 50.0 | 0.67 | 40e | 3.90 | 0.094 | 0.549 |
|  |  |  |  | 0.67 | 97c | 9.45 | 0.094 | 1.331 |
| VB9 | 650 | 44.0 | 57.5 | 1.28 | 84e | 8.19 | 0.193 | 1.235 |
|  |  |  |  | 0 | 82c | 7.99 | 0 | 1.205 |
| VB9 |  |  | 50.0 | 1.22 | 100e | 9.75 | 0.184 | 1.470 |
|  |  |  |  | 0 | 38c | 3.70 | 0 | 0.558 |
| VB10 | 650 | 52.1 | 75.0 | 1.67 | 109 | 11.6 | 0.231 | 1.600 |

For slabs VB8 and VB9 the first two rows relate to conditions when the bars with the lower bond strengths reached their maximum forces and the second two rows relate to ultimate loads. The highest V's are ultimate shears.

1. $F_s$ = force in main bar, an average for all bars in VB5-VB7, otherwise the letters 'e' and 'c' denote edge and centre bars.

2. In slabs VB5 the bars had end hooks and failure was by destruction of the end zone and not by slip of the bars. The ultimate load was 0.9 times the value calculated by equations (8) to (10) for a compression failure at the load.

3. $f_y = 510$ N/mm$^2$

## Table 4 – Beams Series S

| Beam No | $f_{cu}$ (MPa) | Main steel | d (mm) | Top or botton cast | Stirrups[1] | Debonding/delamination | $V_{cr}$ (kN) | $V_u$ (kN) | Failure mode |
|---------|------|-----|-----|------|--------|----------------|------|------|---------|
| S1 | 49.0 | 2T20 | 270 | btm | R6@200 | debonded near support | 37.5 | 55.0 | flexure |
| S2 | 53.2 | 2T20 | 270 | btm | - | debonded near support | 40.0 | 43.0 | shear |
| S3 | 55.4 | 2T20 | 270 | btm | R6@200 | debonded near load | 40.0 | 55.0 | flexure |
| S4 | 53.6 | 2T20 | 270 | btm | - | intermittent debonding | 45.0 | 45.0 | shear |
| S5 | 39.2 | 2T16 | 272 | btm | - | c' = 0 | 36.7 | 56.7 | anchora |
| S6 | 39.7 | 2T16 | 272 | top | - | c' = 0 | 33.3 | 36.0 | anchora |
| S7 | 47.6 | 3T16 | 272 | btm | - | c' = 0 | 50.0 | 50.0 | shear |
| S8 | 47.6 | 3T16 | 272 | top | - | c' = 0 | 40.0 | 46.7 | shear |

(1) stirrups $f_y = 260$ N/mm$^2$


## Table 5 – Beams Series U

| Beam No | $f_{cu}$ (N/mm2) | Main Steel detail | $\dfrac{100 A_s}{bd}$ | N° of loads | $P_u$ (kN) | Failure mode [1] | $\dfrac{P_u}{P_{calc}}$ |
|---------|------|------|------|------|------|---------|------|
| U1[2] | 51.7 | 2T25 | 2.18 | 1 | 200 | shear | - |
| U2 | 49.0 | 2T25 | 2.18 | 1 | 198 | flexure — c | 132 |
| U3 | 52.3 | 2T25 | 2.18 | 2 | 170 | flexure — c | 0.99 |
| U4 | 59.2 | 2T25 | 2.18 | 3 | 234 | flexure — c | 0.95 |
| U5 | 55.6 | 2T16 | 0.89 | 1 | 96 | flexure — c | 0.94 |
| U6 | 33.1 | 2T20 | 1.99 | 1 | 70 | flexure — c | 1.26 |
| U7 | 49.6 | 2T20 | 1.99 | 1 | 79 | flexure — c | 1.12 |
| U8 | 51.3 | 2T20 | 1.99 | 2 | 68 | flexure — c | 0.84 |

Note: (1)    flexure — c — compression without yield

flexure — t — yield followed by compression

(2)    in U1 the unbonded length was 1500 mm in place of 2400 mm

(3)    $f_y$ = approx 500 N/mm$^2$ for main bars.

## Table 6 – Beams Series MV

| Beam No | fcu (MPa) | Delamination | $V_u$ (kN) | Notes |
|---|---|---|---|---|
| MV1 | 55.7 | c' = 0, full length except supports | 47.5 | flexural tension |
| MV2 | 47.8 | debonded except at supports | 30.0 | anchorage |
| MV3 | 52.7 | debonded near load | 42.5 | flexural compression |
| MV4 | 38.9 | debonded near supports | 45.0 | flexural tension |

Note: (1) For MV1 $f_{bu} \geq V_u/z\sum u = 2.03$ N/mm$^2$. With $A_{ss}/s\phi = 0.0105$ calculated; $f_{b4} = 1.92$ N/mm$^2$

(2) For MV2 ultimate load calculated from equations (8)-(10) = 1.12 $V_u$. Anchorage capacity calculated with $f_b = 0.7\sqrt{f_{cu}} + 2p = 0.95$ x experimental value.

(3) For MV3 ultimate load calculated from equations (8) to (10) see text = $V_u$.

(4) For MV4 ultimate load calculated from equations (8) to (10) = 91% experimental value.

(5) Main steel $f_y = 510$ N/mm$^2$, stirrups $f_y = 260$ N/mm$^2$

STUDIES AND RESEARCHES – V.29, 2009
Graduate School in Concrete Structures – Fratelli Pesenti
Politecnico di Milano, Italy

# EXPERIMENTAL INVESTIGATION ON POST-INSTALLED METAL ANCHORS SUBJECTED TO SEISMIC LOADING IN R/C MEMBERS

Alberto Franchi[1], Gianpaolo Rosati[1], Sara Cattaneo[2],
Pietro Crespi[2], Giovanni Muciaccia[3]

## ABSTRACT

The paper presents the results of an experimental investigation on the behavior of post-installed expansion metal anchors fastened to R/C pre-cracked columns and subjected to transverse reverse loading.

Post-installed anchors in reinforced concrete are of crucial importance for the mechanical resistance and stability of both structural and non-structural members, like façade panels and balconies, both connected to the slabs.

In seismic regions, fasteners are expected to transfer cyclic actions as reliably as possible, from the member in question to the concrete. The anchors behavior, however, is still not completely understood in seismic conditions, even if a number of scientific contributions have been lately devoted to this issue, that requires also the definition of appropriate experimental techniques to certify the mechanical properties of the anchors.

The aim of this research project is to investigate the behavior of mechanical anchors, by performing a few pull-out tests on anchors installed in pre-cracked R/C columns. The anchors were installed along the cracks, and the effect of crack opening-closing could be studied. In fact, the increasing damage in the concrete and in the anchor, because of the closing-opening process in the cracks, plays a decisive role in impairing the residual pull-out capacity of the anchors.

---

[1] Professor, Dept. of Structural Engineering, Politecnico di Milano, Milan, Italy
[2] Assistant Professor, Dept. of Structural Engineering, Politecnico di Milano, Milan, Italy
[3] Post-Doctoral Fellow, Dept. of Structural Engineering, Politecnico di Milano, Milan, Italy

# 1. INTRODUCTION

Earthquakes affect anchors in two different ways. First, they induce cracking and crack cycling in the primary structure, and, second, the movement of the structure generates dynamic tensile and shearing forces on anchors (Sippel and Rieder, 2007).

The European product guideline ETAG 001 (2007) and design standard EN 1992-1-1 (2004) deal with the assessment (through CE marking) and design rules for mechanical, chemical and plastic anchors, respectively. No specific provisions, however, have been approved so far in the European Community, with reference to seismic loadings.

This is not the case in USA, where ACI 355.2-04 (2004) defines specific tests based on 140 sinusoidal tension - and shear - loading cycles to be performed on the installed anchor, according to a loading procedure based on a number of blocks of cycles, with a decreasing amplitude and a frequency ranging from 0.1 to 2 Hz. Anchors are installed along hairline cracks that are later opened and closed up to a maximum crack width of 0.5 mm. These tests are pass/fail tests, since the test is considered successful if the anchor exhibits a minimum residual capacity equal at least to 80% of the monotonic pull-out capacity. In such a case, the anchor is considered suitable for seismic applications.

The results of this approval tests improved the understanding of anchor behavior in seismic conditions and provided the background for the development of enhanced prequalification methods for anchors (Guillet and David, 2007; Hoeler and Eligehausen, 2008).

The experimental research presented in this paper aims to evaluate the behavior of a wedge-type expansion anchor (approved according to ETAG001 option 1 for the use in cracked concrete) installed in different positions in life-size beam-column joints, inside and outside the plastic hinges, under cyclic loading. The considered beam-column joint was designed according to the provisions of Eurocode 2 (EN 1992-1-1, 2004).

The test program consists of six tests, where increasing-amplitude cycles are applied to simulate seismic effects (see - for instance - Fig. 8b). After pre-cracking each specimen (as will be explained later), at least 10 anchors were installed in different positions and an LVDT transducer monitored the crack opening close to each installed anchor. At the end of the load cycles, each single anchor was subjected to a residual pull-out test.

The objectives of this research project are:

- to evaluate the maximum crack opening in the specimens;

- to propose a reference crack-width to be used in the approval tests;

- to evaluate the pull-out residual capacity of the anchors and to define the reduction coefficient to be applied to the characteristic capacity in cracked concrete (according to the relative European Technical Approval).

## 2. TEST SPECIMENS

The geometry was chosen to simulate the actual behavior of floor-column connections at the ground level of a multi-storey building with rigid floors and a regular spacing of the columns, over a 4×4 m grid.

The same structural model was tested by Macchi et al. (1993, 1996) and Franchi et al. (1996). Under these assumptions, the column can be considered as a part of a shear-type frame, with an interstorey spacing of 3.4 m, subjected to a horizontal drift at the upper end. These considerations are instrumental in allowing the construction of rather small full-scale specimens, representative of many commonly-found buildings.

Since structural ductility is highly dependent on the detailing of the reinforcement, the design of the reinforcement (longitudinal bars and stirrups) was carried out on the basis of Eurocodes 2 and 8.

Eurocode 2, however, turned out to be more appropriate for the design of the specimens, for at least two reasons:

- the spacing of the stirrups required by Eurocode 8 (EN 1998-1, 2004) in the plastic-hinge regions is so small that a correct installation of the anchors is hardly possible and the formation of the typical concrete cone at failure may be prevented because of the interaction with the stirrups;

- the design of the stirrups according to Eurocode 2 provides more free room for anchor installation, with the formation of a more limited number of cracks, that are more distant and more opened.

The geometry of the specimens is shown in Figure 1: the height of the column is 1700 mm (= half the inter-storey distance of an hypothetic building), while the depth of the foundation is 650 mm. The foundation is required for fixing the column to the strong floor of the testing apparatus. (The foundation block is fixed via 8 Ø 22 mm threaded bars and two steel plates connecting the top of the foundation block to a steel beam fixed to the strong floor, Figs. 2 and 4). The cross section of the column is 250×300 mm. At the top, two vertical steel plates confine the column to avoid any possible local crushing of the concrete under the pressure of the electromechanical jack.

The details of the steel reinforcement are shown in Figure 1; the longitudinal reinforcement consists of 4 Ø 16 mm rebars placed near the corners of the cross section, the stirrups are Ø 10 mm with a 250 mm spacing. In the plastic-hinge zone (the lower 300 mm, as prescribed by EC2), the spacing of the stirrups is limited to 150 mm. A total of six specimens were cast.

Concrete grade is C28/35 (according to EN206, 2000), as commonly found in cast-in-place structures. For the longitudinal and transverse reinforcement, B450C ribbed bars were used (NTC, 2008).

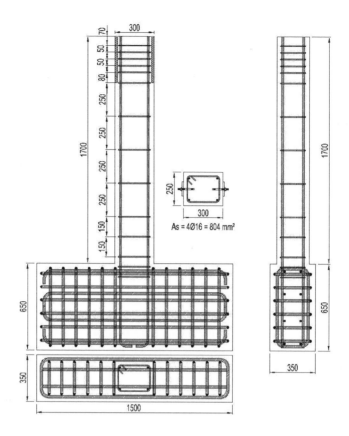

Figure 1 - Geometry of the specimens.

Figure 2 - View of the bottom part of a column and of the foundation block anchored to the strong floor.

## 3. ANCHORS

Wedge-type torque-controlled expansion metal anchors were adopted in the experimental campaign. The selected anchors are made of galvanized carbon steel (Steel Class 8.8), with a nominal diameter of 12 mm (M12 is extensively used in most applications). The geometric and mechanical properties are given in Table 1 and Figure 3. It is worth noting that the characteristic pull-out capacity of the selected anchor type is approved for a crack opening $\Delta w = 0.3$ mm (ETAG001 Option 1).

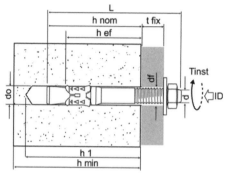

Figure 3 - Wedge-type torque-controlled expansion metal anchor.

| | $d_0$ | $h_1$ | $h_{nom}$ | $h_{ef}$ | $d_f$ | $h_{min}$ | $T_{inst}$ | $c_{cr,N}$ | $s_{cr,N}$ | Steel Class | 8.8 |
|---|---|---|---|---|---|---|---|---|---|---|---|
| | mm | mm | mm | mm | mm | mm | Nm | mm | mm | $f_{yk}$ (MPa) | 640 |
| **M12** | 12 | 100 | 81 | 72 | 14 | 150 | 60 | 108 | 216 | $f_{uk}$ (MPa) | 800 |
| | | | | | | | | | | E (GPa) | 210 |

Table 1 - Summary of the technical specifications of M12 anchor type.

## 4. TEST PROCEDURE

The specimens described in the previous section were tested at the Material Testing Laboratory of the Department of Structural Engineering of the Politecnico di Milano (Milan, Italy), where both static and dynamic tests on full-scale specimens can be carried out.

The loading frame (Figure 4) can apply any displacement history at the top end of the column, without limiting its rotation, by means of an electromechanical jack, which can be positioned at different distances from the strong floor. The testing apparatus is completed by two lateral frames, supporting two steel plates, that guide the column head in order to prevent any out-of-plane deflections of the specimen during the loading process.

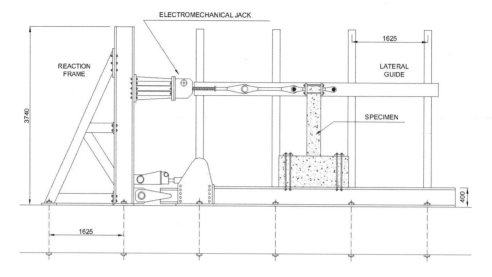

Figure 4 – Loading set-up, including the specimen.

The selected M12 expansion anchors were installed in all six R/C columns at different positions from the foundation block, as shown in Figure 5. A detailed description of the position of each anchor is presented in Table 2, where - for each column - the distance of the installation point from the foundation block is indicated.

The length of the column was subdivided into four different regions (Fig.5), each characterized by a different crack severity (rather numerous cracks in the plastic-hinge zone PH at the base of the column, 1st Region; no cracking in the 4th Region at the top, UZ). The assumed lengths of the regions are reported in Table 3.

In service conditions, anchors installed in concrete are subjected to a variety of loads acting in the axial or transverse direction, as well as in any inclined direction. In the first and second case, the load produces an axial and a shearing force, respectively, while in the third - and most general - case there is a combination of axial and shearing forces. Of course, all the combinations of the design loads, earthquake loading included, must be resisted by the anchor.

| $h_i$ (mm) | A1 | B1 | A2 | B2 | A3 | B3 | A4 | B4 | A5 | B5 | A6 | B6 |
|---|---|---|---|---|---|---|---|---|---|---|---|---|
| Column 1 | 150 | 160 | 270 | 270 | 450 | 450 | 680 | 680 | 930 | 930 | 1090 | 1090 |
| Column 2 | - | 150 | 270 | - | - | 450 | 680 | 680 | 930 | 930 | 1090 | 1090 |
| Column 3 | - | 170 | 330 | - | - | - | 560 | 540 | 750 | 840 | 1040 | 1040 |
| Column 4 | - | 170 | 200 | - | - | 410 | 605 | 625 | 860 | 840 | 1080 | 1050 |
| Column 5 | - | 120 | - | - | 360 | 400 | 600 | 660 | 860 | - | 1100 | 1110 |
| Column 6 | 140 | - | - | 225 | 430 | - | 625 | 610 | 850 | 850 | 1080 | 1080 |

Table 2 - Positions of the anchors in the columns.

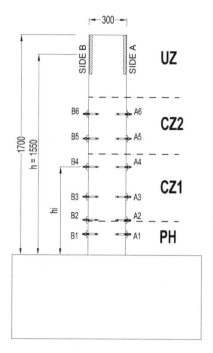

Figure 5 - Positions of the anchors and regions characterized by different crack severity.

| Regions with different crack severity | Length mm | Notes |
|---|---|---|
| PH | 260 | Severe cracking (length equal to the effective depth of column cross-section) |
| CZ1 | 520 | Mild cracking (length twice as much the effective depth of column cross-section) |
| CZ2 | 220-420 | Light cracking |
| UZ | 350-550 | No cracking |

Table 3 - Assumed lengths of the regions with different crack severity.

In the following, for the sake of simplicity and as a first step, the tests will be limited to axial loading. To this end, a calibrated ring was used to apply the axial load to the anchor. The threaded end of the shank of the anchor passes through the base of the ring and goes through the opposite part of the ring, where the threaded bar ("threaded rod" in Fig.6) can be tightened by turning a nut via a torque wrench (Fig. 6). The ring is in equilibrium between the force exerted by the nut and the reaction exerted by the concrete through the base of the ring. During the tightening of the shank, the ring deforms and the deformation is registered by means of a dial gauge. Consequently, the load on the anchor can be controlled after each loading cycle, and can be kept constant (equal - for instance - to the design load).

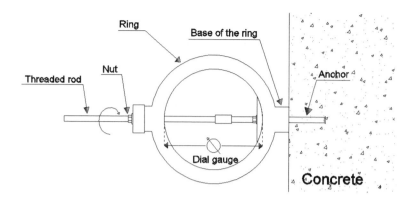

Figure 6 - Loading ring and its instrumentation.

Figure 7 - Calibrated rings and LVDT transducers installed on column surface.

Assuming that the anchor remains within the elastic range during the test, the calculation of the radial shortening of the ring "s" (measured by the dial gauge) to be applied to induce an axial design load $F_d$ (= $N_{Rk}/\gamma_{Mc}$) in the anchor is given by the following relationship:

$$s = \frac{F_d}{K} = \frac{N_{Rk}}{\gamma_{Mc} \cdot K} \tag{1}$$

where K is the calibrated ring stiffness, $N_{Rk}$ is the characteristic capacity of the anchor in cracked concrete ($\Delta w = 0.3$ mm) according to ETAG001 and $\gamma_{Mc} = 1.5$

is the partial safety factor of the concrete. The conditions of constant or variable axial load in the anchor can be reproduced by tightening the anchor at the end of each cycle during the test. Figure 7 shows the calibrated rings and the LVDT applied to the column surface to monitor the width of the crack.

The specimens were pre-cracked by applying a horizontal load (*pre-load*) sufficient to cause steel yielding in the tension zone of the column. The hairline cracks resulting from pre-loading were not randomly distributed, since - as it is well known - the stirrups act as crack inducers, forcing concrete cracking to localize in the planes containing the stirrups.

As a consequence, in most cases the anchors could not be installed exactly along the cracks. In such cases, the anchors were installed as close as possible to the cracked planes, but in some cases the cracked plane did not intersect the hole containing the anchor, while in other cases the cracked plane intersected the hole rather eccentrically or even tangentially, this being one of the reasons why the load-displacement curves measured during the pull-out tests were rather dispersed. (It must be observed that the localization of the cracks in the planes containing the stirrups may be avoided by creating in the concrete crack inducers – in the form of *superficial grooves* - placed half-way between the stirrups; this solution, however, was not adopted in the experimental campaign, because the intention was to investigate anchors behavior in R/C members, as closely as possible to the in-situ conditions).

Last but not least, since crack opening was expected to be a crucial parameter with reference to anchors pull-out capacity, no axial load was applied to the columns during the tests. (Any axial load would have improved the pull-out capacity of the anchors).


## 5. CYCLIC LOADING HISTORIES

In Seismic Engineering, the choice of the loading history is one of the basic problems. By denoting with $\delta_y$ the horizontal displacement at the top of the column corresponding to the first yielding of the reinforcement in the bottom section, $\delta_y$ can be analytically calculated or, alternatively, experimentally determined.

The loading histories applied at the top of the six columns were related to the ductility level of the structure, defined as the ratio between the ultimate and the yielding displacement at the top of the column. The columns were designed for a behavior factor $q = 1.5$ (as required by EN1992-1-1). Nevertheless, the ductility level reached during the tests was larger (up to 4.0).

It should also be noted that, for the same damage level (i.e. for the same level of cracking and crushing in the concrete, and of yielding in the steel), the tests on the shaking table and the static tests (like those carried out in this project) should be considered as equivalent, if a certain number of cycles is applied.

| No. cycles | Column 1 $\delta_y$=10 mm | Column 2 $\delta_y$=10 mm | Column 3 $\delta_y$=15 mm | Column 4 $\delta_y$=15 mm | Column 5 $\delta_y$=16 mm | Column 6 $\delta_y$=18 mm |
|---|---|---|---|---|---|---|
| 3 | $\pm\delta_y$ | $\pm\delta_y$ | $\pm\delta_y$ | $\pm\delta_y$ | $\pm\delta_y$ | $\pm\delta_y$ |
| 3 | $\pm2\delta_y$ | $\pm2\delta_y$ | $\pm1.5\delta_y$ | $\pm1.5\delta_y$ | $\pm1.5\delta_y$ | $\pm1.5\delta_y$ |
| 3 | $\pm3\delta_y$ | $\pm3\delta_y$ | $\pm2\delta_y$ | $\pm2\delta_y$ | $\pm2\delta_y$ | $\pm2\delta_y$ |
| 3 | - | - | $\pm4\delta_y$ | $\pm4\delta_y$ | $\pm4\delta_y$ | $\pm3.5\delta_y$ |
| Total No. | 9 | 9 | 12 | 12 | 12 | 12 |
| | Variable load | | Constant load | | | |

Table 4 - Loading histories for all columns.

The loading histories adopted are reported in Table 4 for all specimens. Two different procedures for the tightening of the anchors were adopted: the first (Columns 1 and 2) simulates the relaxation of the anchor due to crack opening, and the second (Columns 3 to 6) simulates anchor behavior under a constant load, as in service conditions.

All tests were displacement-controlled (displacement rate = 0.38 mm/s). Given the low value of the loading rate, the tests can be considered as quasi-static.

At the top of each column, the horizontal force and the displacement were measured by means of a 100 kN loading cell (placed along the axis of the electro-mechanical jack) and a LVDT (0-200 mm HBM WA), respectively.

Fig. 8 shows the hysteretic loops and the plots of the displacement histories of Column 5. (Similar loops and plots were obtained for the other columns).

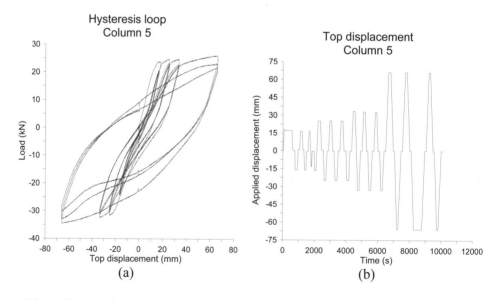

(a)                                                    (b)

Figure 8 - (a) Hysteretic loops; and (b) top-displacement history of Column 5.

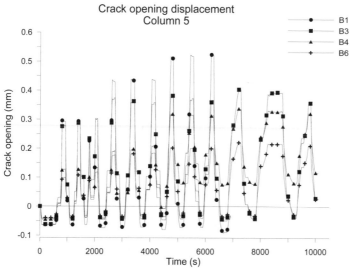

Figure 9 - Crack-opening displacement vs. time in Column 5.

The crack width (or crack-opening displacement) in the columns was measured by means of eight HBM LVDTs (stroke 10 mm), placed astride the cracks. All instruments were connected to a data-acquisition system (HBM Spider 8). In Figure 9 the crack-opening displacement is plotted as a function of time (Column 5), while in Figure 10 the maximum crack opening measured during the test of Column 5 is plotted as a function of the position along the column (the abscissa measures the distance from the foundation block). The typical crack-opening evolution of a cantilever member can be easily recognized. (As a matter of fact, the trend is mostly linearly decreasing, in accordance with the linearly-decreasing distribution of the bending moment).

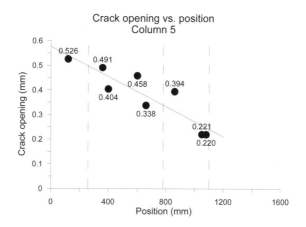

Figure 10 - Maximum crack opening displacement vs. anchor position (Column 5).

287

## 6. PULL-OUT TESTS ON ANCHORS

After being installed in the pre-cracked specimens, past the load cycles, the anchors were tested to evaluate their residual pull-out strength. The tests were performed by using a steel frame, which supported an hydraulic jack in series with a 100 kN loading cell placed along the axis of the anchor (Figs. 11 and 12).

The relative displacement between the anchor and the concrete was measured by means of two LVDTs (0-50 mm) placed at both sides of the anchor; and the average value of the two displacements was recorded by the data-acquisition system. The test results are summarized in Figs.13-15.

Figure 11 - Test rig for the pull-out tests.

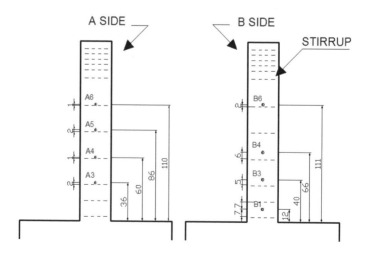

Figure 12 - Anchors and stirrups positions (Column 5).

288

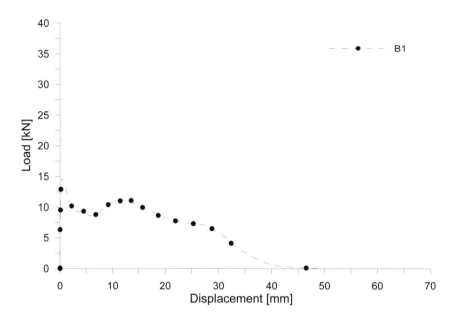

Figure 13 - Pull-out load of anchor B1 vs. displacement (Column 5 - Plastic Hinge Zone = severe cracking).

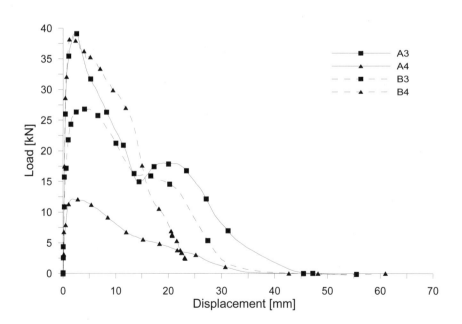

Figure 14 - Pull-out load of anchors A3, A4, B3, B4 vs. displacement (Column 5 - Cracked Zone 1 = mild cracking).

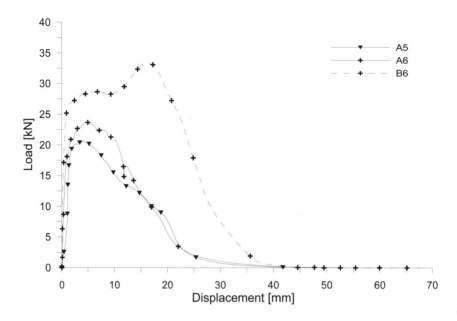

Figure 15 - Pull-out load of anchors A5, A6, B6 vs. displacement (Column 5 - Cracked Zone 2 = light cracking).

After the tests, all specimens exhibited a typical pull-trough failure, that was characterized by the extraction of the shank, because of its sliding inside the expansion element, which remained stuck to the concrete surface of the drilled hole. The failure load of the anchors turned out to be strongly dependent on anchor position. In general, higher values for the pull-out capacity were observed far from plastic-hinge regions.

In Figure 12 the installation position of the anchors with respect to the position of the stirrups in Column 5 is presented, while - for the same column - in Figures 13, 14 and 15 the load-displacement responses of the installed anchors are shown.


## 7. DISCUSSION

In Fig. 16, the maximum crack opening is plotted as a function of the position of the anchors along the column. Among the 48 values reported in Fig. 16, 9 values refer to the Plastic-Hinge Zone (severe cracking), 24 to Cracked Zone 1 (mild cracking) and 15 to Cracked Zone 2 (light cracking).

The maximum crack opening outside the plastic hinge exhibits a lower scatter than within the plastic hinge; furthermore, the distribution along the column height is approximately linear outside the plastic hinge, as required by the linear diagram of the bending moment. The average and the characteristic least-square fittings for the values outside the plastic hinge are also reported (Fig. 16, dashed and full curves, respectively). In particular, a characteristic value $\Delta w_{k,max}$ at the boundary of the plastic hinge (90% probability with 90% confidence level) of 0.60 mm is suggested. This value can be proposed for the definition of future seismic approval tests. (It should be noted that the above-mentioned crack-width value is significantly larger than the values 0.30 and 0.50 mm required by ETAG001 for static loads and by ACI355 for seismic loads, respectively).

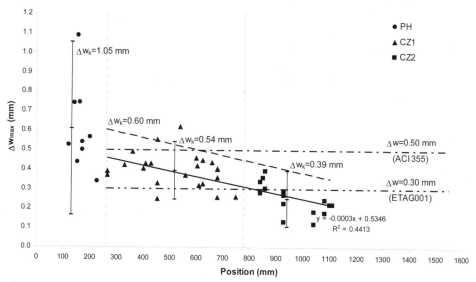

Figure 16 - Maximum crack opening vs. anchor position (all tests).

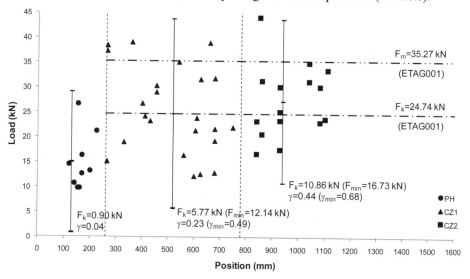

Figure 17 - Residual pull-out load vs. anchor position (all tests).

As for the correlation between the pull-out residual capacity of the anchors and their position along the column (Fig. 17), because of the milder cracking outside the plastic-hinge zone the residual capacity exhibits higher values than in the plastic zone. The characteristic values of the residual capacity $F_k$ (95% probability with 90% confidence level) measured in the different regions of the columns are lower than those reported in the approval of the anchors. (It should be remarked that the scatter of the results is very large, especially for those anchors installed in the lower part of the column, because of the influence of many factors, such the distance of the anchor from the crack or the different loading histories applied to the columns, see Table 4).

In order to quantify the possible capacity in seismic conditions, a reduction factor $\gamma$ equal to the ratio between the pull-out residual capacity $F_{k,test}$ obtained in the experimental campaign and the characteristic capacity $F_{k,ETAG001}$ determined during the approval tests in cracked concrete (ETAG001 option 1) is here proposed:

$$\gamma = \frac{F_{k,tests}}{F_{k,ETAG001}} \tag{2}$$

The computed values of $\gamma$ clearly show that the installation in the plastic-hinge results in really unsafe conditions ($\gamma = 0.04$). Outside the plastic-hinge zone the situation improves with $\gamma = 0.23$ for Cracked Zone 1 and $\gamma = 0.44$ for Cracked Zone 2. These reduction factors are very low because the scatter of the experimental results is very large and the number of the tests is limited (hence the characteristic capacity $F_{k,tests}$ is rather low). If the above considerations are made with reference to the minimum capacity $F_{min,tests}$ and not to $F_{k,tests}$ the reduction factors turn out to be $\gamma_{min} = 0.49$ for CZ1 and $\gamma_{min} = 0.68$ for CZ2.

As for the relationship between the residual capacity and the maximum crack opening, Figure 18 shows all the results obtained in the three different regions. Obviously, the results concerning the installation inside the plastic hinge are characterized by higher values for the crack width and by a lower residual capacity, while the opposite is true for the installation far from the plastic hinge. (The results of the approval tests in either cracked or uncracked concrete, concerning the residual capacity, agree with the results of this experimental campaign, outside the plastic-hinge zone; however, the scatter of the approval tests is much lower than that of the seismic tests).

On the basis of the results of this campaign a possible safe domain for seismic applications outside the plastic hinges can be identified (dashed domain in Fig. 18). For the type of anchors investigated in this project, the residual seismic pull-out capacity may be assumed as 5.77 kN, for any installations outside the plastic hinge, which means 23% of the characteristic capacity under monotonic loading in cracked concrete.

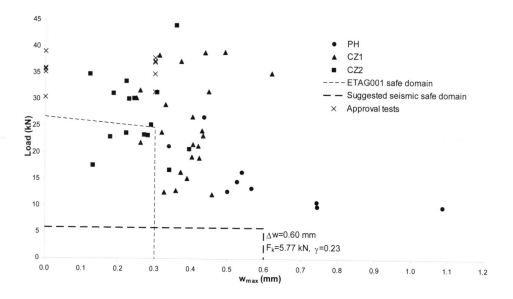

Figure 18 - Residual pull-out load vs. maximum crack opening (all tests).

## 8. CONCLUSIONS

The seismic characterization of post-installed anchors is based on conventional tests (see - for instance - ACI 355.2), where a sinusoidal load is applied to the anchor, whilst crack width is kept constant. In actual seismic conditions, the seismic excitation activates a cycling opening-closing process in the cracks and a variation of the load applied to the anchor.

In this project, the tests were performed by cycling the crack width under constant load (= load applied to the anchor). The tests show that the value of the crack width representative of real seismic conditions should be taken equal to 0.60 mm, rather than 0.80 mm, as suggested by other authors (Hoeler and Eligehausen, 2008).

The commonly-accepted unfavorable behavior of the anchors installed inside the plastic hinges is confirmed by the results of this project. However, also in the zones other than those where plastic hinges form, the residual load-bearing capacity of the anchors is rather low with respect to the capacity in static conditions, because of many uncertainties (not more than 50% of the capacity in static conditions).

This is a remarkable result indeed, since anchors behavior under constant loading and cycling cracking appears to be more exacting than cyclic loading in itself (keeping the crack width constant), which usually brings in a reduction factor not smaller than 0.80.

## ACKNOWLEDGEMENTS

The authors are grateful to G.D.M. Costruzioni S.p.A. for casting the specimens and to the European Consortium of Anchors Producers - ECAP for supplying the anchors to be tested. Sincere thanks are also due to MS Eng. Giorgio Angioletti and MS Eng. Andrea Bono for their valuable cooperation during the tests, to the technicians of the Laboratory for Testing Materials of Politecnico di Milano, and specifically to Mr. Daniele Spinelli.

## REFERENCES

ACI355.2-04 (2004). *Evaluating the Performance of Post-Installed Mechanical Anchors in Concrete.* American Concrete Institute.

EN1992-1-1 (2004). *Eurocode 2: Design of Concrete Structures. Part 1-1: General Rules and Rules for Buildings.* CEN/TC 250.

EN1998-1 (2004). *Eurocode 8: Design of Structures for Earthquake Resistance. Part 1: General Rules, Seismic Actions and Rules for Buildings.* CEN/TC 250.

EN206-1 (2000). *Concrete – Part 1: Specification, Performance, Production and Conformity.* CEN/TC 104.

ETAG001 (2007). *Guideline for European Technical Approval of Metal Anchors for Use in Concrete. Part 1-6.* EOTA, Bruxelles.

Franchi A., Riva P., Ronca P., Roberti R. and La Vecchia M. (1996). "Failure Modalities of Reinforcement Bars in Reinforced Concrete Elements under Cyclic Loading". *Studies and Researches – Politecnico di Milano.* Ed. and pub. by Italcementi (Bergamo, Italy), Vol. 17-1996, pp. 157-187.

Guillet T. and David E. (2007). "A New Seismic Test for Metal Anchors". *Proc. 2nd Int. Symposium on Connections between Steel and Concrete*, Stuttgart, Germany, 4-7 September 2007, Vol. 1, pp. 677-686.

Hoeler M. S. and Eligehausen R. (2008). "Behavior and Testing of Anchors in Simulated Seismic Cracks". *ACI Structural Journal*, Vol. 105, No.3, pp. 348–357.

Macchi G., Pinto P. and Sanpaolesi L. (1996). "Ductility Requirements for Reinforcement under Eurocode 2". *Structural Engineering International*, Vol.4, pp. 249-254.

Macchi G., Pinto P., Sanpaolesi L., Cantù E., Magenes G., Del Corso R., Froli M. and Nuti C. (1993). "Experimental Research on the Minimum Requirements for the Reinforcing Bars Suitable for Seismic R/C Structures" (in Italian). *Associazione Tempcore Italia – TEMPCORIT.*

NTC (2008). *Technical Norms for Buildings (in Italian).* Official Gazette No.29, Feb. 4 - 2008.

Sippel M. and Rieder A. (2007). "Behavior of Fastenings under Realistic Earthquake Excitations". *Proc. 2nd Int. Symposium on Connections between Steel and Concrete*, Stuttgart, Germany, 4-7 September 2007, Vol. 1, pp. 693-701.

Technical Notes

STUDIES AND RESEARCHES – V.29, 2009
Graduate School in Concrete Structures – Fratelli Pesenti
Politecnico di Milano, Italy

# SOME ISSUES CONCERNING CONCRETE IMPREGNATION WITH SILANES

Ralejs Tepfers[1]

## ABSTRACT

Concrete protection against severe environmental conditions, such as wind-driven rain water, is often a must, even more since rain may contain marine salt. Impregnating concrete structures with silanes is a possible solution, that involves producers, users and experts in concrete impregnation with chemical products. Their opinions, however, are still far apart regarding the efficiency of the impregnation and the most suitable technologies.

Having in mind users' point of view, this paper raises and discusses some questions, still awaiting an answer, but does not present a final solution for concrete impregnation with silanes.

There are many factors coming into play, such as what type of silanes should be used? How deep the impregnating layer should be? Impregnation should be limited to the surface, or should be deeper, especially if wind-driven rain is expected to occur?

Surface orientation should be also taken into consideration, since the success of the impregnation depends on whether the surface is vertical or horizontal at the top of the structural member or at the underside.

Further factors like entrapped air, gravity and moisture content seem to influence the impregnation with silanes, as well as the penetration of water, and should be considered.

Other questions are: is it possible to renew the impregnation by cleaning concrete surface? How is it possible to measure any changes in the water-repellent effect of the layer impregnating the concrete? Is there any influence of the silane layers on water diffusion out of concrete?

The above-mentioned unanswered questions may be the reasons why there are so many diverging opinions about the efficiency of silane impregnation.

---

[1] Professor Emeritus, Department of Civil and Environmental Engineering, Structural Engineering, Concrete Structures, Chalmers University of Technology, Göteborg, Sweden.

# 1. INTRODUCTION

Silane ($SiH_4$) is a chemical compound, that has the same structure of methane ($CH_4$), but with an atom of silicium instead of an atom of carbon in the molecule. Like the atom of carbon in methane, the atom of silicium in silane - is placed in the centroid of a tetrahedron, whose vertexes are occupied by 4 atoms of hydrogen.

At ambient temperature silane burns naturally, since no ignition sources are required.

Silanes are more complex chemical compounds, consisting in chains of silicium atoms, having covalent links with hydrogen atoms. The easy decomposition of silanes at room temperature depends on the rather weak link among silicium atoms, this link being weaker than that among carbon atoms in hydrocarbons.

To avoid their decomposition at room temperature, silanes are generally found on the market as solutions, emulsions or gels, that – once sprayed or placed on a surface – are subjected to the combination with the silicates (as in the case of concrete surfaces) and to oxidation, with the formation of water and silicium dioxide ($SiO_2$, whose tiny particles fill the voids of the material). Hence these chemical compounds are often used in water-repellent products, and have been proposed for the protection of concrete surfaces and stone walls.

Protecting the stone walls of a 100 years old church in Sweden close to the North Sea (Skagerak) , whose granite blocks were jointed by means of layers of hydraulic-lime mortar, was the starting point of this paper. The protection of the structure was required by its exposure to heavy winds and rain.

In this context, impregnation of concrete with silanes was studied, and questions arose about the reliability of this technique. Contradicting opinions from engineers about the efficiency of the impregnation and the depth of the protective layer came up as well.

Furthermore, neither the recent tests and the state-of-art studies by Johansson (2006), and Johansson et al. (2006a-d), nor the companies manufacturing and selling impregnation products provide the end users with all necessary information.

In this paper, the author presents his opinions on several still-open questions and, whenever possible, gives their ideas, having in mind the end users..

As previously mentioned, many are the opinions concerning the protection provided by the impregnation of concrete surfaces with silanes in a moist environment. Some researchers believe that the water-repellent ability is good, while others have doubts about the efficiency of the impregnation. There are also different views on how deep the impregnated layer should be and to what extent the penetration depth may guarantee the impregnating effect.

Because of the many aspects still open to investigation, many efforts are today devoted to the research on concrete impregnation, even more since - beside the possible benefits - the technology still arises many questions, without answers, that are crucial for the applications.

Depending on the properties of the specific silanes adopted in concrete impregnation, the penetration should be minimal (i.e. limited to concrete surface), or extended to the walls of the capillaries. (The coating on the walls tends to close the capillaries and to increase concrete resistance to water diffusion). Today's opinion is that the duration of the impregnation is about ten years. Renewing the impregnation makes the capillaries more closed and favours a further reduction of the diffusion, that may even be totally blocked.

Some people think that the solution containing the silanes should be aimed at covering the concrete surface. In this way the silanes do not have the time to penetrate into the capillaries, since their molecules rapidly react with the silicates contained in the concrete. Thereby, concrete surface becomes hydrophobic, the capillaries are undisturbed and water vapour diffusing from inside the concrete can evaporate through the open capillaries. Others think that the waterproofing layer should be preferably 20mm deep, in order to better prevent water intrusion.

The tests concerning the penetration of the silanes in the concrete are always carried out by dipping the sub-surface of the concrete sample in the solution containing the silanes, that are sucked-up against gravity. The results are clear, though limited to the bottom face (*intrados*) of any given structural member, something that occurs very rarely, since generally the sides and top face (*extrados*) are exposed to the water. The intrados, however, may be covered by a film of condensed water, as it is usually the case, when the environment warms up very quickly after a spell at very low temperature. Normally, the sides and the top surface of a structural member are exposed to the rain and should be protected by means of impregnation.

Gravity has no effects on the capillary suction along the lateral surfaces of a concrete structure, but wind pressure may force the water through a too-thin impregnated layer, into the capillaries. As a matter of fact, wind-driven rain forms water films on vertical concrete walls and these films are exposed to wind pressure. The wind pressure deforms the films and pushes them through the impregnated hydrophobic layers into the capillaries, where the water molecules get in contact with the ionic electrically-loaded capillary walls and stick to them.

Tech-Dry Building Protection Systems (see website in References) mentions the above-mentioned risk, which increases with increasing wind pressure and may create *water bridges* through the impregnating layer. These "channels" favour water transport into the concrete. Of course, a deep impregnation may prevent this migration to happen. Furthermore, close to sea coast the water may contain wind-borne salts (*chlorides*), that follow the water into concrete pores.

Along any concrete top surface, the pressure of the rain water increases with the thickness of the water film. The deformed volume of water is forced through the impregnating layer into the capillaries. If water bridges are created through the protecting layer, capillary suction is activated. The air entrapped in the concrete pores, however, has to get out against the water intrusion and is hindered by the water trying to come in.

Cracks affect water intrusion as well, since any excessive opening of the cracks nullifies the benefits of impregnation, that cannot stop the incoming water. Subsequently, the penetration of soft rainwater dissolves the calcium contained in the hydrated cement, and - if water penetration allows the water to flow through the concrete – the hardened cement is depleted of calcium and concrete weakens.


## 2. WATER STRUCTURE

In Civil Engineering capillary suction is usually treated by means of empirical equations and diagrams concerning the various chemo-physical processes. In this way, a lot of information is obtained, to the detriment of the understanding. Hence, to better understand how silane impregnation works, a thorough examination of water properties and atomic structure is necessary. The water molecule consists of two hydrogen atoms and one oxygen atom covalently bounded to each other (because of *electron sharing*). The negative electrons tend to be located between the positive atomic nuclei. This means that the two hydrogen nuclei become outwardly positive poles. The oxygen nucleus becomes a negative pole, because of the surrounding surplus of negatively-charged electrons (Fig.1).

Water molecules are mutually bonded by the electrical attraction between poles having opposite sign (*hydrogen bonding*). The binding is quite weak but sufficient to hold together the volume of water in the form of droplets. In liquid water, the bond is continuously broken and re-established because of *thermal vibrations*; as a result, the molecules can occupy the entire available space. In solid water (*ice*) there are less thermal vibrations, and the hydrogen bonds do not break and the molecules cannot occupy the entire space (this is an explanation of why the volume of ice is larger than that of liquid water, by 9%, for a certain given mass).

Because of their electric polarity, water molecules are attracted by the electrically-charged ionic structures, and this is the case of concrete.

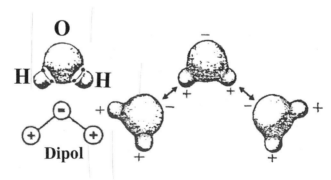

Figure 1 - Simplified structure of water molecules.

The ions strongly bind water molecules among themselves. Ions with positive and negative electrical charges attract water molecules, since these have both positive and negative poles. At temperatures above absolute zero, the molecules vibrate because of thermal excitation. Vibration intensity varies between molecules. Overactive water molecules can jump from ion to ion along the capillary walls, pulling other water molecules, in so forming water layers and volumes, that are held together by hydrogen bonds. The ionic capillary walls becomes hydrophilic and their surfaces become wet, Fig. 2a. If the capillary walls have no electrical charges (as after being impregnated and covered by silanes), the surfaces become hydrophobic and water is repelled, Fig. 2b. The water is not attracted by the capillary walls devoid of ionic electric charges, and the internal hydrogen bonds hold together the water molecules, by forming droplets or layers outside the capillaries. To have water in a hydrophobic capillary, water has to be pressed in.

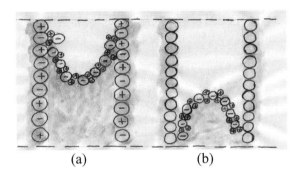

(a)                              (b)

Figure 2 - Water intrusion (a) in a hydrophilic capillary with electrically-charged ionic structure; and (b) in hydrophobic capillary, where water intrusion requires some pressure, since the capillary is electrically uncharged.


The wind pressure acting on a water film covering a concrete surface can deform this film and push it into the capillaries.

Thermally vibrating water molecules can penetrate among thermo-vibrating ions in ionic materials, where water molecules force the structure of the material to swell, see Fig. 3. On the contrary, when the concentration of the water molecules in the environment decreases, the same molecules are expelled and the structure of the material shrinks. It is a reversible process.

Should enough water molecules be around an ion, this ion may move away from the ionic structure, to become a part of the solution, see Fig. 4. In this way, calcium ions are dissolved out of the cement binder and follow the water flow. When the water comes out of a crack in a structural member and evaporates, carbonated calcium remains in the form of white calcareous coating.

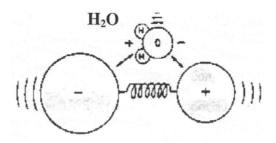

Figure 3 - Thermal vibrations allow the water molecules to penetrate into the ionic structure.

## 3. HYDRATION PRODUCTS (CEMENT GEL) AND WATER

The structure of the cement gel is ionic, as shown in Fig. 5 (electron microscope), where the capillaries are not visible in the form usually adopted in modelling, even if their aim is clear: "sucking" water. The structure has ions with electric charges and is attracting polar water molecules.

In a polar structure the water molecules are able to climb by taking advantage of the temperature-induced vibrations of the molecules, that create layers and layers of water molecules. As a result, menisci are formed and further water molecules are drawn ("capillary suction"). Depending on the direction of the sucking process, gravity counteracts, is neutral or favours water intrusion – "suction".

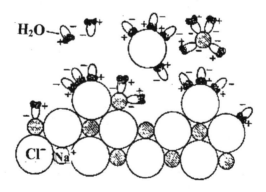

Figure 4 - Several water molecules around an ion can expel the ion from the ionic structure, forcing it to join the solution.

Figure 5 - Enlarged cement-gel particle, as observed by means of an electron microscope.

## 4. THE IMPREGNATING EFFECTS OF SILANES

Silanes come as solutions, emulsions or gels. When applied to concrete surfaces, silanes react rapidly with the silicates of the cement gel and cover concrete surface with a hydrophobic layer. If for some reasons the reaction is delayed, the silanes can be progressively and partially sucked into the capillary system, before the reaction takes place. There are different opinions about the depth required by the impregnating layer to guarantee a reliable protection (between $\sim$ 0.1 mm and 20 mm). According to current knowledge, the impregnation can last for as many as 10 years, though with decreasing efficacy.

The aim of concrete impregnation with silanes is to prevent water from entering into the concrete. As a matter of fact, a correctly-performed impregnation with silanes breaks water continuity into the capillary system, prevents water intrusion and hinders the migration of chlorides or other ions into the concrete (Wittman, 2007). However, silane impregnation does not hinder concrete carbonation, since carbon dioxide - $CO_2$ can penetrate the open capillaries. The requirements for the carbonation to start the corrosion of steel reinforcement (Ljungkranz et al., 1994) are as follows:

(a) the temperature should exceed $4°$ C;
(b) the moisture content in the concrete should be in the range 0.7-1.5%, which corresponds to RH = 50-75% (i.e. ordinary conditions);
(c) the amount of carbon dioxide in the environment should be adequate (this condition is always met).

One should remember that *wet concrete is unaffected by carbonation*, and that impregnated concrete is generally accompanied by internal conditions that favour carbonation. Furthermore, steel reinforcement in concrete corrodes, if the relative humidity exceeds 60%, pH is below 11.8 and adequate oxygen is available. In ordinary concrete, were pH is above 12 and there are few chloride ions, the reinforcement does not corrode.

## 5. QUESTIONS BEFORE DECIDING WHETHER TO IMPREGNATE

Concrete impregnation aimed to prevent water intrusion brings in a lot of questions that are well-known to end users from a qualitative point of view, but should be answered by the scientific community from a quantitative point of view:

(a) Does the impregnation have different effects - for the same penetration depth of the silanes - if applied to the underside surfaces, side surfaces or top surfaces of any given concrete structure? In the three above cases, gravitation is unfavourable, neutral or favourable with reference to penetration. More specifically, in the case of silanes applied to the top surfaces impregnation prevents the entrapped air from getting out of the concrete pore system. Consequently, the air can hinder the penetration of silanes into the capillaries. However, the same yields for water penetration into the pore system.

(b) Since water inside the capillaries is known to have a negative influence on silane intrusion, how should the moisture content in the concrete mass be determined? What is the best method for measuring water content inside the concrete? What is the maximum moisture content, that may still guarantee a successful impregnation? Does it depend on the direction of the intrusion?

(c) Before surface impregnation, may active measures be used in order to reduce moisture content in the concrete? Can drying pistols be used or are there other tools? Since a sudden rain shower during the impregnation process increases concrete moisture and requires specific checks, are there any indications on when to resume working?

(d) How deep should the impregnating layer be? Does wind-carried rain (that creates a water film on vertical concrete surfaces) reduce impregnation effects, because of the wind pressure deforming the film and forcing it into the capillaries? As a matter of fact, gust-induced wind pressure is comparable to that of a water depth of several decimetres. Should the impregnating layer be thin, water bridges would form and water transport through these bridges would occur, making a deeper impregnation layer necessary.

(e) What is the durability of a silane-based impregnated layer covering a concrete surface? Do thicker impregnating layers last longer? After the fading in a number of years (say ten years) of the first emulsion-based silane impregnation, does re-impregnation with updated agents (for instance gel-type silanes) provide the same durability? (Re-impregnation may even last longer).

(f) To what extent any dirt on concrete surface and into the capillaries may be detrimental to the efficacy of silane impregnation? Dirt is usually hydrophilic and can favor water transport into concrete pores. To what extent cleaning concrete surface with pressurized water containing appropriate chemical products can restore the effects of silane impregnation? (Before waxing the body of a car, that is dirt because of pollution, the water-repellent properties of the "sealing" can be guaranteed by using a high-pressure water jet containing some specific chemical products).

(g) What is the best way to impregnate a concrete surface? By spraying the emulsion, or by using a brush, or are there other methods to have the best results?

(h) Does silane impregnation reduce water diffusion through the impregnated concrete layer and towards the external environment, as some scholars declare? When re-applying the impregnation (after the first impregnation has lost most of its efficacy), does the new impregnation reduce capillary size to such an extent that water diffusion out of the concrete may be markedly impaired?

(i) What should be done when the re-impregnation process fills the external capillaries and water diffusion out of the concrete may be hindered? It is not always possible to remove the old impregnated layers, because in this way the concrete cover around the reinforcing bars may become too thin. As an alternative to concrete removal, could a layer of sprayed concrete be applied on a previously-impregnated concrete surface, in order to allow the new layer to be impregnated at a later stage?

# 6. CONCLUDING REMARKS

There are still many open questions requiring an answer from the scientific community on whether, or to what extent, or with what technology a concrete structural member should be impregnated with silanes. What type of silanes should be used? How deep the impregnated layer should be? Answers are instrumental in decision making!

It seems appropriate to limit the impregnation to the surface, without any intrusion, when the surface is not exposed to the combination of rain and high wind-pressure. However, if wind-driven rain is expected, the impregnated layer should be deeper.

Surface orientation has also some relevance in terms of impregnation success. If the surface to be impregnated is vertical or horizontal (belonging to the extrados – top surface - or to the intrados – sub-surface of the given structure), the success of the impregnation process tends to be rather different. Gravity seems to influence the intrusion of the silanes, as well as water penetration, something that should be investigated more thoroughly. The amount of moisture in the pore system is another important factor to be evaluated prior to impregnation. Also the air entrapped by the film of the silanes during the impregnation process along concrete top surfaces should be looked at carefully, since air may endanger any adequate impregnation.

Other questions: is it possible to renew the impregnating effect by cleaning the surface? How can be measured any in-time changes in the water-repellent silane-induced capability? Is it possible to restore the impregnation effects induced by the silanes without altering the water diffusion from the concrete to the environment? Answering these questions requires further research efforts indeed!

Summing up, science has still (a) to give many answers to end users on a number of properties related to the coupling of concrete and silanes, and (b) to clear the way from the many diverging opinions about the efficiency of concrete silane impregnation, something badly needed for concrete preservation against environmental attacks.

## REFERENCES

Johansson A. (2006). *Impregnation of Concrete Structures. – Transportation and Fixation of Moisture in Water-Repellent Treated Concrete*. The Royal Institute of Technology, Department of Architecture and Built Environment, TRITA-BKN. Bulletin 84, ISSN 1103-4270, ISRN KTH/BKN/B—84—SE, Stockholm 2006, 68 pp.

Johansson A., Janz M., Silfwerbrand J. and Trägårdh J. (2006a). "Impregnation of Concrete Structures - Introduction to a PhD-project". *Proc. 4th International Conference on Water-Repellent Treatment of Building Materials (2005)*, Aedificatio Publishers, pp. 59-68.

Johansson A., Janz M., Silfwerbrand J. and Trägårdh J. (2006b). "Moisture Transport in Impregnated Concrete – Moisture Diffusion Coefficient, Modeling, Measurement and Verification. *Restoration of Buildings and Monuments - Bauinstandesetzen und Baudenkmalpflege*, V.12, No.1, pp. 13-24.

Johansson A., Janz M., Silfwerbrand J. and Trägårdh J. (2006c). "Moisture Fixation in Concrete Treated with a Water-Repellent Agent. Swedish Cement and Concrete Research Institute, Stockholm, Sweden, 14 pp.

Johansson A., Janz M., Silfwerbrand J. and Trägårdh J. (2006d). *Penetration Depth for Water-Repellent Agents on Concrete as a Function of Humidity, Porosity and Time*. Swedish Cement and Concrete Research Institute, Stockholm, Sweden, 16 pp.

Ljungkranz C., Möller G. and Petersons N. (1994). *Betonghandbok (Concrete Handbook, in Swedish)*, Svensk Byggtjänst (Swedish Constructions), Stockholm, pp. 785-808.

Tech-Dry Building Protection Systems PTY. LTD. 177-179 Coventry Street, South Melbourne, Victoria, 3205, Australia. **Website: www.techdry.com.au.**

Wittman F. W. (2007). "Effective Chloride Barrier for Reinforced-Concrete Structures in Order to Extend the Service-Life". *Advances in Construction Materials*. Springer Berlin, Heidelberg. ISBN 978-3-540-72447. Part V. pp. 427-437.

STUDIES AND RESEARCHES – V. 29, 2009
Graduate School in Concrete Structures – Fratelli Pesenti
Politecnico di Milano, Italy

# APPLICATION OF THE YIELD-LINE METHOD TO A HEAVY-DUTY REINFORCED-CONCRETE SLAB

Roberto Guidotti[1], Andrea Titi[1]

## ABSTRACT

A rather thin R/C slab resting on six square columns is studied in this technical note, under the loads due to two large silos, each containing roughly 60 tons of desiccated sludge. Limit analysis in the form of the Yield-Line Method is applied to identify the weakest resistant mechanism among several global and local mechanisms, that are kinematically admissible for the given restraints, loads and cut-outs of the slab.

In this application, both bending-controlled and punching-controlled mechanisms are investigated, and a parametric analysis is carried out, in order to assess the sensitivity of each mechanism - and related ultimate load - to the top reinforcement as a fraction of the bottom reinforcement.

This technical note shows once more the value of the Yield-Line Method, that is a "quick" means to have useful information on the ultimate structural behavior and a handy instrument to check the results obtained by means of more refined structural codes, with the peculiar merit of providing a physical insight into the failure modes, allowing the designer to optimize quickly and easily the structural performance.

---

[1] PhD Candidate, Dept of Structural Engineering, Politecnico di Milano (Italy)

# 1. INTRODUCTION

Rigid-plastic modelling of structural behavior, exemplified by the "plastic-hinge" and "yield-line" methods for frames and bi-dimensional structures respectively, is a rather simple but powerful means to investigate the collapse (or ultimate behavior) of rather complex structures. These methods have a sound theoretical background based on the kinematic theorem of the Theory of Plasticity (see for instance Moy, 1981; Chen, 1982; Nielsen, 1984), and obey to an intuitive understanding of the structural behavior (Johansen, 1962 and 1972).

In the present technical, note the Yield-Line Method is used in a case, that is at the same time rather simple and general (Figure 1): a heavy-duty R/C slab supported by six columns, bearing two desiccated-sludge silos and designed with the working-stress approach (Bamonte and Gambarova, 2009). The slab is divided into two roughly square fields, each with a cut-out close to its centroid, and the reinforcement has a uniform distribution (different from top to bottom).

Different bending-controlled and punching-controlled collapse mechanisms are studied, and for each of them not only the "weakest" mechanism (i.e. the most probable) is identified, but a 3D graphic representation of the deformed shape is given, to improve the understanding of the kinematics of each mechanism.

For each mechanism, a parametric analysis is carried on in order to study the sensitivity of the collapse load to the ratio between the limit moments developed by the top and bottom bars.

In spite of its relative simplicity, the slab under investigation exhibits a sizable number of rather different resistant mechanisms. Moreover, since there are no lateral restraints (except the columns), the membrane forces developed along the boundary are rather limited. Consequently, one of the limits of the Yield-Line Method (which cannot take care of the stiffening effect caused by the membrane behavior) has no role. Hence, the weakest mechanism and related collapse load predicted by the Yield-Line Method give a realistic picture of the ultimate behavior of the slab under investigation, and may be a realistic reference for any more complex linear or nonlinear analysis.

Figure 1 - View of the slab and of the columns (by courtesy of the firm "Milano Depur", Nosedo Waste-Water Treatment Plant, Milan, Italy).

Being a classical approach to slab analysis, the Yield-Line Method is treated in many papers and books. For R/C slabs, most of the references can be found in the excellent and well-known books by Ferguson et al. (1988), Favre et al. (1990), Park and Gamble (2000), and Kennedy and Goodchild (2003), while at the Italian level the compact book by Gambarova et al. (2008) may be useful to beginners and designers. The same slab investigated in this paper is treated in Bamonte and Gambarova (2009), although with a different objective (fire safety, see also Krause, 2009).

Rigid-plastic analysis is the backbone of many models suggested in the design codes (see for instance EC-2, 2003).

## 2. GEOMETRY OF THE SLAB AND PROCEDURE OF THE ANALYSIS

The Yield-Line method is applied to the analysis of a rectangular R/C slab (sides = 7.00 m and 12.70 m; thickness = 35 cm), supported by 3 pairs of columns (two along the short sides and two along the transverse axis of symmetry; section of each column 60 x 60 cm, Figure 2). The slab bears two silos, whose total weight (own weight + weight of the desiccated sludge) is 600 kN, that increases up to 900 kN in fire conditions, because of the water poured into each silo.

The transverse spacing of the axes of the columns is 5.20 m, while the longitudinal spacing is 5.25 m; the cut-out of each field is slightly off-center, being closer to the short side, than to the line connecting the two intermediate columns.

In each silos, the cylindrical mantle (external diameter 5.00 m; height 4.50 m) is surmounted by a truncated cone. The content of the silos is desiccated sludge (specific weight 6.9 kN/m³; maximum volume 80 m³).

The Yield-Line Method is applied to the slab according to the following steps:

1. Identification of a suitable set of possible collapse mechanisms, and evaluation of the associated ultimate loads; in this step, both the loads and the geometry are simplified (Figure 3: the loads transmitted by the silos are transformed into an equivalent uniform load; the columns are considered as point-like supports; and the slab is limited to the part enclosed by the lines connecting the centroids of the columns).

2. Identification of the most probable mechanism, that is characterized by the least ultimate load among the various computed ultimate loads.

3. Parametric analysis of the collapse mechanisms as a function of the ratio between the negative and positive limit moments.

Two different load cases have been considered, with/without the load acting on area of the cut-out (Figure 4). The geometry adopted in step 1 is as follows (Figure 3):

- a = 520 cm; b = 525 cm;

- a' = 128 cm; b' = 168 cm;

- c = 136 cm; d = 221 cm.


## 3. EVALUATION OF THE PLASTIC MOMENTS DEVELOPED BY THE REINFORCEMENT

In any given unit section, the plastic moments developed by the reinforcement are evaluated assuming (a) full plasticization in tension for the steel; and (b) a block-type distribution for the compressive stresses in the concrete, extended to 80% of the depth of the neutral axis, see EC2 (2003), and Gambarova et al. (2008).(In concrete plasticity the stress block should be extended to the entire depth of the neutral axis, by introducing an "effectiveness factor" for concrete strength; however, extending the stress block to 80% of the depth is like adopting the same value for the effectiveness factor, with minor differences in terms of internal lever arm; lower values for the effectiveness factor are generally adopted in shear and torsion, where the stress state is more complex and tension plays a sizable role). Consequently, the ratio between the internal moment lever-arm z (distance between the centroid of the stress block and the centroid of the tensile reinforcement) and the effective depth d depends on the mechanical steel ratio $(A_s f_{yd}\}/A_c f_{cd})$. The effective depth depends in turn on bar diameter Ø and net cover c (= 1.5Ø).

In detail:

- Bottom reinforcement (positive bending): 1Ø16/10 in both x and y directions; isotropic reinforcement, steel ratio = 0.58 %.

- Top reinforcement (negative bending): 1Ø16/20 in both x and y directions; isotropic reinforcement, steel ratio = 0.29%.

- Steel characteristic/design strength at yielding: $f_{yk}/f_{yd}$ = 432/375 MPa.

- Concrete characteristic strength in compression: $f_{ck}$ = 25 MPa.

- Concrete design strength in compression: $f_{cd}$ = 13 MPa.

- Effective depth:

  o d' = h – c - Ø/2 = 35 - 1.5x1.6 - 1.6/2 = 31.8 cm (for the bar layers closest to the concrete surface = "external" bar layers;

  o d''= h – c – Ø - Ø/2 = 35 - 1.5x1.6 - 1.6 - 1.6/2 = 30.2 cm (for the bar layers farthest from the concrete surface = "internal" bar layers;

  o d (mean value adopted in the analysis) = 31 cm.

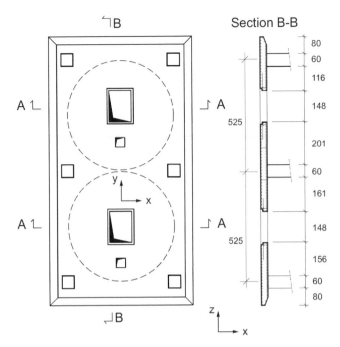

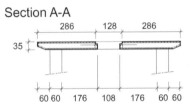

Section A-A

Figure 2 - Typical R/C slab resting on columns (the dashed circles are the footprints of the two silos). Measures in cm. The load due to the two silos has been introduced has an uniformly distributed load in the analysis.

| | Bottom bars | Top bars |
|---|---|---|
| Plastic moments *[kNm/m]* | 213.20 | 111.45 |
| Depth of the neutral axis *[x/d]* | 0.17 | 0.13 |
| Max. strain of the compressed concrete *[$\varepsilon_{c,max}$]* | -3.5 ‰ | -3.5 ‰ |
| Max. strain of steel *[$\varepsilon_{s,max}$]* | 16.88 ‰ | 24.41 ‰ |

Table 1 - Plastic moments developed by the tensile reinforcement.

The value of the plastic moments per unit length are listed in Table 1. No maximum value was enforced for the ultimate strain of the carbon steel (= unlimited ductility, no hardening). In under-reinforced sections, this assumption (see EC-2, 2003) leads to the same values of the resistant moments generally found by introducing the very popular limitation $\varepsilon_{s,max} = 10‰$.

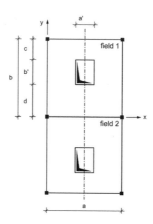

Figure 3 - Plan view of the slab.

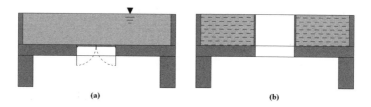

Figure 4 - Different cases for the load acting on the cut-out area: (a) liquids or very loose materials; and (b) rather cohesive materials (the load may be prevented from falling through the cut-out by providing non-structural walls along the sides of the cut-out).

Because of reinforcement isotropy, $m_x^+$ and $m_y^+$, $m_x^-$ and $m_y^-$ coincide:

$$m_x^+ = m_y^+ = \mathbf{m}^+ = \mathbf{213\,kNm\,/\,m}$$

$$m_x^- = m_y^- = \mathbf{m}^- = \mathbf{111\,kNm\,/\,m}$$

where (+) and (-) refer to the moments developed by the bottom and top reinforcement, respectively. In the following, the yield lines where the positive limit moments are activated ("positive" yield lines) will be indicated with full thick lines, while those where the negative moments are activated ("negative" yield lines) will be indicated with dashed thick lines. The former [latter] yield lines represent steel plasticization and concrete cracking induced by sagging (positive bending) [hogging (negative bending)].

It is worth recalling that - according to a well-known conservative assumption by Johansen – any local bending and shear deformations of the bars crossing the yield lines may be neglected. Consequently, the complementary resistant mechanisms called "dowel action" and "kinking" may be neglected as well.

## 4. COLLAPSE MECHANISMS

The R/C slab under investigation is subjected to a rather uniform load and, because of the restraints and the cut-outs, may fail according to a number of different collapse mechanisms, either global (i.e. implying the failure of the whole slab) or local (i.e. limited to a single field), each characterized by a different yield-line pattern. As shown in the following, thirteen different yield-line patterns were identified (six bending-controlled and seven punching-controlled), either fully defined or requiring the evaluation of one unknown parameter.

The mechanisms were selected taking into account: (a) the linearly-elastic bending behavior analyzed by means of a FE code (Bamonte and Gambarova, 2009); (b) the slab behavior suggested by a simplified "equivalent" system of strips; and (c) the geometry, that is characterized by cut-outs and point-like supports. Whether any mechanism was a combination of other "independent" mechanisms was considered of minor relevance.

The ultimate loads were computed according to the Principle of Virtual Works, by using the Virtual Work Equation (Park and Gamble, 2000; see also Bamonte and Gambarova, 2009), with the load applied to the area of the cut-out and with this area unloaded (Cases "a" and "b", respectively, Fig. 4). In the former case, the load acting on the cut-out "works" because of slab sagging; in both cases, the reinforcement stopped along the sides of the cut-out develops no limit moments and does not contribute to the internal work (Bamonte and Gambarova, 2009). Hence, for a given virtual displacement field, the internal work does not change, while the external work diminishes, if there is no load applied to the cut-out area. Consequently, the collapse load increases and is larger than in the case with the load applied to the cut-out area.

Since the Yield Line Method leads to upper-bound solutions, that overestimate the collapse load, lower-bound solutions should possibly be worked out in order to assess the accuracy of the results. In the case of R/C slabs, the rather simple and intuitive Hillerborg's Strip Method (Hillerborg, 1996) may be used. Such further step, however, was beyond the scope of this study.

### 4.1 Mechanism No.1 (local failure)

This mechanism (Figure 5a) requires the evaluation of a single unknown parameter concerning the position of the positive yield line. This position should be determined by minimizing the collapse load, that here (as in the following) is evaluated with no load applied to the cut-out area. Since the relationship between the collapse load $p_{u1}$ and the unknown parameter x is rather complex, the minimum was identified numerically (Figure 12a, Appendix I), where the minimum of the collapse load occurs for x = 232 cm and has the following value:

$$p_{u1} = 71 \; kN / m^2$$

315

In Figure 5a, the lateral diagram of the virtual displacements refers to any longitudinal section not crossing the cut-out. For the expression of the collapse load, see Table 3a (Appendix II).

## 4.2  Mechanism No.2 (global failure)

This mechanism (Figure 5b) is based on a single positive yield line running along the longitudinal axis of symmetry. The mechanism is fully determined and the rather simple formulation of the collapse load $p_{u2}$ leads to the following value:

$$p_{u2} = 50 \ kN \ / \ m^2$$

In Figure 5b the bottom diagram of the virtual displacements refers to any transverse section not crossing the cut out. For the expression of the collapse load, see Table 3a (Appendix II).

## 4.3  Mechanism No.3 (local failure)

This mechanism (Figure 5c) is based on the formation of four positive yield lines connecting the columns of each field with the corners of the cut-out, and of one negative yield line along the transverse axis of symmetry (connecting the two intermediate columns). The mechanism is fully determined and the rather complex formulation of the collapse load $p_{u3}$ leads to the following value:

$$p_{u3} = 198 \ kN \ / \ m^2$$

In Figure 5c, the diagrams of the virtual displacements refer to the sections aligned with the edges of the cut-out. For the expression of the collapse load, see Table 3a (Appendix II).

## 4.4  Mechanism No.4 (local failure)

This mechanism (Figure 6a) is based on the formation of three positive and one negative yield lines. The negative yield line and the two diagonal positive yield lines are the same as in the previous case, while the third positive yield line runs along the longitudinal axis of symmetry. The mechanism is fully determined and the rather complex formulation of the collapse load $p_{u4}$ leads to the following value:

$$p_{u4} = 115 \ kN \ / \ m^2$$

In Figure 6a, the top diagram of the virtual displacements refers to any transverse section comprised between the cut-out and the top free edge, while the lateral diagram refers to the section aligned with the longitudinal axis of symmetry. For the expression of the collapse load see, Table 3a (Appendix II).

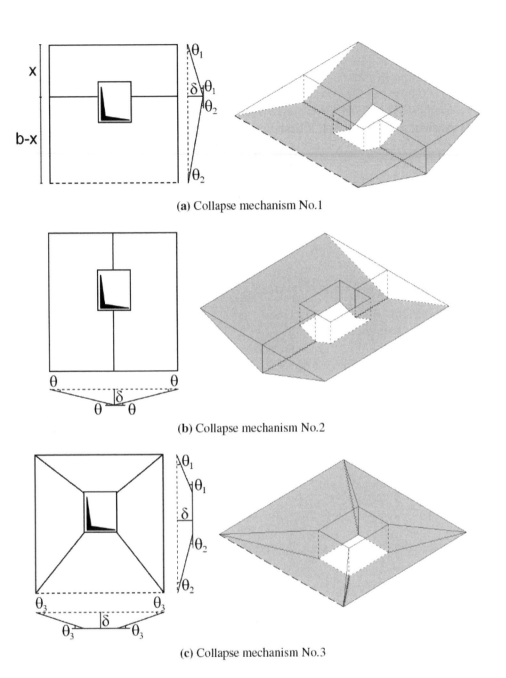

**(a)** Collapse mechanism No.1

**(b)** Collapse mechanism No.2

**(c)** Collapse mechanism No.3

Figure 5 - Bending-controlled mechanisms No.1, 2 and 3 (plan view and 3D representation.

## 4.5 Mechanism No.5 (global failure)

This mechanism (Figure 6b) is based on three positive yield lines in each field, two connecting the extreme columns with the nearest corners of the cut-out, and the third running along the longitudinal axis of symmetry between the cut-outs. The mechanism is fully determined and the rather complex formulation of the collapse load $p_{u5}$ leads to the following value:

$$p_{u5} = 102 \ kN \ / \ m^2$$

In Figure 6b, the bottom diagram of the virtual displacements refers to any transverse section comprised between the cut-out and the axis connecting the two intermediate columns, while the lateral diagram refers to the section aligned with the longitudinal axis of symmetry. For the expression of the collapse load, see Table 3a (Appendix II).

## 4.6 Mechanism No.6 (global failure)

This mechanism (Figure 6c) is based on four positive and two negative (albeit aligned in the plan view) yield lines, but has a single unknown parameter, that has to do with the position of the intersection points between the positive yield lines and the longitudinal sides of the slab. The coordinate of these points should be determined by minimizing the collapse load. Since the relationship between the collapse load $p_{u6}$ and the unknown parameter x is rather complex, the minimum was identified numerically, as shown in Figure 12b (Appendix I), where the minimum of the collapse load occurs for x = 235 cm and has the following value:

$$p_{u6} = 93 \ kN \ / \ m^2$$

In Fig. 6c, the diagrams of the virtual displacements refer to the free edges of the slab field. For the expression of the collapse load, see Table 3a (Appendix II).

## 4.7 Some comments on bending- and punching-related mechanisms

The first five mechanisms examined so far are clearly related to bending, and specifically to the principal bending moments (Bamonte and Gambarova, 2009). These mechanisms are mostly characterized by the extension of the yield lines to the whole field. The controlling factor is the bending behavior rather far from the supports and not the local effects close to the supports. The sixth mechanism is a "transition" mechanism, since the layout of the yield lines indicates a stronger role for the supports.

The next seven mechanisms are strongly affected by the supports - or by some of the supports – and in at least one case exhibit a number of yield lines radiating from the supports. For these reasons these mechanisms are termed "punching-related mechanisms", even if they are bending- and not shear-controlled.

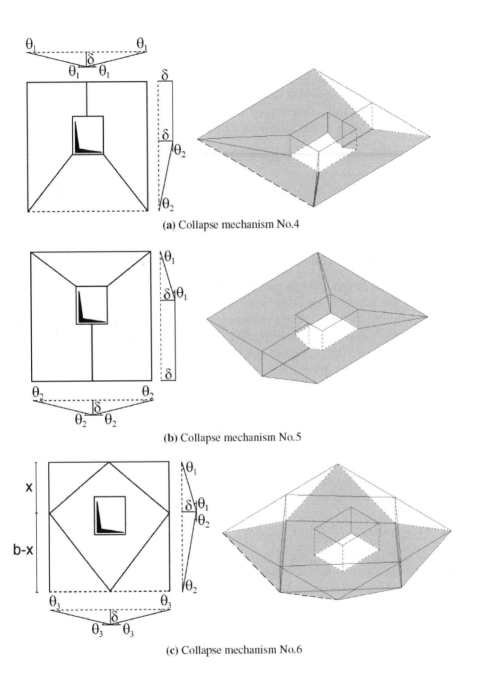

**(a)** Collapse mechanism No.4

**(b)** Collapse mechanism No.5

**(c)** Collapse mechanism No.6

Figure 6 - Bending-controlled mechanisms No.4, 5 and 6 (plan view and 3D representation).

### 4.8   Mechanism No.7 (global failure)

This mechanism (Figure 7a) is based on eight positive and four negative yield lines connecting the columns of each field with the corners of the cut-out. The mechanism is fully determined and the rather complex formulation of the collapse load $p_{u7}$ leads to the following value:

$$p_{u7} = 131 \ kN \ / \ m^2$$

In Figure 7a, the diagrams of the virtual displacements refer to the sections aligned with the longitudinal and transversal edges of the slab. For the expression of the collapse load, see Table 3b (Appendix II).

### 4.9   Mechanism No.8 (local failure)

This mechanism (Figure 7b) is based on the formation of four positive yield lines connecting the edges of the slab with the extreme corners of the cut-out, and of three negative yield lines, two connecting the extreme columns with the nearest corners of the cut-out and one running along the transverse axis of symmetry (connecting the two intermediate columns). The mechanism is fully determined and the rather complex formulation of the collapse load $p_{u8}$ leads to the following value:

$$p_{u8} = 127 \ kN \ / \ m^2$$

In Figure 7b, the diagrams of the virtual displacements refer to the sections aligned with the longitudinal and transversal edges of the slab. For the expression of the collapse load see Table 3b (Appendix II).

### 4.10   Mechanism No.9 (local failure)

This mechanism (Figure 7c) is similar to the previous one, with two more positive yield lines, aligned with the transverse edges of the cut- out. The mechanism (characterized by six positive and three negative yield lines) is fully determined and the rather complex formulation of the collapse load $p_{u9}$ leads to the following value:

$$p_{u9} = 115 \ kN \ / \ m^2$$

In Figure 7c, the diagrams of the virtual displacements refer to the sections aligned with the longitudinal and transversal edges of the slab. For the expression of the collapse load, see Table 3b (Appendix II).

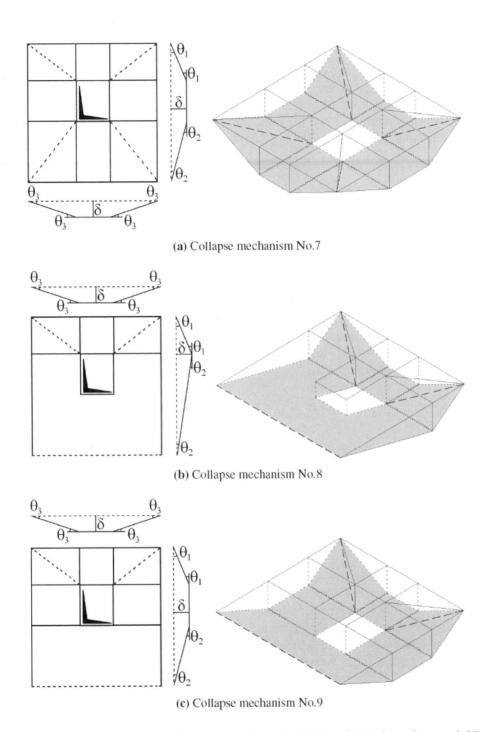

(a) Collapse mechanism No.7

(b) Collapse mechanism No.8

(c) Collapse mechanism No.9

Figure 7 – Punching-controlled mechanisms No.7, 8 and 9 (plan view and 3D representation).

### 4.11 Mechanism No.10 (global failure)

This mechanism (Figure 8a) is similar to mechanism 8, but the intermediate columns are involved. There are no negative yield lines along the transversal axis of symmetry. The mechanism (characterized by 4 positive and two negative yield lines) is fully determined and the rather complex formulation of the collapse load $p_{u10}$ leads to the following value:

$$p_{u10} = 106 \ kN / m^2$$

In Figure 8a, the diagrams of the virtual displacements refer to the sections aligned with the longitudinal and transversal edges of the slab. For the expression of the collapse load see Table 3b (Appendix II).

### 4.12 Mechanism No.11 (global failure)

This mechanism (Figure 8b) is similar to mechanism 9, but the intermediate columns are involved. As in the previous case, there are no negative yield lines along the transversal axis. The mechanism (characterized by six positive and two diagonal negative yield lines) is fully determined and the rather complex formulation of the collapse load $p_{u11}$ leads to the following value:

$$p_{u11} = 103 \ kN / m^2$$

In Figure 8b, the diagrams of the virtual displacements refer to the sections aligned with the longitudinal and transversal edges of the slab. For the expression of the collapse load, see Table 3b (Appendix II).

### 4.13 Mechanism No.12 (global failure)

This mechanism (Figure 9a) is based on four positive yield lines "cutting"' the corners of the slab and two negative yield lines along the transversal axis. Since the positive yield lines are assumed to be at 45° to slab sides, there is one single unknown parameter, concerning the position of the intersection points between the positive yield lines and the longitudinal (and transversal) sides of the slab. The coordinate of these points should be determined by minimizing the collapse load. Since the relationship between the collapse load $p_{u12}$ and the unknown parameter x is rather complex, the minimum was identified numerically, as shown in Figure 12c (Appendix I), where the minimum of the collapse load occurs theoretically for x = 0 cm (*) and has the following value:

$$p_{u12} = 77 \ kN / m^2$$

In Figure 9a, the diagrams of the virtual displacements refer to the sections aligned with the longitudinal and transversal edges of the slab. For the expression of the collapse load, see Table 3b (Appendix II).

(*) Since for x = 0 no mechanism can form (because of kinematic incompatibility) and the collapse load is rather constant close to x = 0 (Fig.12c), the yield lines may form at a distance not smaller than x = d from the axes of the columns, where d is the side of the square sections (= yield lines tangent to the sections of the columns and passing through the corners). Of course, the position of the inclined yield lines is highly questionable.

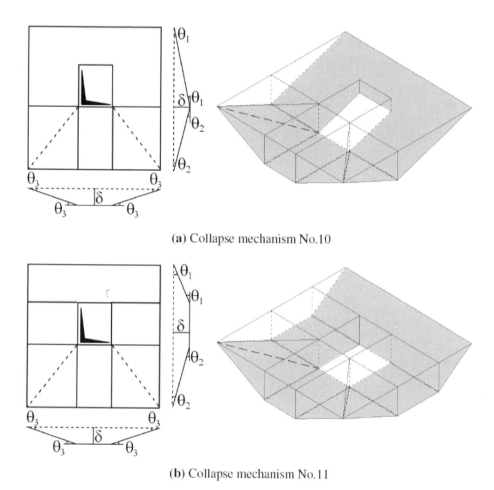

(a) Collapse mechanism No.10

(b) Collapse mechanism No.11

Figure 8 – Punching-controlled mechanisms No.10 and 11 (plan view and 3D representation).

## 4.14  Mechanism No.13 (global failure)

This mechanism (Figure 9b) is characterized by circular positive yield lines developing around the columns of the slab and negative yield lines radiating from the columns ("fan-type" mechanism). The mechanism has a single unknown parameter concerning the position of the intersection points between the positive yield lines and the longitudinal/transversal sides of the slab. The coordinate of these points should be determined by minimizing the collapse load. Since the relationship between the ultimate load $p_{u13}$ and the unknown parameter r is rather complex, the minimum was identified numerically, as shown in Figure 12d (Appendix I), where the minimum of the collapse load occurs theoretically for r = 0 cm (**).

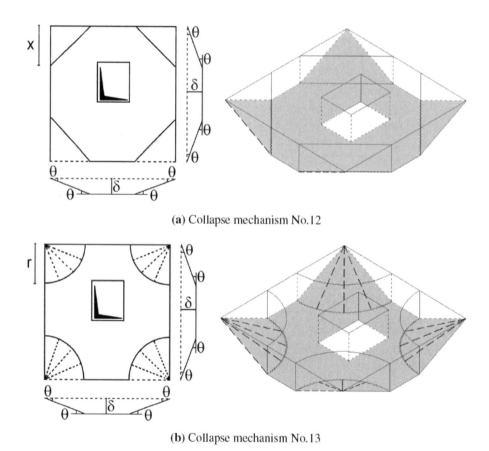

(a) Collapse mechanism No.12

(b) Collapse mechanism No.13

Figure 9 – Punching-controlled mechanisms No.12 and 13 (plan view and 3D presentation).

The value of the collapse load is as follows:

$$p_{u13} = 81 \ kN \ / \ m^2$$

In Figure 9b, the diagrams of the virtual displacements refer to the sections aligned with the longitudinal and transversal edges of the slab. For the expression of the collapse load, see Table 3b (Appendix II).

(**) As in the previous case, since for r = 0 no mechanism can form (because of kinematic incompatibility) and the collapse load is rather constant close to x = 0 (Fig.12d), the circular yield lines may form at a distance not smaller than r = d/(2 cos45°) from the axes of the columns, where d is the side of the square sections (= circular yield lines tangent to the sections of the columns and passing through the corners). Of course, the position of the circular yield lines is highly questionable.

## 4.15 Summary of the results

In Table 2, for each collapse mechanism (first column) the key parameters and the type of collapse are indicated, as follows:

- The type of collapse (second column), "global" with the simultaneous failure of the two slab fields or "local" with the failure of a single field (the local failure does not exclude the simultaneous failure of the two fields).

- The collapse load $p_u$ (third column), assuming that no load be applied on the cut-out area, see Figure 4b.

| Mechanism | Collapse | $p_u$ $[kN/m^2]$ | $p_u^*$ $[kN/m^2]$ |
|---|---|---|---|
| 1 | Local | 71 | 62 |
| 2 | Global | 50 | 43 |
| 3 | Local | 198 | 164 |
| 4 | Local | 115 | 96 |
| 5 | Global | 102 | 87 |
| 6 | Global | 93 | 84 |
| 7 | Global | 131 | 119 |
| 8 | Local | 127 | 113 |
| 9 | Local | 115 | 102 |
| 10 | Global | 106 | 96 |
| 11 | Global | 102 | 92 |
| 12 | Global | 77 | 71 |
| 13 | Global | 81 | 75 |

Table 2 - Summary of the collapse types and of the collapse loads.

- The collapse load $p_u^*$ (fourth column), assuming that the full load be applied on the area of the cut-out (Figure 4a), which means that the slab bears also the load distributed over the cut-out area, with the the cut-out providing no resistant moments to the slab. Note that including the load acting on the cut-out area leads to a decrease of the collapse load, comprised between -8% and -17% (average value -12%).

The ultimate loads plotted in Figure 10 show that the most probable collapse mechanism is No.2.

In Appendix II (see Table 4) there are the expressions of the collapse loads for the different mechanisms considering the load applied on the cut-out.

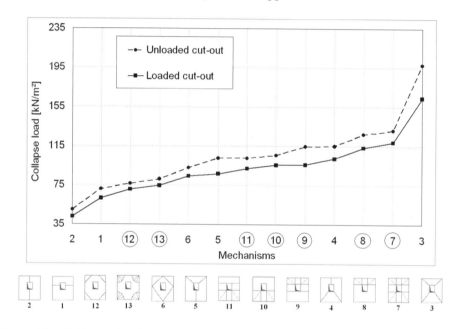

Figure 10 - Collapse loads. For the slab in question, the collapse load is $p_{u2}$ = 43-50 kN/m$^2$ (with/without the load acting on the cut-outs, Table 2). Numbers within circles refer to punching-related mechanisms.

According to the plan view of Fig.3, the mass of the two silos (120.000 kg) and of the slab (45-48.000 kg, with/without cut-outs) exerts a distributed load $p_d$ on the slab close to 30 kN/m$^2$. Hence, under the service loads the safety coefficient $p_{u2}/p_d$ is 1.43-1.67 (with/without the load acting on the cut-outs). This range of values agrees with code requirements, but since the Yield-Line Method provides upper-bound values for the collapse load, the actual safety factor is smaller, and a more refined analysis should be carried out (see – for instance – Gambarova et al., 2008), taking into consideration the favorable contributions of the cantilever strips placed along the sides of the slab (Bamonte and Gambarova, 2009).

## 5. PARAMETRIC ANALYSIS

As previously mentioned, the sensitivity of the collapse mechanisms - and related collapse load – is here investigated with reference to the ratio between the limit moments developed by the top and bottom bars, respectively. The objective is to ascertain to what extent the ratio $(m^-/m^+)$ can modify the mutual relationship among the various collapse mechanisms so far investigated, with obvious consequences on the collapse loads.

Five different values of the negative limit moment are considered, while the positive limit moment is kept constant; for each value of the $(m^-/m^+)$ ratio, the collapse load is calculated without the load acting on the cut-out area:

- $m^+ = 213 \text{ kNm/m}$   ;   $m^-/m^+ = 0.25 - 0.50 - 0.75 - 1.00 - 1.25.$

Looking at Fig.11, the following remarks can be made:

- In all cases, mechanism 2 is the most probable collapse mechanism;

- Mechanisms 2 and 5 are unaffected by the limit-moment ratio, since the negative limit moment does not contribute to the internal work;

- The smaller the $m^-/m^+$ ratio, the smaller the ultimate load;

- Among the punching-controlled mechanisms, reducing $m^-/m^+$ makes mechanism 13 *(with fan-type yield lines)* smaller than mechanism 12 *(with straight yield lines)*.

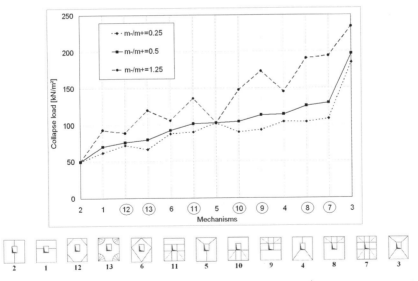

Figure 11 - Comparison between the extreme cases $(m^-/m^+ = 0.25$ and $1.25)$ and the reference case $(m^-/m^+ = 0.50)$. No load applied on the cut-out (see Fig.4b). Numbers within circles refer to punching-related mechanisms.

327

## 6. CONCLUSIONS

This paper demonstrates once more the efficacy of the Yield-Line Method within the kinematic theorem of the Theory of Plasticity. Through a worked example, that is at the same time rather simple and rather general, this technical note is also an "open invitation" to many designers to take advantage of such a powerful and handy approach.

The Yield-Line Method may be considered as a "quick" means to have useful information on the ultimate structural behavior of R/C slabs, with the added unvaluable merit of providing a physical insight into the collapse mode. Furthermore, the value of the collapse load worked out with the yield lines may be a reference value for the results obtained by means of more or less complex codes based on either linear or nonlinear analysis.

Moreover, since – with certain limitations - the Yield-Line Method is a tool for optimizing the reinforcement, the steel amounts and arrangement worked out in this way may also be a reference for various R/C optimization problems, solved by means of linear-programming methods.

In the present work, different flexural collapse mechanisms have been investigated, some being bending-controlled and some punching-controlled. The results show that the most critical bending-controlled collapse mechanisms are those characterized by the simplest kinematics, i.e. with the smallest number of yield lines. As for the punching-controlled mechanisms, the most critical are those with the yield lines "cutting" the corners.

Finally, the parametric analysis carried out to investigate the role of the ratio between the top and bottom reinforcement (for the same bottom reinforcement), shows that the order of the mechanisms – from the weakest to the strongest in terms of collapse load - may change by varying the top reinforcement, something that (a) should be expected, but that is seldom considered by designers, and (b) may help in optimizing the reinforcement.

## ACKNOWLEDGEMENTS

The results presented in this technical note were obtained by the authors in partial fulfillment of the requirements of the PhD course in Structural, Seismic and Geotechnical Engineering of the Politecnico di Milano.

## REFERENCES

Bamonte P. And Gambarova P.G. (2009). "Analysis at the Ultimate State of a R/C Slab Supporting Desiccated-Sludge Silos". *European Journal of Civil and Environmental Engineering – EJCEE*, V.13, No.6, pp. 685-706.

Chen W.F. (1982). *Plasticity in Reinforced Concrete.* McGraw Hill.

EC-2 (2003). *Eurocode 2: Design of Concrete Structures - Part 1-1: General Rules and Rules for Buildings.* European Committee for Standardization (CEN).

Favre R., Jaccoud J.P., Koprna M. and Radojicic A. (1990). *Dimensionnement des Structures en Béton – Dalles, Murs, Colonnes et Fondations"(Design of Concrete Structures – Slabs, Walls, Columns and Foundations, in French).* Presses Polytechniques et Universiateires Romandes, Lausanne (Switzerland).

Ferguson P.M., Breen J.E. and Jirsa J.O. (1988). *Reinforced Concrete Fundamentals.* John Wiley & Sons.

Gambarova P.G., Coronelli D. and Bamonte P (2008). *Guidelines for R/C Slab Design (in Italian).* Patron Editore (Bologna, Italy).

Hillerborg A. (1996). *Strip Method Design Handbook.* Spon, London.

Johansen K.W. (1962). *Yield-Line Theory.* Cement and Concrete Association.

Johansen K.W. (1972). *Yield-Line Formulae for Slabs.* Cement and Concrete Association.

Krause U. (2009). *Fires in Silos: Hazard, Prevention and Fire Fighting.* Ernst & Sohn.

Moy S.S.J (1981). *Plastic Methods for Steel and Concrete Structures.* The MacMillan Press.

Nielsen M.P. (1984). *Limit Analysis and Concrete Plasticity.* Prentice-Hall.

Park R. and Gamble W.L. (2000). *Reinforced Concrete Slabs.* John Wiley and Sons.

## APPENDIX I – Minimization of the collapse load

Mechanisms No. 1, 6, 12 and 13 require the minimization of the collapse load to identify the unknown geometrical parameter and the relative collapse load, that is the "true" collapse load. In Figs. 12a-d the collapse load is plotted as a function of the unknown parameter; the minimums give at the same time the value of the unknown parameter and the collapse load.

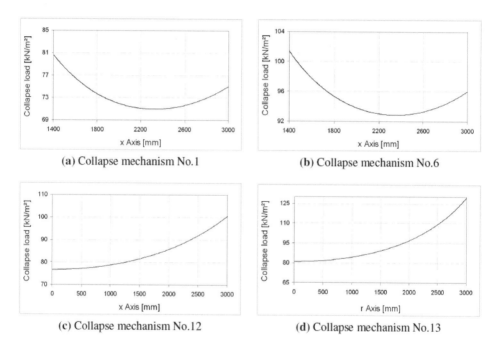

(a) Collapse mechanism No.1

(b) Collapse mechanism No.6

(c) Collapse mechanism No.12

(d) Collapse mechanism No.13

Figure 12 – Plots of the collapse load as a function of the unknown geometrical parameter, whose values correspond to as many kinematically-admissible collapse mechanisms.

## APPENDIX II – Expressions of the collapse load

---

$$p_{u1}(x) =$$
$$= \frac{m^+(a-a')(\theta_1+\theta_2)+m^- a\theta_2}{\left[\frac{1}{2}(b-x)a+\frac{1}{2}xa\right]-\left[a'(x-c)\frac{c}{x}+\frac{1}{2}(x-c)a'\left(1-\frac{c}{x}\right)+a'(b-x-d)\frac{d}{b-x}+\frac{1}{2}(b-x-d)a'\left(1-\frac{d}{b-x}\right)\right]}$$
$$\theta_1 = \frac{\delta}{x} \qquad \theta_2 = \frac{\delta}{(b-x)}$$

---

$$p_{u2}(x) =$$
$$= \frac{m^+(b-b')2\theta}{\left[\frac{1}{2}ab\right]-2\left[\frac{1}{2}a'b'\frac{a-a'}{a}+\frac{1}{4}a'b'\left(1-\frac{a-a'}{a}\right)\right]}$$
$$\theta = \frac{2\delta}{a}$$

---

$$p_{u3}(x) =$$
$$= \frac{2m^+d\theta_3+2m^+c\theta_3+m^+(a-a')\theta_2+m^+(a-a')\theta_1+m^- a\theta_2}{4\left[\frac{1}{12}c(a-a')\right]+\left[\frac{1}{12}d(a-a')\right]+\frac{1}{2}ca'+\frac{1}{2}da'+2\left[\frac{1}{4}b'(a-a')\right]}$$
$$\theta_1 = \frac{\delta}{c} \qquad \theta_2 = \frac{\delta}{d} \qquad \theta_3 = \frac{2\delta}{(a-a')}$$

---

$$p_{u4}(x) =$$
$$= \frac{2m^+d\theta_1+m^+(a-a')\theta_2+m^+c2\theta_1+m^- a\theta_2}{\left[a\frac{b-d'}{2}+\frac{a}{3}d'\right]-2\left[\frac{a'}{2}(b-d'-c)\left(1-\frac{a'}{a}\right)+\frac{a'}{2}(d'-d)\left(1-\frac{a'}{a}\right)+\frac{a'^2}{4a}(b-d'-c)+\frac{a'^2}{6a}(d'-d)\right]}$$
$$\theta_1 = \frac{2\delta}{a} \qquad \theta_2 = \frac{(a-a')\delta}{ad}$$

---

$$p_{u5}(x) =$$
$$= \frac{2m^+d2\theta_2+m^+(a-a')\theta_1+2m^+c\theta_2}{\left[a\frac{b-d'}{2}+\frac{a}{3}d'\right]-2\left[\frac{a'}{2}(d'-c)\left(1-\frac{a'}{a}\right)+\frac{a'}{2}(b-d'-d)\left(1-\frac{a'}{a}\right)+\frac{a'^2}{4a}(b-d'-d)+\frac{a'^2}{6a}(d'-c)\right]}$$
$$\theta_1 = \frac{(a-a')\delta}{ac} \qquad \theta_2 = \frac{2\delta}{a}$$

---

$$p_{u6}(x) =$$
$$= \frac{2m^+(b-x)\theta_3+m^+ a\theta_2+2m^+ x\theta_3+m^+ a\theta_1+m^- a\theta_2}{\frac{5}{6}ab-a'b'}$$
$$\theta_1 = \frac{\delta}{x} \qquad \theta_2 = \frac{\delta}{b-x} \qquad \theta_3 = \frac{2\delta}{a}$$

---

Table 3a – Collapse loads for the bending-controlled mechanisms No.1-6 (no load applied on the cut-out).

$$p_{u7}(x) =$$
$$= \frac{2m^- d\theta_3 + 2m^- c\theta_3 + m^-(a-a')\theta_2 + m^-(a-a')\theta_1 + m^+(a-a')\theta_1 + m^+(a-a')\theta_2 + 2m^+ c\theta_3 + 2m^+ d\theta_3}{[ab] - \left[a'b' + \frac{1}{3}c(a-a') + \frac{1}{3}d(a-a')\right]}$$

$$\theta_1 = \frac{\delta}{c} \quad \theta_2 = \frac{\delta}{d} \quad \theta_3 = \frac{2\delta}{(a-a')}$$

$$p_{u8}(x) =$$
$$= \frac{m^- a\theta_2 + 2m^- c\theta_3 + m^-(a-a')\theta_1 + 2m^+ c\theta_3 + m^+(a-a')(\theta_1+\theta_2)}{[ab] - \left[\frac{1}{3}(a-a')c + \frac{1}{2}a(b'+d) + a'b' - a'\frac{b'^2}{2(b'+d)}\right]}$$

$$\theta_1 = \frac{\delta}{c} \quad \theta_2 = \frac{\delta}{b-c} \quad \theta_3 = \frac{2\delta}{(a-a')}$$

$$p_{u9}(x) =$$
$$= \frac{m^- a\theta_2 + 2m^- c\theta_3 + m^-(a-a')\theta_1 + 2m^+ c\theta_3 + m^+(a-a')\theta_1 + m^+(a-a')\theta_2}{[ab] - \left[\frac{1}{3}c(a-a') + \frac{1}{2}ad + a'b'\right]}$$

$$\theta_1 = \frac{\delta}{c} \quad \theta_2 = \frac{\delta}{d} \quad \theta_3 = \frac{2\delta}{(a-a')}$$

$$p_{u10}(x) =$$
$$= \frac{2m^- d\theta_3 + m^-(a-a')\theta_2 + m^+(a-a')(\theta_1+\theta_2) + 2m^+ d\theta_3}{[ab] - \left[\frac{1}{3}d(a-a') + a'b' + \frac{1}{2}(b-d)a - \frac{1}{2}\frac{b'^2}{b-d}a'\right]}$$

$$\theta_1 = \frac{\delta}{b-d} \quad \theta_2 = \frac{\delta}{d} \quad \theta_3 = \frac{2\delta}{(a-a')}$$

$$p_{u11}(x) =$$
$$= \frac{2m^- d\theta_3 + m^-(a-a')\theta_2 + m^+(a-a')\theta_1 + m^+(a-a')\theta_2 + 2m^+ d\theta_3}{[ab] - \left[\frac{1}{3}d(a-a') + \frac{1}{2}ac + a'b'\right]}$$

$$\theta_1 = \frac{\delta}{c} \quad \theta_2 = \frac{\delta}{d} \quad \theta_3 = \frac{2\delta}{(a-a')}$$

$$p_{u12}(x) =$$
$$= \frac{8m^+ x\theta + 2m^- x\theta}{[ab] - \left[a'b' + \frac{2}{3}x^2\right]}$$

$$\theta = \frac{\delta}{x}$$

$$p_{u13}(x) =$$
$$= \frac{2\pi(m^+ + m^-)}{[ab] - \left[a'b' + \frac{1}{3}\pi r^2\right]}$$

$$\theta = \frac{\delta}{r}$$

Table 3b - Collapse loads for the punching-controlled mechanisms No.7-13 (no load applied on the cut-out).

$$p_{u1}(x) =$$
$$= \frac{m^+(a-a')(\theta_1+\theta_2)+m^-a\theta_2}{\left[ab-\frac{1}{2}xa-\frac{1}{2}a(b-x)\right]}$$
$$\theta_1 = \frac{\delta}{x} \qquad \theta_2 = \frac{\delta}{(b-x)}$$

$$p_{u2}(x) =$$
$$= \frac{m^+(b-b')2\theta}{\frac{1}{2}ab}$$
$$\theta = \frac{2\delta}{a}$$

$$p_{u3}(x) =$$
$$= \frac{2m^+d\theta_3+2m^+c\theta_3+m^+(a-a')\theta_2+m^+(a-a')\theta_1+m^-a\theta_2}{\left[\frac{1}{2}a'(c+d)+a'b'+\frac{1}{6}(a-a')(2c+3b'+2d)\right]}$$
$$\theta_1 = \frac{\delta}{c} \qquad \theta_2 = \frac{\delta}{d} \qquad \theta_3 = \frac{2\delta}{(a-a')}$$

$$p_{u4}(x) =$$
$$= \frac{2m^+d\theta_1+m^+(a-a')\theta_2+m^+c2\theta_1+m^-a\theta_2}{\left[\frac{1}{2}ab-\frac{1}{6}\frac{a^2d}{a-a'}\right]}$$
$$\theta_1 = \frac{2\delta}{a} \qquad \theta_2 = \frac{(a-a')\delta}{ad}$$

$$p_{u5}(x) =$$
$$= \frac{2m^+d2\theta_2+m^+(a-a')\theta_1+2m^+c\theta_2}{\left[\frac{1}{2}ab-\frac{1}{6}\frac{a^2c}{a-a'}\right]}$$
$$\theta_1 = \frac{(a-a')\delta}{ac} \qquad \theta_2 = \frac{2\delta}{a}$$

$$p_{u6}(x) =$$
$$= \frac{2m^+(b-x)\theta_3+m^+a\theta_2+2m^+x\theta_3+m^+a\theta_1+m^-a\theta_2}{\frac{5}{6}ab}$$
$$\theta_1 = \frac{\delta}{x} \qquad \theta_2 = \frac{\delta}{b-x} \qquad \theta_3 = \frac{2\delta}{a}$$

Table 4a – Collapse loads for the bending-controlled mechanisms No.1-6 (load applied on the cut-out).

$$p_{u7}(x) =$$
$$= \frac{2m^- d\theta_3 + 2m^- c\theta_3 + m^- (a-a')\theta_2 + m^- (a-a')\theta_1 + m^+ (a-a')\theta_1 + m^+ (a-a')\theta_2 + 2m^+ c\theta_3 + 2m^+ d\theta_3}{[ab] - \left[\frac{1}{3}d(a-a') + \frac{1}{3}c(a-a')\right]}$$
$$\theta_1 = \frac{\delta}{c} \quad \theta_2 = \frac{\delta}{d} \quad \theta_3 = \frac{2\delta}{(a-a')}$$

$$p_{u8}(x) =$$
$$= \frac{m^- a\theta_2 + 2m^- c\theta_3 + m^- (a-a')\theta_1 + 2m^+ c\theta_3 + m^+ (a-a')(\theta_1 + \theta_2)}{[ab] - \left[\frac{1}{2}a(d+b') + \frac{1}{3}c(a-a') - \frac{1}{2}\frac{a'b'^2}{d+b'}\right]}$$
$$\theta_1 = \frac{\delta}{c} \quad \theta_2 = \frac{\delta}{b-c} \quad \theta_3 = \frac{2\delta}{(a-a')}$$

$$p_{u9}(x) =$$
$$= \frac{m^- a\theta_2 + 2m^- c\theta_3 + m^- (a-a')\theta_1 + 2m^+ c\theta_3 + m^+ (a-a')\theta_1 + m^+ (a-a')\theta_2}{[ab] - \left[\frac{1}{3}c(a-a') + \frac{1}{2}ad\right]}$$
$$\theta_1 = \frac{\delta}{c} \quad \theta_2 = \frac{\delta}{d} \quad \theta_3 = \frac{2\delta}{(a-a')}$$

$$p_{u10}(x) =$$
$$= \frac{2m^- d\theta_3 + m^- (a-a')\theta_2 + m^+ (a-a')(\theta_1 + \theta_2) + 2m^+ d\theta_3}{[ab] - \left[\frac{1}{2}a(c+b') + \frac{1}{3}d(a-a') - \frac{1}{2}\frac{a'b'^2}{c+b'}\right]}$$
$$\theta_1 = \frac{\delta}{b-d} \quad \theta_2 = \frac{\delta}{d} \quad \theta_3 = \frac{2\delta}{(a-a')}$$

$$p_{u11}(x) =$$
$$= \frac{2m^- d\theta_3 + m^- (a-a')\theta_2 + m^+ (a-a')\theta_1 + m^+ (a-a')\theta_2 + 2m^+ d\theta_3}{[ab] - \left[\frac{1}{3}d(a-a') + \frac{1}{2}ac\right]}$$
$$\theta_1 = \frac{\delta}{c} \quad \theta_2 = \frac{\delta}{d} \quad \theta_3 = \frac{2\delta}{(a-a')}$$

$$p_{u12}(x) =$$
$$= \frac{8m^+ x\theta + 2m^- x\theta}{[ab] - \frac{2}{3}x^2}$$
$$\theta = \frac{\delta}{x}$$

$$p_{u13}(x) =$$
$$= \frac{2\pi(m^+ + m^-)}{[ab] - \frac{1}{3}\pi r^2}$$
$$\theta = \frac{\delta}{r}$$

Table 4b – Collapse loads for the punching-controlled mechanisms No.7-13 (load applied on the cut-out).

STUDIES AND RESEARCHES – V.29, 2009
Graduate School in Concrete Structures – Fratelli Pesenti
Politecnico di Milano, Italy

# DAMAGE ASSESSMENT IN THE VELASCA TOWER OF MILAN : A PROCEDURAL APPROACH

Paola Ronca[1], Luca Bertolini[2], Pietro Crespi[3], Antonio Migliacci[1], Federica Lollini[4], Elena Redaelli[4]

## ABSTRACT

The mechanical properties and the potential of reinforced concrete as a major structural material appeared clearly at the beginning of the XX Century. Since then, concrete revolutionary and appealing characteristics have favored the scientific and technological progress in the construction field, as demonstrated by the many well-known names of architects and engineers active in the early decades of the past century. The architectural works of that period started a new architectural style, and paved the way to the so-called "Modern Movement".

However, the scientific interest and the great amount of work done in the domain of historical monuments had the effect of diverting the attention from the development of a specific culture on modern heritage restoration.

Such lack of attention, however, clashes with the sensitivity to degradation of the materials used in modern structures and in the finishing details of their façades. Hence, having specific guidelines for the inspection procedures and maintenance techniques to be adopted in "Modern Heritage" is one of today's top priorities in Architecture and Civil Engineering.

These open issues are treated in this paper, where first the most relevant steps required to set appropriate procedures in damage assessment are recalled, and later the mostly chemical tests – and their results – concerning corrosion effects are presented and discussed, with reference to the façade panels and structural members of the Torre Velasca high-rise building in Milan.

---

[1] Professor, Department of Structural Engineering
[2] Professor, Department of Materials Chemistry and Chemical Engineering
[3] Assistant Professor, Department of Structural Engineering
[4] Assistant Professor, Dept. of Materials Chemistry and Chemical Engineering
  Politecnico di Milano, Milan, Italy

# 1. INTRODUCTION

Milan is recognized as one of the most significant urban example in Europe of the 20th Century new deal in Architecture, because of either its "neo-liberty buildings", or the more recent buildings designed within the rationalist framework, the so-called "Modern Movement". Many well-known architects, still mentioned at the international level, worked in Milan and left in downtown outstanding examples of buildings designed and built between the twenties and the sixties of the last century.

Representative names of the Modern Movement, among the many, are Albini, Gardella, Ponti and the BBPR Group, i.e. Banfi-Belgioioso-Peressuti-Rogers, who worked mostly in Milan. One of the best building is Torre Velasca, tht was among the first tall buildings built in Italy.

As it is well known, the Modern Movement has its roots in the increasing confidence of both Engineers and Architects in dealing with the peculiar properties of concrete and reinforced-concrete members, and in the increasing attention (especially from the Architects) to the social aspects of their work, this being typical of the period immediately past the First World War.

The great attention devoted at the turn of the 19th Century and at the beginning of the 20th Century to steel as a new material, that suited new architectural shapes, gave the opportunity to design large-span, tall and slender buildings, something never achieved in the history of constructions.

In spite of their representing the highest expression of recent Italian architecture - in terms of quality of the design and distinction of the authors -, these buildings still need to be recognized as a cultural asset, and still are waiting for the dignity and respect reserved to historical architecture.

With regard to the latter point, Italian architecture, a model for centuries, was mostly ignored by the European culture in the decades before and after the beginning of the 20th Century, since the Eclectism of that period was in Italy more a rhetorical imitation of the past styles, than a critical and intelligent historical interpretation, as occurred in Great Britain.

At the same time, Italy was not touched by the Liberty, which arrived much later, after the many successes this revolutionary and provocative style had obtained in other countries, like Belgium and Austria. In Italy, the Liberty was rather a formal and uncritical movement.

Only Rationalist Architecture, also born in the northern countries, was interpreted with originality and got some autonomy, that gave the Italian designers the opportunity to interact at par with the European artistic avant-garde culture.

Buildings erected in that period in Italy, however, are not highly regarded, in spite of their historical and artistic relevance, and have been often modified, altered, abandoned or even destroyed.

The problems affecting modern architecture can be subdivided into four categories (Artioli, 2009):

(a) negligence from managers, owners and those responsible for the tutelage, who do not consider modern architecture as belonging to "monuments".

(b) structural fragility - and therefore limited resistance to time wearing - because of some peculiar characteristics, either typological (flat roofs, absence of waterproofing systems and gutters, sharp corners), or technological (use of new, hardly tested materials), or even ideological (buildings are a "product", thought and designed to have a certain useful life, i.e. to be worn out by the use);

(c) difficulties during the restoration phase in finding the original materials, whose production has already been discontinued and whose reproduction is not possible;

(d) lack of education concerning the specific problems brought in by the restoration of "modern" architecture, because of lack of experience and poor circulation (so far) of data about the experience accumulated on the methodologies and materials to be used in this particular field.

Within this framework, the paper describes the comprehensive approach, that has been adopted for the assessment of the rather compromised conditions of the "Torre Velasca" tall building in Milan.

## 2. THE SIGNIFICANCE AND ACTUALITY OF TORRE VELASCA

The Torre Velasca building (simply called "the tower" in the following), which is 106 m tall, can be divided in three zones: (1) the zone from the ground level to the $15^{th}$ floor, with a rectangular plan (21.08 m × 38.46 m); (2) the zone from the $16^{th}$ to the $18^{th}$ floor characterized by the presence of a system of strut and tie beams which support the expanded zone above; and (3) the zone from the $19^{th}$ to the $26^{th}$ floor (27.04 m × 44.78 m), see Fig. 1a.

The tower is centered around a core, characterized by reinforced-concrete walls. The perimeter of the tower is exhibit a number of slender pilasters, that spread out in the form of inclined struts from the $15^{th}$ to the $18^{th}$ floor, to support - together with a couple of tie-beams - the upper projecting part of the building (Fig. 1b). The façade pattern is marked by the presence of small pilasters, parapets, prefabricated panels and window ledges. According to the available documentation, the visible R/C structural members (pilasters, struts and tie beams) are coated with a cement plaster containing red crushed Verona marble, while small pilasters, parapets and window ledges are entirely made of a concrete containing the same crushed Verona marble (from the archives of the owner Immobiliare Lombarda S.p.A.).

The tower, that is still a cornerstone in the debate about the issues of modern architecture, is worldwide recognized as an outstanding and innovative example of the evolution of the Modern Movement in the Fifties. Immediately after its construction, however, the innovative aspects of the tower aroused some criticism (Samonà, 1959; Patané, 1960) by those who stigmatized the discontinuity in the urban context, as well as by the supporters of the so-called orthodoxy within the Modern Movement.

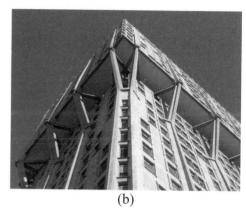

(a)                                                      (b)

Figure 1 - View of the Torre Velasca (a); and of its expanded top (b).

It should also be remembered that the design and construction processes took eight years, a rather long period, which was characterized by a remarkable evolution of the European Rationalism, because of the opportunities offered by the improving knowledge of materials physical, mechanical and structural properties. A clear sign of this evolution can be found in the previous design proposals for the Torre Velasca, published past its construction (Fiori and Prizzon, 1982).

These proposals show the many challenging issues, that the designers had to face and that are still highly debated in terms of architectural and engineering aspects. (Which is the best material in tall buildings: steel or reinforced concrete?, see Fiori and Prizzon, 1982; however, nowadays both solutions are equally good, after the introduction of high-performance concrete).

As a matter of fact, at the beginning of the Fifties, few examples could be found of tall buildings with their structural skeleton made of reinforced concrete, since the vast majority had a steel skeleton. For such reason, BBPR architects went to South America to have first-hand information on reinforced-concrete skyscrapers and on their response under wind action.

The final structural solution was progressively found through the strict cooperation between the architects and the structural engineers (Prof. Arturo Danusso recognized that he had never worked with such static-oriented architects, see Fiori and Prizzon, 1982).

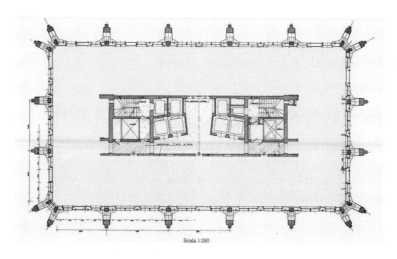

Figure 2 – Structural plan view of the Torre Velasca (15th floor).

Among the most significant details, that confirm the actuality of the tower, are such innovative (and still adopted) structural and architectural solutions as the central core and the peripheral sequence of the pilasters (Fig. 2), and the widespread use of pre-cast industrialized R/C finishing elements. The formal sequence of the façades consists of a series of visible vertical and horizontal main structural elements, with the characteristic inclination of the pilasters/struts from the 15th to the 18th floor, and the inter-storey peripheral beams, together with the partitioning non-structural members (called "small pilasters" or "pilastrini" in the original drawings) and the marble-grit panels (Fig. 3).

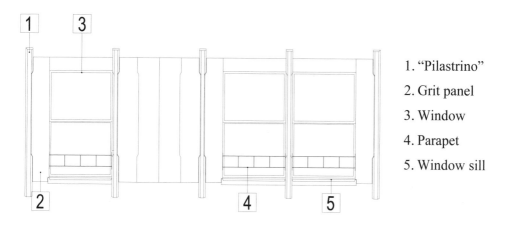

1. "Pilastrino"
2. Grit panel
3. Window
4. Parapet
5. Window sill

Figure 3 - The precast elements of the façade ("pilastrino" = small pilaster)

With particular reference to the small pilasters and to the marble-grit panels (that are clearly self-bearing elements), the next chapter will describe the steps of the procedure adopted for the damage assessment.

## 3. FIRST INSPECTION PHASE FOR DAMAGE ASSESSMENT

The significance of Torre Velasca, as a monument of Modern Heritage, has been briefly recalled in the previous chapter. Particular aspects of the building are the complexity of the interaction between the architectural and the structural frameworks, something that should be taken in due consideration to understand the steps of the procedure utilized in damage assessment (Ronca et al., 2009).

The damage-assessment challenging aspects of the so called "Historic Heritage" have attracted the attention of many researchers and scholars in the last decades and have been treated in a rather general way, since the issues about the most suitable inspection techniques and the acquisition/treatment of the results are still open discussion (Ronca et al., 2004).

Different approaches are required whenever the rehabilitation of modern architecture is at issue, not only because of materials variety, but also because of some peculiar aspects, not strictly related to materials and structures (CEB Bulletin n° 243, 1998; Fib TG 5.1, 2002; ISO2394, 1998).

(a)                                             (b)

Figure 4 – Inspecting anchor rebars of precast elements with a pachometer (a); and a driller (b).

For instance, the buildings born from the "Rationalism Movement" are characterized by formally-simple façades, compared to those of Historic Heritage, but the extensive use of industrialized overhanging façade elements (as in the case of Torre Velasca) are a source of great concern. Their durability-performance assessment is a challenging issue, not only because of visible material degradation and/or corrosion, but also because of the rather undefined connection systems to the load-bearing elements. Figure 4 shows some phases of the test campaign aimed at identifying the anchors of the main finishing components of the façades (the small pilasters and the marble-grit panels).

Even more than in historic heritage, the inspection procedures for the damage assessment in modern heritage should be non-destructive.

All these aspects should be taken into account in order to appropriately plan the tests, and to adopt the best - often unusual - techniques.

In the following, the initial phases of the damage-assessment procedure adopted in the case of Torre Velasca are briefly recalled, because of these phases being instrumental in planning the subsequent tests and in choosing the best suitable tools, according to a scale of priority. (For a detailed description of the tests, see the report issued by Consorzio CIS-E 2008 (CIS-E, 2008).

The phases of the damage-assessment procedure are as follows:

(a) identification of the geometry and of the materials, to compare the design documents and the in-situ situation; to this end, a complete drawing of the façade has been considered as a first necessary step; the tower was subdivided in three zones: A, B and C, to take into account the variability of the microclimate and of the layout, as shown in Figure 5;

(b) consultation of the documents about previous repairing interventions, and examination of their actual effectiveness and consistency, with specific reference to the repairing materials (R.A.S., 1995), see Figs. 6 and 7;

(c) observation of the cracks and of the spalling of the concrete;

(d) execution of mini-invasive tests and extraction of small cores to calibrate the non-destructive tests (specifically those aimed at locating the small bars required to connect the finishing façade elements to the structural members (Fig. 4);

(e) definition of the cores (number and location) to be tested;

(f) execution of the in-situ and laboratory tests (pull-out, chemical and electro-chemical tests), as shown in Figure 8;

(g) suggestions for reliable and sustainable repair interventions.

Of course, a specific team was set up, for inspecting the building, from the top to the bottom (Fig. 9), in order to give an answer to the previous points, and particularly to check the position of the different precast elements (Fig.5) and the consistency of previous repairing works (see Figures 6 and 7).

Cracking and spalling - or delamination - of the plaster layers were examined with special tools. The same was done to detect the direction and the size of the rebars, by using a pachometer, both in the main structural members and in the precast elements (Figure 10).

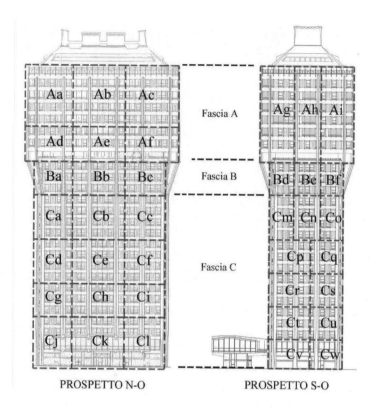

Figure 5 - Different levels of the façade.

Figure 6 – Details of previous repairing.

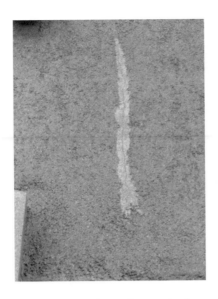

Figure 7 - Reopening of a repaired crack.

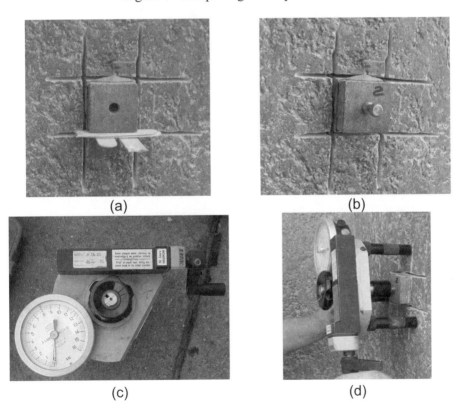

Figure 8 - Pull-out tests.

Figure 9 – Inspection team at work.

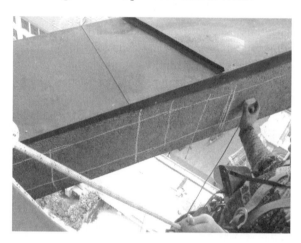

Figure 10 – Detection of the rebars.

The ultra-sonic technique gave various useful results, that were obtained by using at first a hammer in a few easily-accessible points. Then it was decided to perform some in-situ pull-out tests.

These tests gave very scattered results exhibiting rather low values for the adhesion of the bars to the concrete.

To have as much as possible information on the entire surface, an advanced and powerful technique based on thermography was used.

The instrumentation was set up for this specific purpose, but a special calibration procedure was necessary for the unusual distance from the source to the surface, in order to guarantee an appropriate precision, see Figs. 11 and 12 (Sineco, 2008).

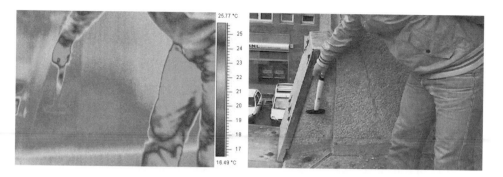

Figure 11 - In situ calibration of thermography (a) by means of manual hammer technique (b).

Figure 12 - Example of a thermographic survey.

Cores were extracted on the four sides of the tower, at different levels and on different elements, to check the thickness of the various layers (plaster, mortar and concrete), and to measure the depth of the carbonation attack (if any).

The main results obtained in the first phase of the damage-assessment activity can be summarized as follows:

345

- previously-repaired cracks tend to open again (Fig.7);

- inspecting the layers by coring is instrumental in checking the integrity and the consistency of the surface layers (Fig. 13);

- coring reveals a generalized light carbonation, but in few cores carbonation penetrated for 50 mm (in 13 cores out of 105; reference was made to the Italian norms UNI EN 14630, 2007);

- thermography reveals a leopard-skin distribution of the adhesion between the plaster layer and the underlying concrete, in agreement with the results of the pull-out tests (Fig.12);

- reinforcement degradation seems to be mainly limited to bar surface. (The quality of the concrete and the thickness of the cover were an effective barrier against carbonation).

Figure 13 - Example of a core (MAPEI Report, 2007).

Two main issues resulted from the tests performed in the first phase of the assessment:

- the need of a more extensive experimental campaign to better characterize the concrete subjected to carbonation and to predict the possible evolution of bar corrosion;

- the need of deeper checks on the small R/C pilasters belonging to the precast façade and on their anchors. (The large number of these small pilasters, their size and their architectural value, together with that of the contour elements of the windows, makes these checks rather demanding, Figs. 3 and 14).

It should be noted that the available drawings where unreliable with reference to the details of the anchors.

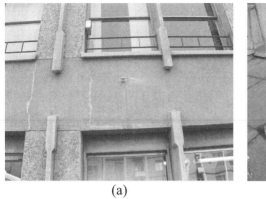 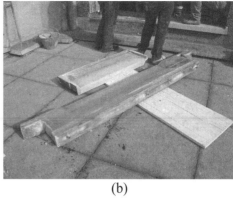

(a)                                                          (b)

Figure 14 - Details of the small pilasters (a); and a small pilaster after being removed (b).


## 4. ASSESSMENT OF THE CORROSION LEVEL

A first survey of the façades was carried out observing from the ground floor and from the surrounding buildings, in order to pinpoint any visible signs of deterioration and to locate accessible areas where on-site tests could be performed. A detailed inspection was carried out on the elements of the $2^{nd}$ floor of the N-W façade, but other elements of the same façade were observed as well (at $6^{th}$, $10^{th}$, $14^{th}$, $18^{th}$, $23^{rd}$ and $25^{th}$ floor), together with some of the S-W façade (at $6^{th}$, $10^{th}$ and $18^{th}$ floor).

The inspection of the façades highlighted some cracking in the plaster of the main pilasters. Most of these cracks were sealed in the past (probably in 1978-1979) with a white product, which makes them clearly visible. Similar cracks were visible on beams, tie-beams and struts (Fig. 6 and 7). No clear signs of corrosion-induced damage (such as concrete spalling with exposed rebars or rust stains) were observed on the structural elements and the causes of plaster cracking were uncertain.

Sealed cracks were also observed on the decorative elements, such as the small pilasters and panels; also the joints of the panels were sealed, although no previous corrosion-related phenomena could be observed on the external surface. The small pilasters, the parapets and the window ledges, however, showed evidence of corrosion, such as cracking and rust stains. In particular, the small pilasters and the parapets of the $25^{th}$ floor showed considerable damage due to rebar corrosion, in spite of the extensive repairing performed in the past.

A few cores were extracted from some selected structural elements, in order to better ascertain the cause of corrosion and to determine the origin of the cracks visible on the outer surface of the plaster layer.

The analyses performed on concrete cores showed that neither chlorides nor other substances (generally responsible for concrete chemical attack) were present, and that the corrosion of the reinforcement induced by concrete carbonation was the only form of deterioration in R/C members (Bertolini et al., 2008). (Concrete carbonation is a natural process that reduces concrete alkalinity. The latter protects the reinforcement from corrosion, but – should concrete alkalinity be reduced or even zeroed – reinforcement corrosion would start and rapidly progress, see Bertolini et al., 2004).

## 4.1 Materials stratification

The cores were analyzed to better investigate the various layers (in terms of thickness and materials) covering the reinforcement.

The observation of the cores extracted from the pilasters lead to the identification of three layers: an external plaster layer (P), an intermediate mortar layer (M1) and the core made of structural concrete (C1), see Fig. 15a.

The plaster layer was usually adherent to the mortar layer, that looked very dense. Conversely, the mortar layer was here and there detached from the underlying concrete. The external surface of the plaster layer was protected by means of an acrylic coating (probably applied during in 1978-1979, see Bertolini et al., 2008).

Figure 16 shows the frequency distribution of the thickness of the three layers (P, M1 and C1), that were measured on 45 cores extracted from the pilasters. The most representative values of the thickness are 10-15 mm for P, and 10-25 mm for M1.

The thickness of each layer, however, was rather variable, and so the total thickness of the two layers. For instance, there were values as low as 15 mm and values as thick as 40 mm. The cores extracted from other structural elements (parapet beams, struts and tie-beams) exhibited a similar stratification (Table 1).

| Element | # | P | | | M1 | | |
|---|---|---|---|---|---|---|---|
| | | m | M | σ | M | M | σ |
| Pillars | 45 | 5 | 27 | 13 | 5 | 50 | 16 |
| Beams | 14 | 5 | 25 | 13 | 6 | 40 | 19 |
| Struts | 2 | 13 | 15 | 14 | 6 | 30 | 18 |
| Tie-beams | 4 | 7 | 17 | 12 | 18 | 25 | 21 |

Table 1 - Number of data (#), minimum (m), maximum (M) and average ($\sigma$) values of the thickness (mm) of the plaster layer (P) and of the mortar layer (M1) measured on cores extracted from the structural members.

As for the decorative elements, the 27 cores extracted from the small pilasters and from the parapets showed the presence of a single material, a mortar containing small red aggregate particles, which was conventionally designated as M2 (Fig. 15b). The external surface of the cores was covered with either an opaque paint (cores taken from floors 20th-25th) or an acrylic coating (cores from lower floors).

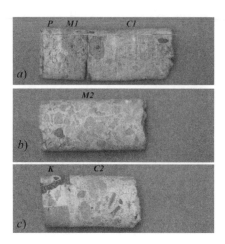

Figure 15 - Cores ($\varnothing$ = 26 mm) extracted from a main pilaster (a), from a small pilaster (b), and from a panel (c), and designation of the layers.

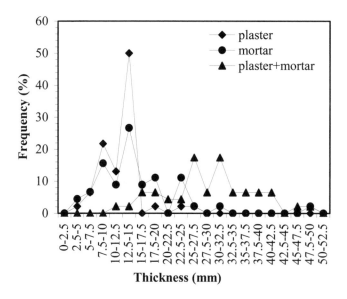

Figure 16 - Distribution of the thickness of plaster (P) and mortar (M1) layers measured on 45 cores extracted from the main pilasters.

Finally, the 19 cores extracted from the prefabricated panels showed the presence of two layers, see Fig. 15c: (1) an external layer made of klinker (K) containing yellow and red ceramic fragments, as well as small red particles, all dispersed in a matrix of cement paste (thickness ranging from 10 to 22 mm; average value = 16 mm) and (2) the underlying layer of concrete (C2).

## 4.2 Carbonation depth

The phenolphtalein test used to measure the carbonation depth (Fig. 17) showed that in the main pilasters the plaster layer P was always fully carbonated, while in the mortar layer M1 and in the concrete C1 the carbonation depth ranged from 0 to 25 mm, and from 2 to 17 mm, respectively.

The total carbonation depth measured from the external surface (i.e. including the thicknesses of P and M1) was between 0 and 45 mm (Fig. 18). Some cores, however, showed an anomalous carbonation, i.e. plaster layers partially or fully alkaline and mortar layers severely carbonated. Two reasons may be cited: the replacement of the plaster layer during previous repair works (although no visual differences were observed in the materials), and the propagation of the carbonation at the interface between the mortar layer and the concrete, since the former was in many zones detached from the latter. (These carbonation depths were not included in the frequency analysis).

The same carbonation levels were found in the beams, struts and tie-beams (Table 2), where both the plaster and mortar layers were often fully carbonated, while negligible carbonation was observed in the concrete.

Figure 17 - Phenolphthalein test on a core extracted from a main pilaster.

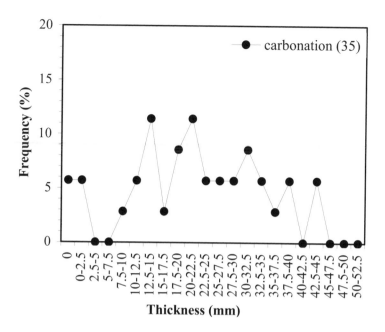

Figure 18 - Distribution of the carbonation depth measured on 35 cores extracted from the main pilasters.

Moreover, carbonation depth was not significantly influenced by such factors as the type of the structural element, the vertical distance from the ground level and the orientation of the façade (Bertolini, 2008). Since pilasters, beams, struts and tie-beams had the reinforcement covered by the same materials and the same carbonation depth, it is reasonable to assume that the structural elements have the same resistance to carbonation.

| Element | # | C | | |
|---|---|---|---|---|
| | | m | M | Σ |
| Main pilasters | 35 | 0 | 45 | 22 |
| Beams | 12 | 5 | 56 | 28 |
| Struts | 2 | 13 | 49 | 31 |
| Tie-beams | 4 | 0 | 43 | 26 |
| Small pilasters | 22 | 0 | >60 | >21 |
| Panels | 18 | 27 | >80 | >52 |

Table 2 - Number of data (#), minimum (m), maximum (M) and average (σ) values of the total carbonation depth c, (mm) measured on cores.

The carbonation depth of the small pilasters (mortar M2) was highly variable, with values ranging from 0 mm (completely alkaline mortar) to 60 mm (equal to core size, Table 2). Two cores were extracted from window ledges and parapets close to the reinforcement. The outer part of the cores was alkaline, while the inner part in contact with the corroded reinforcement was carbonated, as if the outer material had been replaced in the past.

Last but not least, the cores extracted from the prefabricated panels were severely carbonated (Table 2).

## 4.3  Concrete cover

The cover depth of the outermost reinforcing bars was detected in all elements (structural and decorative) by means of a magnetic-type covermeter. The depth of the rebars was always measured from the external surface (hence, it includes the plaster and mortar layers, if any).

In both the stirrups and the longitudinal rebars the cover exhibited a marked variability: for instance, in the main pilasters the cover of the stirrups varied between 25 and 60 mm, while the cover of the longitudinal rebars was comprised between 40 and 70 mm (Fig. 19).

The cover of the stirrups and of the longitudinal rebars in the beams, struts and tie-beams had characteristics similar to those of of the main pilasters (Table 3).

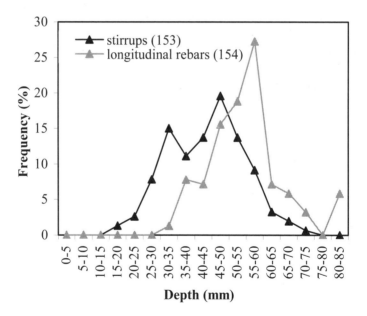

Figure 19 - Cover-thickness distribution in the reinforcement of the main pilasters (sample number between brackets).

| Element | Stirrups | | | | Longitudinal rebars | | | |
|---|---|---|---|---|---|---|---|---|
| | # | m | M | σ | # | m | M | σ |
| Main pilasters | 153 | 20 | 75 | 44 | 154 | 35 | 85 | 56 |
| Beams | 77 | 22 | 80 | 42 | 115 | 30 | 85 | 56 |
| Struts | 60 | 23 | 68 | 37 | 47 | 22 | 75 | 34 |
| Tie-beams | 27 | 19 | 42 | 31 | 19 | 23 | 44 | 33 |
| Small pilasters | 100 | 5 | 57 | 27 | 24 | 8 | 46 | 24 |
| Window ledges | 24 | 8 | 48 | 31 | 23 | 17 | 50 | 32 |
| Parapets | 27 | 10 | 26 | 18 | 14 | 15 | 31 | 25 |
| Panels | 23 | 19 | 28 | 22 | 36 | 21 | 30 | 26 |

Table 3 - Number of data (#), minimum (m), maximum (M) and average values (σ) of cover thickness.

Comparing the average value of the carbonation depth with the average value of concrete-cover thickness shows that most of the reinforcement is still enrobed by basic concrete and so in passive conditions. However, wherever the concrete cover is thin (smaller than 10-15 mm) and carbonation has reached the structural concrete (Tables 1 and 2), the reinforcement is no longer in passive conditions and the concrete runs the risk of cracking because of steel corrosion. It is not possible, however, to identify these areas, on the basis of the few available samples.

The reinforcement of the small pilasters consists of two adjacent longitudinal bars ($\varnothing$ = 6 mm) anchored to the structure by means of bent steel wires. The longitudinal bars and the horizontal wires are located at 20-40 mm and 5-40 mm from the external surface, respectively (the wires are not parallel to the surface). The depth of the reinforcement in both window ledges and parapets is comprised between 25 and 40 mm. Since carbonation depth in small pilasters, window ledges and parapets has a great variability, and the thickness of these elements is rather small, full carbonation cannot be ruled out; hence, the reinforcement is surrounded by carbonated concrete and it is no longer passivated, and corrosion can propagate.

The panels are reinforced with a wire mesh ($\varnothing$ = 5-6 mm) located at 20-30 mm from the external surface (Table 3), and its reinforcement is in contact with carbonated concrete.

## 4.4 Corrosion of the reinforcement

Electrochemical measurements were carried out to investigate the corrosion level in the reinforcement (Bertolini et al., 2004). The corrosion potential of the steel was mapped on the concrete surface by using a CSE (Cu/CuSO4) reference electrode. The electrical resistivity was measured by placing a resistivity probe (connected to a conductivimeter) on the outside surface. In carbonated concrete, the conditions of active corrosion of the reinforcement are usually characterized by potential values lower than -200 mV/CSE and by low values of electrical resistivity for both the concrete and the mortar. Both parameters are affected by the moisture of the concrete cover, that is the governing factor in the propagation of carbonation-induced corrosion (Bertolini et al., 2004).

The measurement of the reinforcement potential was carried out during a very rainy period, on structural and decorative elements in the low part of the building. It was not possible to carry out electrochemical measurements on elements above the 19th floor (parapets at the 25th floor are an exception), which are more subject to rain, and on the panels, because there were no exposed rebars to be used as electrical connection.

The electrical resistivity was measured only on the surface of the elements at the 2nd floor.

The reinforcement potential of the elements at floors below 15th and of the tie-beams showed values higher than 0 mV/CSE (Fig. 20), while the electrical resistivity measured on their surface was between 100 and 3000 W×m, and in most cases above 1000 W×m (Fig. 21). These electrochemical measurements indicate that – in spite of the very wet period – the elements at any floors lower than the 18th floor were relatively dry, probably due to the sheltering effect of the upper part of the tower. Hence, the corrosion risk is negligible.

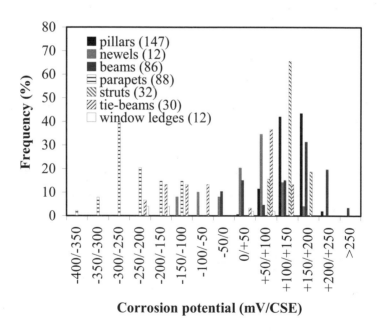

Figure 20 – Distribution of the steel potential in the reinforcement of different elements (sample number between brackets).

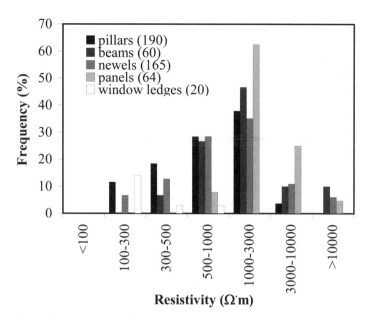

Figure 21 – Distribution of the electrical resistivity measured in different elements (sample number between brackets).

The electrochemical potential of the struts (measured on the external surfaces), was comprised between -200 and +150 mV/CSE (the more negative the values, the greater the risk of active corrosion), see Fig.21. It should be noted that the external surfaces of the tie-beams, unlike the struts, are unsheltered from the rain.

Negative values of the reinforcement potential were also measured on the parapets at 25th floor (between -250 and +100 mV/CSE on the window ledges at the lowest floors). Low values of electrical resistivity, between 100 and 300 W×m, were measured on the mortar of the window ledges, this being an indication that the mortar was wet at the moment of the inspection (Fig. 21). For these elements the corrosion risk cannot be neglected.

Though limited to 25th floor parapets, the measurements reasonably indicate that for the elements above the 18th floor (more subject to rain) the risk of corrosion is higher and the situation is more critical.

## 4.5 Cracking assessment

During the inspections, visible formerly-sealed cracks were observed in the plaster layers of some structural members. Since previous analyses had not allowed to clearly establish why these cracks had opened again, some cores were extracted astride the cracks. Phenolphthalein tests showed that the inner concrete layers were always alkaline. It was also observed that, in some cases, cracking propagated only inside the plaster layer, while in other cases cracking reached the reinforcement, whose surface was covered with a small amount of corrosion products (not enough to produce cracking). As a result, it can be concluded that cracks in the plaster layers are likely to be due to other causes than corrosion, and that the corrosion in the embedded steel is a consequence rather than a cause. No matter what is the cause of cracking, the plaster layers run the risk of getting detached from the façades and a repairing strategy is mandatory. This strategy, however, should take into account that the plaster layer has certainly contributed to limit carbonation and to keep concrete dry; hence, should this layer be left in place and keep its adhesion to the concrete, its beneficial role in reducing concrete moisture and steel corrosion rate would be substantial.

## CONCLUSIONS

Modern Heritage deserves the same attention deserved by Historical Heritage, even if with different approaches and objectives, since in the former case the buildings are "living" buildings, which need not only to be preserved, but whose functions need to be guaranteed.

Within such a framework, this paper is meant to contribute to the definition of a rehabilitation strategy, with different interdisciplinary means implying mechanical, physical and chemical tests, that should always be as little invasive as possible.

The case in question - Torre Velasca -, however, demonstrates once more that there is a number of issues still open to further attention, like those concerning the compatibility of the rehab techniques with the structural and architectural framework, the functions to be guaranteed during the rehab works, and the reliability, sustainability and durability of the rehab techniques.

Finally, the difficulties met by the teams at work on complex architectural shapes should not be taken lightly, because they may significantly increase the time and the cost of rehab processes.

## ACKNOWLEDGEMENTS

The authors are grateful to "Immobiliare Lombarda S.p.A" for entrusting CIS-E Consortium - Politecnico di Milano with the task of damage assessment in Torre Velasca, and particularly to MS Engs. Roberto Ostoni, Gianandrea Grasso and Umberto Valente, who provided all the necessary documentation and cooperated with their extraordinary experience.

The team of the young MS Engineers and Architects - Tatiana Matallo, Giuditta Pezzotta, Alessandro Zichi and Francesca Marsan - is to be thanked as well, for they worked with never-ending enthusiasm and with increasing technical skills in a rather unusual environment.

Last but not least, the technical support by MAPEI S.p.A. and SINECO S.p.A. in both in-situ and laboratory tests was instrumental in guaranteeing a regular and high-quality data acquisition.

# REFERENCES

Artioli A. (2009). "The Safeguard of Modern Architecture: Legal Provisions and Operative Procedures". *Proc. Int. Conf. on Protection of Historical Buildings – Prohitech.* Ed. by F.M. Mazzolani, pub. by Taylor and Francis Group, London, UK, keynote lecture.

Bertolini L. (2008). *Inspection Interventions Aimed at the Definition of Guidelines for the Restoration of the Façades of Torre Velasca in Milan (in Italian).* Technical report, Politecnico di Milano.

Bertolini L., Carsana M. and Redaelli E. (2008). "Conservation of Historical Reinforced-Concrete Structures Damaged by Carbonation-Induced Corrosion by Means of Electrochemical Realkalisation". *Journal of Cultural Heritage*, Vol.9, No.4, pp. 376-385.

Bertolini L., Elsener B., Pedeferri P. and Polder R.B. (2004). *Corrosion of Steel in Concrete: Prevention, Diagnosis, Repair.* Wiley-VCH, Weinheim.

Bertolini L., Lollini F. and Redaelli E. (2008). "Corrosion Assessment of Structural and Decorative Reinforced Concrete of Torre Velasca in Milan". *Proc. Int. Conf. on Protection of Historical Buildings – Prohitech.* Ed. by F.M. Mazzolani, pub. by Taylor and Francis Group, London, UK, pp. 495-500.

CEB Bulletin n° 243 (1998). *Strategies for Testing and Assessment of Concrete Structures".*

CIS-E (2008). *Risanamento facciate dell'edificio "Torre Velasca" a Milano (Façade Rehabilitation in the Torre Velasca Building in Milan", in Italian).* CIS-E Technical Report.

Fib TG 5.1 (2002). *State-of-the-Art Report on Monitoring and Safety Evaluation of Existing Concrete Structures.*

Fiori L. and Prizzon M. (1982). *"BBPR: la Torre Velasca: Disegni e Progetto della Torre Velasca (Drawings and Design of the Torre Velasca in Milan, in Italian).* Pub. by Abitare Segesta, Milan.

Immobiliare Lombarda S.p.A. Archives. *Original Design Drawings of Torre Velasca.*

ISO 2394 (1998). *General Principles on Reliability for Structures.*

MAPEI S.p.A. (2007). *Torre Velasca: Analisi dei campioni" (Torre Velasca: Sample Analysis, in Italian).* Technical Report.

Patané G. (1960). "Une ouvre discutèe: la Torre Velasca à Milan" (A Debatable Building : the Torre Velasca in Milan, in French). *Journal de la Construction de la Suisse Romande*, n. 6, 7, 8, 9.

R.A.S. S.p.A. (1995). *Opere di ripristino del copriferro di due pilastri al 17° piano dell'immobile di Piazza Velasca 5 – Milano (Repairing of the Concrete Cover in Two Columns at the 17th Floor of the Building of Velasca Square in Milan, in Italian)*. Technical Report.

Ronca P. et al. (2004). "New Developments of Sonic Tests Applied to Thick Masonry Structures". *Proc. Int. Conf. on Advances in Assessment, Structural Design and Construction*. CIMNE, ed. by P. Roca and C. Molins, Barcellona (Spain), pp. 221-230.

Ronca P., Franchi A. and Migliacci A. (2009). "Open Issues for the Conservation Problems of Modern Land-Mark Architecture: the Case Study of Torre Velasca in Milan". *Proc. Int. Conf. on Protection of Historical Buildings - Prohitech*, ed. by F.M. Mazzolani, pub. by Taylor and Francis Group, London (UK), pp. 557-562.

Samonà G. (1959). "Il grattacielo più discusso d'Europa: la Torre Velasca" (The Most Criticized Tall Building in Europe: the Torre Velasca, in Italian). *L'Architettura*, No. 40.

Sineco S.p.A. (2008). *Rapporto tecnico - Rilievo termografico (Technical Report – Thermographic Survey", in Italian)*. Technical Report.

UNI EN 14630 (2007). *Prodotti e sistemi per la protezione e la riparazione delle strutture di calcestruzzo. Metodi di prova. Determinazione della profondità di carbonatazione di un calcestruzzo indurito con il metodo della fenolftaleina (Products and Technologies for Structural-Concrete Repair. Test Methods. Assessment of the Carbonation Depth in a Hardened Concrete by means of the Phenolphtalein Method, in Italian)*. Italian Standardization Agency.

# ACKNOWLEDGEMENTS

The Editorial Board is grateful to Georgy Balazs (H), Duilio Benedetti (MI), Luigi Biolzi (MI), Fabio Biondini (MI), Luigi Cedolin (MI), Dario Coronelli (MI), Frank Dehn (DL), Liberato Ferrara (MI), Giorgio Macchi (PV), Franco Massazza (IC), Annibale Materazzi (PG), Gabriella Mulas (MI), Aurelio Muttoni (CH), Marco Pisani (MI), Giovanni Plizzari (BS), Paolo Riva (BG), Gaetano Russo (UD), Miguel F. Ruiz (CH), Giuseppe Spadea (CS), Sergio Tattoni (CA) and GianDomenico Toniolo (MI), who were asked to review the papers in the years 2007-09.

The Editorial Board acknowledges also the valuable cooperation of Dr. Patrick Bamonte (MI), who checked the compliance of the manuscripts with the format and the submission rules.

BG = University of Bergamo, Bergamo – Italy
CA = University of Cagliari, Cagliari - Italy
CH = Ecole Polytechnique Fédérale de Lausanne – EPFL, Lausanne - Switzerland
CS =  University of Calabria, Rende (Cosenza) - Italy
DL = Technical University of Leipzig , Leipzig - Germany
H   = Technical University of Budapest, Budapest - Hungary
IC  = Italcementi Group, Bergamo - Italy
MI  = Politecnico di Milano, Milan - Italy
PG = University of Perugia, Perugia  – Italy
PV  = University of Pavia, Pavia – Italy
UD = University of Udine, Udine - Italy

# PREPARATION OF MANUSCRIPTS

## General

- Size of the volume: 165 x 240 mm.
- Area in which the text must be typed: 129 x 195.
- Upper, lower, left and right margins: 20, 25, 18 and 18 mm.
- Abstract, text, references, captions, titles of the tables: single spaced, left- and right-justified, 11 Times New Roman.
- Figures, tables and captions: skip two lines between the text and each figure or table, skip one line between each figure (table) and its caption (title), skip two lines between each caption (title of the table) and the text.
- Tables: put the title underneath the table.
- Maximum suggested number of pages: 30.

## First page

- Top left corner: identification of the volume (3 lines, 11 Times New Roman) as in the papers published in V.26; then skip at least three lines.
- Title: centered, upper-case letters, bold characters, 13 Times New Roman; then skip at least two lines.
- Authors' names: centered, upper and lower case, 11 Times New Roman; then skip at least three lines.
- Abstract: preceded by the heading **ABSTRACT**, left- and right-justified, any length with the only limit of being contained in the $1^{st}$ page (together with the keywords), 11 Times New Roman.
- Keywords: preceded – on the same line - by **KEYWORDS**, up to 5 keywords should be indicated (left- and right-justified, 11 Times New Roman; skip two lines between the last line of the abstract and the keywords).
- Indentation: 5 spaces at the beginning of each paragraph, except the first paragraph.
- Affiliation: at least two lines below the abstract, preceded by a full straight line, at the foot of the page, with academic or professional position, department or division, employer (university, research center, company, firm ...), city, state.

## Following pages

- Indentation: 5 spaces at the beginning of each paragraph, except the first paragraph following the heading or sub-heading of each chapter or sub-chapter.
- Headings:

  **1. INTRODUCTION**      ($1^{st}$ level, chapters)
  **1.1 Materials**      ($2^{nd}$ level, sub-chapters)
  1.1.1 Concrete      ($3^{rd}$ level, sub-chapters)

- Skip two lines between the end of a chapter and the heading of the following chapter.
- Skip one line between the end of a sub-chapter and the heading of the following sub-chapter.
- Skip one line between each heading or sub-heading and the following text.
- Fill each page with text/figures/tables/references in order to avoid half-filled pages. If the last page is not full, place the references in two partial columns of similar length.
- Fill each page in such a way that its last line be aligned with the last lines of the other pages, in accordance with the page format.

**Captions, quotations, references and appendixes**

- Captions and titles (to be placed always under the figures and the tables): short captions or titles (less than one line) should be centered; long captions or titles (two or more lines) should be left- and right-justified.

  Examples:

  Figure 1 – Fracture energy vs. temperature.

  Table 1 – Geometry of the specimens: L = span; b = section width; $\Delta$L = distance between the point loads; and d',t' = depth and thickness of the mid-span notch.

- Quotations within the text: ..... Chopra (1995) or ..... Black and White (1998) or .... Black et al. (2000) or ... (White, 1995; Black, 2002; Gray, 2003a) [add a letter like "a", "b", "c", ..... if two or more papers published in the same year by the same author(s) are cited in the references].

- References: should be in alphabetic order (numbered references, like [5], are accepted whenever the references are very numerous and/or cumbersome):

  Black K. and White E. (1998). "Experimental Studies on Concrete". *Journal of Concrete Constructions*, Vol.00, No.00, pp. 0000-0000.

  Black K., Gray C. and White E. (2000). "Concrete Modeling". *Proc. 4th Int. Conf. on Advances in Concrete Mechanics*, ed. by B. Green and W. Brown, City, State, Vol.1, pp. 0000-0000.

  Chopra A.K. (1995). *Dynamics of the Structures*, pub. by Prentice-Hall, Upper Saddle River, New Jersey (USA).

- Skip 6pt between two successive references.

- Appendixes: the sections "References" and "Notation" should not be indicated as appendixes; any appendix should be placed past the sections "References" and "Notation", and should be indicated with Roman numbers.

- For the quotation of a paper published in Studies and Researches, adhere to the following example:

Regan P.R. and Kennedy reid I.L. (2009). "Assessment of Concrete Structures Affected by Cover Delamination – Part 1: Effect of Bond Loss". *Studies and Researches – Annual Review of Structural Concrete*. Politecnico di Milano, Vol. 29, pub. by Starrylink (Brescia, Italy), pp.245-275.

**Format of the keywords**

**KEYWORDS :** bond, chlorides, corrosion, reinforced concrete, shear capacity

**Paper submission**

The papers should be submitted to any member of the Editorial Board, preferably as a word file, within the month of June of the year of publication. Each paper will be reviewed by at least two independent reviewers, and the reviews will be sent back to the author(s) within 5 weeks since the submittal of the paper.

Design-oriented papers, short contributions on specific scientific or professional topics, and experimental or numerical reports  are welcome, and will be published in the Section "Technical Notes".

*Presidente Prof. Antonio MIgliacci – Direttore Prof.ssa Paola Ronca*

# Scuola Master F.lli Pesenti
# Attività nell'anno accademico
# 2008/2009

# F.lli Pesenti Master School – Politecnico di Milano

## (FPMS – PoliMi)

### Academic Year 2008-09

#### *President's Message*

Entriamo ora nell'anno 2010, consci dell'incombere sempre più pressante di varie emergenze gravanti sul nostro pianeta, talvolta mascherate dai sensazionali passi in avanti della Scienza e della Tecnologia.

Come è ben noto, senza voler stabilire un ordine di priorità, ma riconoscendone le strette interconnessioni, le emergenze del nostro pianeta possono essere così elencate: gli incrementi e gli squilibri demografici, il riscaldamento globale e la destabilizzazione climatica, le emissioni inquinanti e l'accentuazione dell'effetto serra, gli assetti energetici mondiali, la disponibilità di acqua, la questione dei profughi ambientali.

Da tempo sono state messe in atto varie iniziative per fronteggiare le emergenze relative al clima e all'ambiente, che parrebbero svincolate da problemi politico-demografici, e sono state sancite risoluzioni concrete, con l'obiettivo anche di premiare le scelte operative orientate alla difesa ed al miglioramento del patrimonio mondiale.

In particolare, nella Conferenza di Copenhagen, appena conclusa, si è ribadito l'obiettivo prioritario di fermare – o almeno di ridurre - la tendenza all'aumento del riscaldamento globale. Anche se questa priorità è stata riconosciuta da quasi tutti i Paesi del mondo già nella Convenzione di Kyoto degli anni novanta del secolo scorso, occorre riconoscere che ad oggi sono assai limitati i risultati raggiunti, da un lato per l'impetuoso sviluppo di alcuni grandi Paesi (che nello spasmodico bisogno di energia non si sono fatti scrupolo d'impiegare massicciamente il carbone ed il petrolio, ambedue altamente inquinanti), dall'altro lato per la staticità tecnico-economica dell'Industria dei Paesi già sviluppati, e anche di quelli meno sviluppati, che non si è lasciata coinvolgere facilmente nella riconversione "verde", viste le relative incertezze tecnico-economiche-finanziarie.

In sostanza, anche se politici ed amministrativi hanno mostrato di avvertire le esigenze mondiali e di condividere totalmente la necessità di affrontarle, ed anche se ormai in parecchi Paesi è stato programmato un piano serio e concreto per l'introduzione di fonti di energia rinnovabili (eolica, solare, geotermica, marina), appare ad oggi ancora lontana la conversione del modello di sviluppo da quello illimitato a quello sostenibile (*). Tuttavia, l'operare nell'ottica della sostenibilità - anche nel solo ambito del Mondo delle Costruzioni - può contribuire a tale auspicata conversione, non certo determinante come quantità, ma fondamentale perché contribuisce ad orientare le coscienze verso la cultura della responsabilità.

In particolare, nel campo delle Strutture, per "muoversi" nell'ottica della sostenibilità, in linea di principio occorre:

- la corretta e coerente concezione del progetto (**Conceptual Design**), al fine di garantire alle strutture resistenza, rigidezza, tenacità, robustezza – anche sotto eventi eccezionali – durabilità, versatilità (adattabilità, riparabilità, sostituibilità), ispezionabilità e manutenibilità;

- la corretta e coerente concezione dell'esecuzione (**Efficient Construction**), con materiali e tecnologie eco-compatibili, impiego del riciclo, prefabbricazione, ottimizzazione dei cantieri, industrializzazione;

- la scelta di appropriate e sicure modalità di uso (**Consistent Use**), al fine di garantire un esercizio coerente a quanto programmato nel contesto in cui esso si svolge.

Questa strategia operativa ha lo scopo di ottenere strutture la cui realizzazione possa appartenere all' "insieme" rappresentato - nella figura seguente - quale intersezione dei tre insiemi rispettosi singolarmente degli aspetti sociali, ambientali ed economici. In sostanza si afferma che le operazioni del costruire vanno orientate all'ottimizzazione: (a) delle esigenze sociali, in specie per la sicurezza (salvaguardia della vita umana) ed il rispetto in esercizio delle necessità fisiologiche delle persone (confort d'esercizio); (b) delle esigenze ambientali, in specie per il rispetto e la conservazione del mondo naturale; e (c) delle esigenze economiche, per i costi e gli oneri sia diretti che indiretti gravanti sulla Società.

In particolare, negli ultimi decenni gli interessi del **Conceptual Design** si sono ampliati da una visione puramente meccanica di materiali e strutture ad una visione più generale, basata sulla sicurezza e sulla durabilità delle opere, all'interno della sostenibilità, con qualche problema di adattamento in Paesi

(*) Si rammenta che lo Sviluppo Sostenibile ha ricevuto la sua prima definizione nel Rapporto del Presidente, Sig.ra Gro Harlem Brundtland, della Commissione Mondiale per l'Ambiente e lo Sviluppo - WCED (UNESCO, 1987), nel modo seguente: "Lo Sviluppo Sostenibile è lo sviluppo che garantisce i bisogni delle generazioni attuali senza compromettere la possibilità che le generazioni future riescano a soddisfare i propri".

Tale formulazione stabilisce le regole di un progetto di vita per tutti i popoli della Terra, allineato alla cultura o etica della Terra, riconosciuta sin dal 1949 dall'americano Aldo Leopold nel suo saggio avente proprio il titolo "The Land Ethics".

Questo progetto è però solo un contributo alla salvezza del pianeta dalla catastrofe verso cui sembra avviarsi, anche se si tratta di un contributo fondamentale poiché sveglia le coscienze promovendo quella "cultura della responsabilità" tanto cara al Prof. Piero Pozzati di Bologna, che ne ha fatto l'oggetto di un suo saggio illuminato. Infatti, nel corso dei decenni che si sono succeduti alla prima dichiarazione d'intenti del 1949, lo Sviluppo Sostenibile ha suscitato parecchi contrasti, ma anche sostegno convinto, come dimostrato - ad esempio - dal consenso allargato ottenuto nella Conferenza di Rio de Janeiro del 1992 (Agenda 21: Masterplan per la sostenibilità del 21° secolo, nel rispetto del "principio di precauzione" sancito a Stoccolma nel 1972).

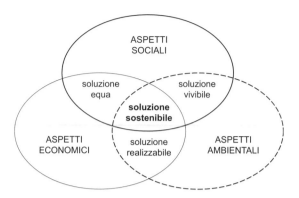

*Definizione dell'insieme rispettoso degli aspetti sociali, ambientali ed economici.*

piuttosto tradizionali come l'Italia, dove il calcestruzzo – ad esempio – è stato considerato da sempre come "eterno" e compatibile con il mondo naturale. Ma così non è! Senza nulla togliere ai pregi del calcestruzzo, è ormai riconosciuto come tale materiale si deteriori né più ne meno delle pietre naturali. Inoltre, l'impatto delle cave sul territorio ed il consumo energetico nella produzione del cemento, unito all'emissione di anidride carbonica, spingono sempre più verso lo sviluppo di conglomerati cementizi ultraperformanti o con minore contenuto di cemento, e di materiali alternativi.

La durabilità e la sostenibilità hanno portato all'introduzione di nuove parole-chiave, come "ciclo di vita", rapporto costo-benefici", "compatibilità ambientale", "progettazione ecologica", "riutilizzo", "riciclo", "riduzione dell'impatto locale", "ottimizzazione dei cantiere", "risparmio energetico", "inerzia termica", "priorità locali", "materiali ecologici", …..). Queste parole chiave stanno avendo un notevole impatto non solo sullo sviluppo dei materiali da costruzione, ma anche sulla stessa progettazione strutturale, sebbene l'orientamento attuale della ricerca sia soprattutto focalizzato sui materiali.

In effetti, i materiali strutturali continuano a giocare un ruolo predominante in riferimento a: (a) costruzioni esistenti (→ ripristino, rinforzo ed adeguamento); (b) costruzioni future (→ versatilità, durabilità, riduzione dell'impatto locale, risparmio energetico); e (c) tecnologie di produzione e movimentazione (→ dalla cava al cantiere, nel caso del calcestruzzo). In dettaglio:

- Costruzioni esistenti: il costo e la criticità (specialmente in aree urbanizzate o di interesse storico) della demolizione e ricostruzione di edifici esistenti consiglia assai spesso il recupero di tali edifici e quindi l'uso di materiali innovativi (quali polimeri fibrorinforzati e conglomerati ad alte/altissime prestazioni) per ripristinare/rinforzare/adeguare le loro strutture, anche a fronte di situazioni ambientali gravose (→ carichi sismici, vibrazioni, impatto, alta temperatura) e di condizioni di cantiere spesso difficili.

- Costruzioni future: la durabilità richiede sempre più di progettare, produrre ed impiegare materiali "ingegnerizzati" (cioè materiali artificiali "ritagliati" su specifiche esigenze), al fine di garantire un'adeguata vita strutturale utile, senza necessità di gravosi interventi manutentivi, pur in presenza spesso di condizioni ambientali estreme (→ incendio, bassissime temperature, radiazioni, sismicità).

- Tecnologie di produzione e movimentazione : le nuove costruzioni devono essere realizzate in ossequio alla sostenibilità, e quindi le loro strutture devono essere progettate e costruite in modo tale da garantire non solo prestazioni adeguate (→ sicurezza e durabilità), ma anche un ridotto impatto sull'ambiente e sulla Società nel suo complesso (→ riduzione delle emissioni di anidride carbonica durante la produzione dei materiali; riutilizzo dei materiali risultanti dalle demolizioni; riciclo di sottoprodotti industriali; contenimento delle aree di cantiere; controllo dei tempi di costruzione; scelta dei materiali e delle tecniche costruttive sulla base della loro disponibilità in prossimità del cantiere; ......).

Tutte queste esigenze - e le regole per soddisfarle che traducono nella pratica delle Costruzioni i principi strategici sopra indicati - vengono raccolti oggigiorno in "codici" fra i quali si può ricordare quello applicato negli USA con la sigla LEED (Leadership for Energy and Environmental Design). Anche in Italia si sta affermando la stessa tendenza, come dimostra l'iniziativa della Regione Lombardia di commissionare la stesura di linee-guida alla Fondazione Politecnico e – per suo tramite – al Consorzio CIS-E (Costruzioni ed Ingegneria Strutturale in Europa).

Si può concludere sottolineando come la sostenibilità tenda sempre più a pervadere le attività umane, costituendo un terreno di confronto e – si spera di intesa - fra Scienza, Tecnologia, Formazione, Politica, Industria, Economia ed Associazioni nazionali/locali, pubbliche/private.

Un contributo piccolo ma significativo è dato da questo volume e dalla Scuola, che possono essere considerati come un'ulteriore dimostrazione del continuo coinvolgimento dell'Ingegneria Strutturale e delle Scienze dei Materiali nella sicurezza, durabilità e sostenibilità delle costruzioni in calcestruzzo armato.

Milano, Dicembre 2009

*Il Presidente della Scuola Master*
*"Fratelli Pesenti"*
*Professor Antonio Migliacci*

# F.lli Pesenti Master School – Politecnico di Milano

## (FPMS – PoliMi)

### Academic Year 2008-09

### *Director's Message*

The last section of the annual volume "Studies and Researches" is traditionally devoted to the illustration of the most recent activities of **FPMS-PoliMi**, which is also the editor of this volume.

The "F.lli Pesenti School for Advanced Studies on Reinforced-Concrete Structures" was established in 1927, by mutual consent of the Politecnico di Milano and the Pesenti family, who is still the major stock-holder in the Italcementi Group.

At that time, the leading ideas were (a) to introduce both young engineers and experienced professional designers to the new design and analytical approaches required by R/C structures, (b) to provide an outstanding educational level through the joint participation of qualified academicians and professional experts working together in the domain of reinforced concrete, and (c) to favor applied research and applications concerning cementitious materials and R/C structures.

More than 80 years of academic and professional heritage in providing graduate education within the scientific community of the Politecnico di Milano have allowed the F.lli Pesenti School (a) to offer a solid highly-respected curriculum, (b) to become a *cornerstone school for Civil Engineers and Architects*, in the field of constructions and infrastructures, and (c) to favor a smooth transition open to innovation, from the past **Specialty School** to to-day's **Master School FPMS-PoliMi.**

In the last decade, the educational program of the Master School has been tailored on the basis of two objectives: promoting research and innovation in the domain of structural cementitious materials and R/C constructions, and encouraging a profession-oriented educational approach, within the framework of the European higher-education system ensuing from the Bologna and Sorbonne agreements of the nineties.

From the first original version offering a single course to today's multi-course organization **providing six accredited Master Courses each of 60 ECTS**, a lot of major events have occurred!

The six courses - open to Engineers and Architects - have the following titles:

1. Master in **Reinforced-Concrete Structural Design (MRC)**
2. Master in **Architecture, Structures and Technologies (MAST)**
3. Master in **Environment-Sustainable Developments (MESD)**
4. Master in **Construction Project-Management (MCPM)**
5. Master in **Architectural-Works Management (MAWM)\***
6. Master in **Seismic-Construction Design (MSCD)**

(\*) In English

Each Master Course is based on a number of "lecture blocks" or "units" under the supervision of academic tutors.

The Master Course MSCD has a specific time schedule and its lecture units are supervised by heads or managers of public/private institutions active in (a) seismic engineering and prevention, and (b) post-earthquake activities, as explained in our web site.

A sizable part of each curriculum can be "tailored" in accordance with the personal interests of each student, with the help of his/her instructor. For more information, see the web site:

http://masterpesenti.stru.polimi.it

Among the objectives of the **F.lli Pesenti Master School**, the link between education and research/innovation has always been cherished, as demonstrated by the publication of this annual volume, whose title has undergone a slight rewording, starting from this Volume 29 – 2009:

**Studies and Researches**
**Annual Review of Structural Concrete**

Finally, it is useful to address the main "pillars" characterizing the educational system of the **F.lli Pesenti Master School**:

- A comprehensive educational team of managers, professional designers and academicians, acting as teachers or instructors, highly qualified in their field and generally registered as Professional Engineers and Architects.

- A co-operative system, which provides each student a working stage in the second semester of the academic year.

- An on-line graduate program, that is at the same time flexible and convenient.

- Many opportunities offered by the research projects in progress at the Department of Structural Engineering of the Politecnico di Milano, under the supervision of those academicians who have strong connections with major private or public developers.

- Many opportunities offered by the industrial milieu of Milan and Lombardy, which are among the most propulsive cities and regions in Europe. (These opportunities very often come in the form of working stages).

- Specific courses addressed to the managerial issues faced today by Engineers and Architects, given by MBA tutors and professors.

- A central geographical location, which plays a pivotal role as a link between Europe and South-Mediterranean countries.

- Job opportunities, that come in recognition of the high-level of our Master Diploma and are favored by the joint activity during the working stages.

- Possibility of continuing and updating one's own education by attending short one-week or on-line non-credit courses.

Milan, December 2009

*The Director of the School*
*Professor Paola Ronca*

*Paola Ronca*

# Le attività della Scuola Master F.lli Pesenti

## Anno accademico 2008-2009

Le seguenti *"pagine gialle"*, come già anticipato nel *Director's remarks,* illustrano, in continuità con la tradizione, il cammino e le attività della Scuola F.lli Pesenti, con particolare riferimento all'anno accademico 2008-2009, e sono articolate nelle sottoelencate sezioni:

- **Completamento delle nuove iniziative** coinvolgenti il triennio 2007-2009;

- **Ampliamento dell'offerta didattica** con specifiche nuove Unità Didattiche

- **Attività collaterali della Scuola** a supporto della diffusione e innovazione dell'offerta didattica;

- **Tesi di Master** svolte durante l'esperienza di stage lavorativo e discusse nelle due sessioni per gli esami di Diploma, rispettivamente in data 27-10-e 27-11 2009.

## Completamento delle nuove iniziative

Si sottolineano schematicamente i **punti salienti**:

- Da una offerta di  3 diversificati Corsi di Master CFU (Crediti Formativi Universitari), con circa 30 docenti, l'edizione 2008-2009 ha attivato 6 Corsi di Master CFU :

     1 Master in " Reinforced Concrete Structural Design" (MRC)
     2 Master in "Architecture, Structure and Technology" (MAST)
     3 Master in "Environment Sustainable Development" (MESD)
     4 Master in "Construction Project Management" (MCPM)
     5 Master in "Architectural Works Management" (MAWM) *(in English)*
     6 Master in "Seismic Construction Design" (MSCD)

- Il corpo docente è attualmente composto, per la sua maggioranza, da docenti di diversi Dipartimenti e Facoltà del Politecnico e altri Atenei (come previsto nel "Regolamento dei Master di Ateneo") e da liberi professionisti, per complessivi 65/70docenti. La docenza dei Master 4 e 5 è fornita dai docenti dei Master MBA della *School of Management* del Politecnico (MIP).

- Con l'edizione 08-09 si è attuata concretamente anche l'offerta completamente on-line dei Corsi di Master, per un totale di oltre 500 ore di lezione registrate su DVD, le relative slides illustrate da ciascun docente e materiale didattico disponibile su supporto informatico.

Di seguito brevemente si illustra come nasce l'idea di tale offerta (*motivazioni*), quali impegno e professionalità si richiedono (*impegno*), quale interesse ha suscitato (*risultati*):

*Motivazioni*:

a) ragguardevole numero di giovani che, lavorando come liberi professionisti, vedono nei nostri Master il percorso ottimizzato per il proprio aggiornamento, attraverso la "continuing education" garantita da una istituzione universitaria, ma con "back to school" di 1 anno impossibile, volendo , o dovendo, conservare il proprio impegno lavorativo.

b) usufruibilità dell'offerta formativa dei Master anche per più brevi periodi di presenza in aula, nel caso di permessi brevi da parte del datore di lavoro o di permessi di soggiorno per gli stranieri.

c) maggiore visibilità internazionale della Scuola F.lli Pesenti.

d) maggiore visibilità delle iniziative nel campo della "long-life education".

*Impegno:*

a) costituzione ex-novo di particolari attrezzature informatiche (server dedicato con processore Intel), di software specifico (S.O.Linus), approntamento di aula per video-riprese e registrazione audio.

b) creazione di sito interattivo, con accesso attraverso password e controllo dell'operatore abilitato.

c) creazione di team dedicato ( 2 ingegneri elettronici e 3 operatori) e disponibile in continuo per interventi immediati e imprevisti.

d) illustrazione, convincimento e training ai docenti per le modalità di svolgimento delle lezioni e la preparazione in formato elettronico del Materiale didattico.

e) traduzione in lingua inglese di tutto il materiale didattico.

*Risultati:*   con l'edizione 2008-2009, in 4 dei 6 Master c'è stata richiesta di frequenza on-line, per un totale di 9 iscritti che seguono a distanza. La richiesta di "frequenza mista" per l'edizione dei Master 2009/2010 si aggira sul 30% del totale delle iscrizioni.

Il grafico successivo riporta l'andamento annuale delle iscrizioni, dopo colloquio di ammissione, all'offerta formativa della Scuola F.lli Pesenti.

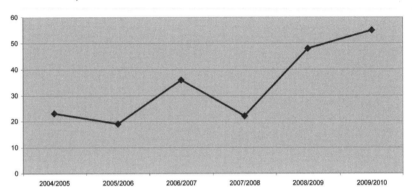

- Trasformazione del Volume *"Studies and Researches"*, per l'adeguamento ai parametri di classificazione come pubblicazione a livello internazionale; meta raggiunta già con i numeri 26, 27 e 28, con presenza, sia nel Comitato Scientifico, sia fra i Revisori di esperti stranieri, sia con l'edizione in lingua inglese; in particolare sul presente volume 29 si registra un cospicuo numero di autori stranieri.

Grazie anche al capillare invio del volume a singoli docenti universitari, professionisti, centri di ricerca, biblioteche universitarie, associazioni di settore, in Italia e all'estero, sempre più numerosi sono i papers inviati per accettazione, e numerose sono le espressioni di apprezzamento per la significatività e grado di approfondimento degli argomenti trattati.

Si riporta di seguito la lettera inviata dal prof. Nawy al prof. Gambarova, principale curatore della diffusione a livello internazionale di *"Studies and Researches"*.

**DR. EDWARD G. NAWY, D.ENG., P.E.**
33 Silver Charm Road
MANALAPAN, NEW JERSEY 07726
PHONE (732) 446-4809
FAX (732) 446-4805
E-mail: nawype@cs.com

LICENSED PROFESSIONAL ENGINEER
IN THE STATES OF NJ, NY, PA, CA, FL
CHARTERED CIVIL ENGINEER

November 16, 2009

DISTINGUISHED PROFESSOR EMERITUS
DEPT. OF CIVIL & ENVIRONMENTAL ENGINEERING
RUTGERS – THE STATE UNIVERSITY OF NEW JERSEY
PISCATAWAY, NEW JERSEY 08854

Professor Pietro G. Gambarova
Ordinario di Tecnica delle Costruzioni
Dipartimento di Ingegneria Strutturale
Politecnico di Milano
Milan, Italy
Tel: +39 02 2399 4391
Fax: +39 02 2399 4220
Email: pietro.gambarova@polimi.it

Dear Professor Gambarova:

............................. I want also to thank you for the autographed excellent book of research papers issued by the Graduate School of the Politecnico di Milano under your direction.

OMISSIS

............................................. I have read all the papers in the book you kindly gave me and I am very impressed at the very high-level extensive research papers presented in the publication and the lucid analyses of the research results. Having myself edited several ACI SP volumes, I am well aware of the extensive efforts that are expended in compiling and editing each paper. So, my congratulations to you and to your co-editor on such a well-edited volume 28 – and in perfect English.

I hope that our paths will cross again, and with my warmest personal regards,

Sincerely yours,

Edward G. Nawy
Distinguished Professor Emeritus
Rutgers -The State University
ACI Honorary Member

- Visibilità internazionale della Scuola: il parametro più significativo è l'aumento di <u>allievi stranieri</u>. In percentuale, per l'anno accademico 08-09, si è raggiunto il 40% degli iscritti (su una media di Politecnico che si aggira su 8%). Il seguente grafico riporta l'incremento numerico degli allievi Master non UE negli anni, comprese le iscrizioni 09-010:

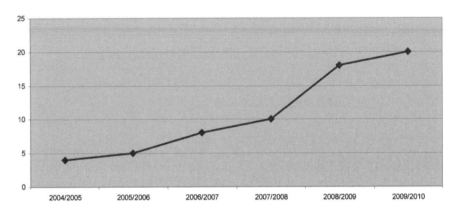

Andamento annuale delle partecipazioni ai Master di allievi non UE

Alcuni allievi stranieri hanno usufruito di Borse di Studio fornite dal Consorzio CIS-E.

La presenza a livello internazionale della Scuola si è concretizzata anche con le due attività parallele, fondamentali e su cui la direzione della Scuola ha prestato da sempre attenzione ed energie :

- lo svolgimento presso i locali della Scuola di cicli di lezioni e/o seminari ad invito di docenti stranieri, come riportato nella sezione "Attività collaterali".

- La disponibilità dei docenti della Scuola, con il supporto della Scuola, a partecipare ad incontri programmatici, ad organizzare "Special Session" in Convegni Internazionali, a tenere seminari in consessi internazionali, come evidenziato nella successiva sezione "Attività collaterali".

# Ampliamento dell'offerta didattica

L'offerta didattica si è arricchita e completata con l'attivazione e svolgimento di 6 Corsi di Master Specializzanti/professionalizzanti, come già precedentemente elencati.

In particolare, si è attivato il nuovo Master in *"Progettazione Sismica delle Strutture Sostenibili in Calcestruzzo"*, che così pone **la Scuola come il più completo polo di riferimento della catena <u>innovazione-formazione-progettazione.</u>**

Il Master è stato diretto dal Prof. G.D. Toniolo del DIS, coadiuvato dal Prof. A. Palermo. Le <u>Unità Didattiche caratterizzanti</u>, sono state affidate ciascuna ai più autorevoli esperti a livello nazionale e internazionale, che puntualmente hanno svolto le lezioni nei locali della Scuola.

La prima, in ordine temporale, di tali Unità, ha trattato i temi della "<u>Sismologia applicata all'ingegneria</u>", come illustrato nella slide introduttiva qui riportata:

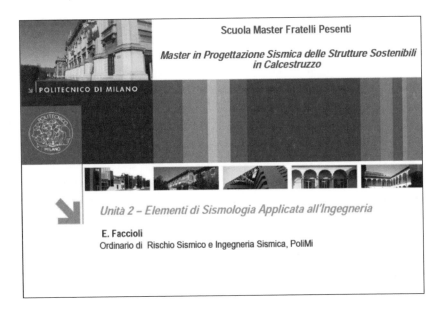

Di seguito l'elenco completo delle Unità Didattiche approvate e svolte per la prima edizione del Master:

Unità 1: Materiali da costruzione – Prof. Franchi
Unità 2: Elementi di sismologia applicata all'ingegneria – Prof. Faccioli
Unità 3: Analisi strutturale – Prof. Perotti
Unità 4: Progettazione degli edifici – Prof. Castellani

Unità 5: Strutture prefabbricate – Prof. Toniolo

Unità 6: Isolamento sismico – Prof. M. Dolce

Unità 7: Ponti – Prof. Mancini

Unità 8: Costruzioni esistenti – Prof. Manfredi

Unità 9: Fondazioni e opere di sostegno – Prof. Lancellotta

Unità 10: Sperimentazione sismica – Prof. Negro

In totale le *Unità Didattiche* in cui gli altri 5 corsi di Master sono articolati, sono cresciute per numero specifico dei moduli didattici e per temi rivisti e rinnovati. Il flow-chart illustra di seguito i percorsi consigliati per ciascun corso di Master.

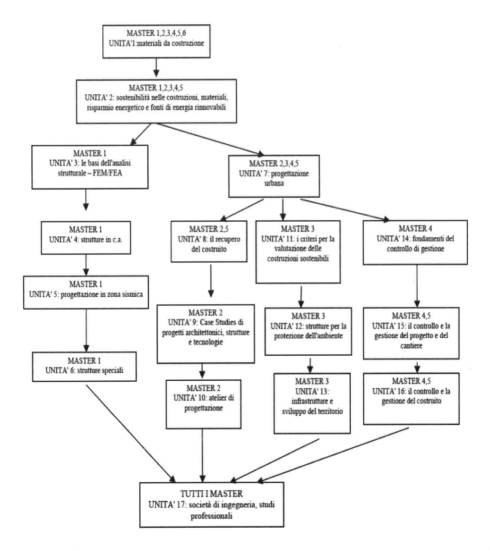

Come già accennato, l'offerta on-line è stata accolta con notevole interesse da giovani già inseriti nel mondo del lavoro, come valida alternativa a forme, più onerose per l'allievo, di didattica part-time. A supporto e completamento dell'offerta on-line si è aperto il *Portale della Scuola,* anche per attivare concretamente la vita della *Alumni E-Community e conseguente Long-life Education.*

*Indirizzo web*: http://masterpesenti.stru.polimi.it

## Attività collaterali della Scuola

Come ogni anno alcuni docenti della Scuola, con il supporto organizzativo e amministrativo della Scuola, si sono attivati nell'organizzazione di visite tecniche, seminari, incontri tecnici, sia presso i locali della Scuola, sia in sedi diverse, e partecipazione a Convegni Internazionali, come di seguito brevemente elencato (in ordine temporale):

### Corso MIDAS

**POLITECNICO DI MILANO**

Dipartimento
di Ingegneria Strutturale

**Italcementi**
Italcementi Group

A world class local business

Scuola Master F.lli Pesenti

# Seminar on:
# Optimization Tools for the Conceptual Design of Structures

Alessandro Beghini, Ph.D., PE, LEED® AP, Associate, Skidmore, Owings & Merrill, LLP
Massimiliano Binci, Ph.D., Skidmore, Owings & Merrill, LLP

Venerdì 19 Dicembre 2008 ore 11.30-13.00 Aula Scuola Pesenti –Politecnico di Milano-

Inspired by the seminal paper by Michell (*Thelimits of economy of material in frame-structures*, 1904), engineers at Skidmore, Owings and Merrill, LLP (SOM) investigated several tools for optimization of structural shapes and systems to be employed during the conceptual phase of the design process. Structural optimization attracts increasing interest in the building industry, especially in the design of high-rise buildings. By selectively distributing the material in the structure, the efficiency of the resulting design can be optimized, often producing aesthetically pleasant forms.

Michell trusses represent a valuable starting point in defining optimal layouts. Unfortunately, analytical solutions have been derived over the years only for relatively simple load conditions and eometries. In recent years, efficient numerical methods have been developed to derive optimal structural shapes for various problems. Among these methods: homogenization method, Evolutionary Structural Optimization (ESO), Bidirectional ESO, etc. The results of the analysis based on these methods provided information about the flow of forces in the structure and helped our designers in the characterization of the structural system. The presentation will outline few applications of Optimization to international projects and the role of a Ph.D. in the development of these methods.

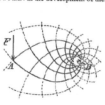

**Alessandro Beghini, Ph.D., PE, LEED® AP**
Biography:
10.2008 – present: Associate at Skidmore, Owings & Merrill, LLP.
07.2005 – 9.2008: Structural Engineer at Skidmore, Owings & Merrill, LLP.
Selected projects:
- Research in Optimal Structural Topologies
- Burj Dubai, Dubai, U.A.E.
- North Carolina Museum of Art Expansion, Raleigh, NC, USA
- Philippines Stock Exchange, Manila, The Philippines
- Shangri-La Hotel, Manila, The Philippines
06.2005 – Ph.D. in Theoretical and Applied Mechanics, Northwestern University, Evanston, IL, USA.
09.2001 – M. Eng. in Civil Engineering, University of Tokyo, Tokyo, Japan.
04.2001 – Laurea (B.S./M.S.) in Structural Engineering, Politecnico di Milano (Polytechnic of Milan), Milan, Italy.

**Massimiliano Binci, Ph.D.**
Biography:
3.2008 – present: Structural Engineer at Skidmore, Owings & Merrill, LLP.
Selected projects:
- Mumbai International Airport, Mumbai, India
- Meeras Twin Tower, Dubai, UAE
- Lotte Busan Tower, Busan, South Korea
01.2008 – Ph.D. in Materials Science and Engineering, Drexel University, Philadelphia, PA, USA.
02.2003 – M.S. in Civil Engineering, Ecole Centrale de Nantes, Nantes, France.
02.2003 – B.S. in Structural Engineering, Polytechnic Institute of Milan (Politecnico di Milano), Milan, Italy.

# *Seminari a cura degli Enti ed Imprese che offrono stages e borse di studio*

La Scuola Master F.lli Pesenti - POLITECNICO di MILANO
p.zza L. da VINCI, 32 - 20133 MILANO
presso Aula Conferenze della Scuola

martedì 24 marzo 2009

**ore 09,30**
*Le torri di Citylife*

**CITYLIFE**
Ing. Piero Bellotti

**ore 11,30**
*Presentazione degli stage offerti*

**IMPRESA CLAUDIO SALINI SpA**
Dott. A Bonificio

**ore 14,30**
*Sistemi PERI: di cantiere e attrezzature speciali*

**PERI**
Ing. Meroni
Ing. Vernò

**ore 16,30**
*Sistemi DOKA di cantierei*

**DOKA**
Ing. M. Maffezzoli

giovedì 26 marzo 2009

**ore 09,30**

**ITALCEMENTI Group**
Ing. Andrea Leidi
Ing. Gennaro Guala
Ing. Gabriele Guala

*Laboratori Italcementi a Dalmine*

**Impresa PANDINI SpA**
Ing. Giovanni Pandini

**ore 11,30**

**HINES Italia – Soc. CAPRERA ITALIA srl**
Ing. Claudio Saibene

*Edifici di Garibaldi Repubblica*

**Impresa COLOMBO Costruzioni SpA**
geom. Luigi Paolo Bertoglio e geom. Gianfranco Cesana
arch. Giacomo De Lisio
**M.S.C. ASSOCIATI srl**
Ing. Danilo Campagna
Ing. Alessandro Aronica

**ore 15,30**

**NUOVO OSPEDALE di BG – AZIENDA OSPEDALIERA**
Ing. Paolo Bosi

*Nuovo Ospedale di Bergamo*

**Impresa DEC SpA**
Ing. Malloni,
Ing. Bassanelli, Ing. Locatelli

venerdì 27 marzo 2009

**ore 15,30**
*Due realizzazioni significative*

**Impresa PIZZAROTTI & C. SpA**
Ing. Stefano Soncini

*Centro Internazionale di Aggiornamento Sperimentale Scientifico*

**OGGETTO: INVITO AL SEMINARIO INTERNAZIONALE CIAS DEL 2010 A MADRID**

Gentilissima Prof. ssa Paola Ronca,

con la presente, a nome del Consiglio Scientifico del Cias, abbiamo il piacere di invitarLa ufficialmente, in qualità di Relatore, al Seminario Internazionale **"EVOLUZIONE NELLA SPERIMENTAZIONE PER LE COSTRUZIONI"** che si svolgerà da sabato 8 a sabato 15 maggio 2010 a Madrid.

Il Seminario si dividerà in quattro Sessioni, ognuna di mezza giornata, che si svolgeranno la mattina del lunedì 10, del martedì 11 e tutto il giovedì 13 maggio 2010.

Nel pomeriggio del lunedì e martedì sono inoltre previste delle lezioni all'Università per gli studenti, aperte anche ai partecipanti del Seminario Cias.

Di seguito sono riportati i titoli delle Sessioni, i Presidenti di Sessione e i Relatori invitati.

Come vede Lei è invitata a prendere parte alla IV Sessione sulla "RIABILITAZIONE DEL COSTRUITO".

**DIPARTIMENTO DI INGEGNERIA STRUTTURALE**

www.luiter.it

Il Consorzio CIS-E e la Scuola Master F.lli Pesenti del Dipartimento di Ingegneria Strutturale - DIS del Politecnico di Milano presentano il Corso:

## Modellazione e simulazione del comportamento statico e dinamico di edifici alti mediante il codice Midas

Il Corso si propone di illustrare i problemi strutturali che si devono affrontare nella progettazione di edifici alti, utilizzando come strumento di calcolo il software Midas. Il sistema fondazionale e l'interazione con il terreno, il pacchetto di impalcato tipo, il sistema di pilastri, il sistema di controventamento e gli eventuali sistemi di smorzamento vengono affrontati con particolare riferimento ad alcuni episodi importanti in corso di costruzione o di progettazione nell'area milanese.

Particolare attenzione verrà posta sulla risposta di tali strutture all'azione del vento.

Relatori Politecnico:
proff. P. Crespi, A. Franchi, F. Perotti e A. Zasso.

Nella prima parte del Corso, alcuni esperti del programma Midas si alterneranno per l'illustrazione di alcune importanti funzioni del programma stesso.
Relatori CSPfea: ingg. L. Griggio e P. Segala.

E' previsto inoltre un contributo didattico da parte dello Studio Favero & Milan Ingegneria Srl.

A chi è destinato il Corso:
Ingegneri strutturisti, studenti di Master o di Dottorato interessati all'Ingegneria Strutturale.

**Giovedì e venerdì 12 e 13 marzo 2009** dalle ore 9,00 alle ore 17,00 nell'Aula Castigliano del Dipartimento di Ingegneria Strutturale del Politecnico di Milano in P.zza Leonardo da Vinci 32

*Il costo è di 300,00 € a partecipante*

Per info: arch. Emanuela Ghidini, consorziocise@stru.polimi.it - Tel: +39 02 2399 4252

Partner

Software solutions for Structural Engineers

# *Corsi brevi di Formazione Permanente*

**"Fondamenti e opere di sostegno"**

Modulo didattico - applicativo all'interno del Corso di Master *"Progettazione Sismica delle Strutture Sostenibili in Calcestruzzo"*

Coordinamento scientifico: prof. Giandomenico Toniolo
Master School F.lli Pesenti
Dipartimento di Ingegneria Strutturale, Politecnico di Milano

**30 Marzo – 02 Aprile 2009**
**Ore complessive: 24**

SEDE: Aule - Master School F.lli Pesenti
Dipartimento di Ingegneria Strutturale, Politecnico di Milano
Piazza Leonardo da Vinci 32, Milano

Corso organizzato da:
**Master School F.lli Pesenti, Dipartimento di Ingegneria Strutturale, Politecnico di Milano**

**Docenti del corso:**

- *coordinatore: prof. Renato Lancellotta -* Politecnico di Torino
- *prof. C. Tamagnini –*
- *prof. C. Di Prisco –* Politecnico di Milano
- *prof.ssa D. Foti –* Politecnico di Bari

**Orari delle lezioni:**

| ora | Lunedì 30 | Martedì 31 | Mercoledì 1 | Giovedì 2 |
|---|---|---|---|---|
| 9.15-10.15 | Lancellotta | Tamagnini | Di Prisco | Foti |
| 10.15-11.15 | Lancellotta | Tamagnini | Di Prisco | Foti |
| 11.15-12.15 | Lancellotta | Tamagnini | Di Prisco | Foti |
| 12.15-13.15 | Lancellotta | Tamagnini | Di Prisco | Foti |
| 14.15-15.15 | Lancellotta | Tamagnini | Di Prisco | Foti |
| 15.15-16.15 | Lancellotta | Tamagnini | Di Prisco | Foti |

**Costo del corso: 400 euro + IVA 20%**

**Contenuti del corso:**

Il Corso ha lo scopo di fornire conoscenze specialistiche per la progettazione e risposta sismica delle fondazioni e opere di sostegno. In particolare verrano trattati i seguenti temi:
a)Caratterizzazione geotecnica del sito;
b)Opere di sostegno: analisi pseudo-statica;
c)Opere di sostegno: simulazione numerica in campo statico;
d)Opere di sostegno: simulazione numerica sotto azione sismica
e)Fondazioni superficiali: interazione sotto carichi sismici;
f)Fondazioni su pali: interazione cinematica e inerziale.

Coordinate bancarie per il versamento della quota di adesione:
Banca Intesa San Paolo - Fil. n° 2587; Via Celoria 2 - Milano
c.c. n°: 6130000000-92
intestato a Consorzio CIS-E
CIN: C; COD. ABI: 03069; C.A.B.: 01749
IBAN: IT39C0306901749613000000092

Per eventuali ulteriori informazioni rivolgersi a:
arch. Emanuela Ghidini o dott.ssa Sara Giussani
Politecnico di Milano - DIS
P.zza Leonardo da Vinci, 32 - 20133 Milano
Tel: 02-2399.4252/4305;
e-mail: scuolamaster@stru.polimi.it
consorziocise@stru.polimi.it
sito web: http://masterpesenti.stru.polimi.it

**"Ponti"**

**Modulo didattico - applicativo all'interno del Corso di Master "Progettazione Sismica delle Strutture Sostenibili in Calcestruzzo"**

Coordinamento scientifico: prof. Giandomenico Toniolo
Master School F.lli Pesenti
Dipartimento di Ingegneria Strutturale, Politecnico di Milano

**4 - 7 maggio 2009**
**Ore complessive: 24**

**SEDE: Aule - Master School F.lli Pesenti**
Dipartimento di Ingegneria Strutturale, Politecnico di Milano
Piazza Leonardo da Vinci 32, Milano

Corso organizzato da:
**Master School F.lli Pesenti, Dipartimento di Ingegneria Strutturale, Politecnico di Milano**

**Docenti del corso:**

- **coordinatore**: *prof. ing. Giuseppe Mancini*
  *- Politecnico di Torino*
- *prof. ing. Donato Sabia - Politecnico di Torino*
- *ing. Agostino Marioni - Alga S.p.A.*
- *ing. Hugo Corres Peiretti – Studio Fhecor*
  *Madrid 01 - Spagna*

Sara' fornito on-line il materiale didattico presentato in aula da tutti i docenti.

**Contenuti del corso:**

Il Corso si articola nei seguenti moduli:
a) Caratteristiche dei ponti (tipologie, comportamento)
b) Problemi specifici di progettazione sismica
c) Adeguamento sismico dei ponti esistenti
d) Appoggi (dispositivi, smorzatori, …)

**Orari delle lezioni:**

| ora | Lunedì 4 | Martedì 5 | Mercoledì 6 | Giovedì 7 |
|---|---|---|---|---|
| 9.15-10.15 | Mancini | Sabia | Marioni | Corres |
| 10.15-11.15 | Mancini | Sabia | Marioni | Corres |
| 11.15-12.15 | Mancini | Sabia | Marioni | Corres |
| 12.15-13.15 | Mancini | Sabia | Marioni | Corres |
| 14.15-15.15 | Sabia | Sabia | Marioni | Corres |
| 15.15-16.15 | Sabia | Sabia | Marioni | Corres |

**Costo del corso: 400 euro + IVA 20%**

Coordinate bancarie per il versamento della quota di adesione:
Banca Intesa San Paolo - Fil. n°2587; Via Celoria 2 - Milano
c.c. n°. 6130000000-92
intestato a Consorzio CIS-E
CIN: C; COD. ABI: 03069; C.A.B.: 01749
IBAN: IT39C0306901749613000000092

Per eventuali ulteriori informazioni rivolgersi a:
arch. Emanuela Ghidini o dott.ssa Sara Giussani
Politecnico di Milano - DIS
P.zza Leonardo da Vinci, 32 - 20133 Milano
Tel: 02-2399.4252/4305;
e-mail: scuolamaster@stru.polimi.it
consorziocise@stru.polimi.it
sito web: http://masterpesenti.stru.polimi.it

388

**"Costruzioni esistenti"**

**Modulo didattico - applicativo all'interno del Corso di Master "Progettazione Sismica delle Strutture Sostenibili in Calcestruzzo"**

Coordinamento scientifico: prof. Giandomenico Toniolo
Master School F.lli Pesenti
Dipartimento di Ingegneria Strutturale, Politecnico di Milano

**11-14 maggio 2009**
**Ore complessive: 24**

SEDE: Aule - Master School F.lli Pesenti
Dipartimento di Ingegneria Strutturale, Politecnico di Milano
Piazza Leonardo da Vinci 32, Milano

Corso organizzato da:
*Master School F.lli Pesenti*, Dipartimento di Ingegneria Strutturale, Politecnico di Milano

**Docenti del corso:**

- **coordinatore**: prof. ing. Gaetano Manfredi
  *Università degli Studi di Napoli "Federico II"*
- prof. ing. Angelo Masi
- *Università degli Studi della Basilicata*
- prof. ing. Gerardo Mario Verderame
  *Università degli Studi di Napoli "Federico II"*

Sara' fornito on-line il materiale didattico presentato in aula da tutti i docenti.

**Contenuti del corso:**

Il Corso si articola nei seguenti moduli:
a) Metodi di indagine (livelli di conoscenza, geometria, dettagli strutturali, materiali)
b) Risposta sismica degli edifici in c.a.: esperienze dei terremoti (collassi tipici, edifici critici, deficienze strutturali)
c) Valutazione della sicurezza sismica (metodi di analisi e criteri di verifica)
d) Strategie e tecniche di intervento (adeguamento, miglioramento, riparazione, interventi globali e locali)

**Orari delle lezioni:**

| ora | Lunedì 11 | Martedì 12 | Mercoledì 13 | Giovedì 14 |
|---|---|---|---|---|
| 9.15-10.15 | Masi | Verderame | Verderame | Manfredi |
| 10.15-11.15 | Masi | Verderame | Verderame | Manfredi |
| 11.15-12.15 | Masi | Verderame | Verderame | Manfredi |
| 12.15-13.15 | Masi | Verderame | Verderame | Manfredi |
| 14.15-15.15 | Masi | Verderame | Verderame | Manfredi |
| 15.15-16.15 | Masi | Verderame | Verderame | Manfredi |

**Costo del corso: 400 euro + IVA 20%**

**Coordinate bancarie per il versamento della quota di adesione:**
Banca Intesa San Paolo - Fil. n° 2587; Via Celoria 2 - Milano
c.c. n°. 6130000000-92
intestato a Consorzio CIS-E
CIN: C; COD. ABI: 03069; C.A.B. : 01749
IBAN: IT39C0306901749613000000092

Per eventuali ulteriori informazioni rivolgersi a:
arch. Emanuela Ghidini o dott.ssa Sara Giussani
Politecnico di Milano - DIS
P.zza Leonardo da Vinci, 32 - 20133 Milano
Tel: 02-2399.4252/4305;
e-mail: scuolamaster@stru.polimi.it
consorziocise@stru.polimi.it
sito web: http://masterpesenti.stru.polimi.it

## "Isolamento sismico"

**Modulo didattico - applicativo all'interno del Corso di Master**
*"Progettazione Sismica delle Strutture Sostenibili in Calcestruzzo"*

Coordinamento scientifico: prof. Giandomenico Toniolo
Master School F.lli Pesenti
Dipartimento di Ingegneria Strutturale, Politecnico di Milano

**16-19 giugno 2009**
**Ore complessive: 24**

**SEDE: Aule - Master School F.lli Pesenti**
Dipartimento di Ingegneria Strutturale, Politecnico di Milano
Piazza Leonardo da Vinci 32, Milano

Corso organizzato da:
**Master School F.lli Pesenti**, **Dipartimento di Ingegneria Strutturale, Politecnico di Milano**

### Docenti del corso:

- **coordinatore**: *prof. M. Dolce*
  *Dipartimento della Protezione Civile*
- *dott. D. Cardone*
  *Università degli Studi della Basilicata*
- *ing. A. Martelli*
  *ENEA*
- *ing. C. Moroni*
  *Università degli Studi della Basilicata*
- *prof. F.C. Ponzo*
  *Università degli Studi della Basilicata*

Sara' fornito on-line il materiale didattico presentato in aula da tutti i docenti.

### Contenuti del corso:

Il Corso si articola nei seguenti moduli:
a) Introduzione all'isolamento sismico delle strutture
b) Le norme sismiche per l'isolamento e la dissipazione di energia
c) Dispositivi antisismici: classificazione, modalità di prova e normative
d) Progetti e realizzazioni in Italia e nel mondo
e) Criteri di progettazione, analisi e verifica di edifici e ponti isolati
f) Esempio di progettazione di edificio nuovo con isolamento sismico
g) Esempio di adeguamento con isolamento sismico di edificio esistente
h) Metodi di progettazione per sistemi controventi dissipativi in edifici in c.a.
i) La progettazione dei ponti isolati: esempi di applicazioni
j) La progettazione di edifici e ponti isolati con il metodo degli spostamenti

### Orari delle lezioni:

| ora | Martedi 16 | Mercoledi 17 | Giovedi 18 | Venerdi 19 |
|---|---|---|---|---|
| 9.15-10.15 | Dolce | Martelli | Ponzo | Cardone |
| 10.15-11.15 | Dolce | Martelli | Ponzo | Cardone |
| 11.15-12.15 | Dolce | Ponzo | Ponzo | Cardone |
| 12.15-13.15 | Moroni | Ponzo | Ponzo | Cardone |
| 14.15-15.15 | Moroni | Ponzo | Cardone | Cardone |
| 15.15-16.15 | Moroni | Ponzo | Cardone | Cardone |

### Costo del corso: 400 euro + IVA 20%

**Coordinate bancarie per il versamento della quota di adesione:**
Banca Intesa San Paolo - Fil. n° 2587; Via Celoria 2 - Milano
c.c. n°. 6130000000-92
intestato a Consorzio CIS-E
CIN: C; COD. ABI: 03069; C.A.B. : 01749
IBAN: IT39C0306901749613000000092

Per eventuali ulteriori informazioni rivolgersi a:
arch. Emanuela Ghidini o dott.ssa Sara Giussani
Politecnico di Milano - DIS
P.zza Leonardo da Vinci, 32 - 20133 Milano
Tel: 02-2399.4252/4305;
e-mail: scuolamaster@stru.polimi.it
consorziocise@stru.polimi.it
sito web: http://masterpesenti.stru.polimi.it

*Lettera di ringraziamento della Protezione Civile – Regione Lombardia per la presenza e il lavoro svolto in Abruzzo dagli allievi della Scuola*

**RegioneLombardia**

Giunta Regionale

Milano, 20 maggio 2009

*Carissimi,*

la grande commozione, suscitata in Italia e nel del mondo dalle tragiche immagini del terremoto in Abruzzo, ha saputo tramutarsi in una gara di solidarietà straordinaria.

In tale circostanza di emergenza e di dolore è stato fondamentale il contributo, la competenza, l'efficienza e la disponibilità, da Voi offerta così generosamente. Grazie per aver saputo rispondere con prontezza, professionalità e tempestività alle esigenze del territorio così duramente colpito e per aver sostenuto e supportato i nostri amici abruzzesi.

È emerso da tutti Voi un forte spirito di compartecipazione, solidarietà e capacità che ha fornito un aiuto prezioso al servizio della sicurezza collettiva, attraverso un sistema di pronta risposta, coordinando i soccorsi e le necessarie attività di verifiche di agibilità degli edifici nel tentativo di ripristinare, in tempi brevi, la normalità.

Il Governo regionale continuerà a sostenere il Vostro operato che contribuisce ad assicurare una risposta competente e tempestiva nei casi di emergenza.

Per questo Vi ringraziamo di cuore e Vi esprimiamo la nostra riconoscenza e gratitudine per quello che avete fatto e state facendo, incoraggiandoVi a proseguire nel Vostro impegno con costanza e passione.

L'Assessore

Stefano Maullu

Il Presidente

Roberto Formigoni

*Organizzazione della <u>Special Session "Modern Heritage"</u>, all'interno del Convegno Internazionale "Prohitech – Protection Historical Buildings" – Roma 21-24 giugno 2009, e presentazione della Keynote Lecture da parte della Prof.ssa Paola Ronca*

**SPECIAL SESSION
MODERN HERITAGE**
KEYNOTE LECTURE
*The safeguard of the modern architecture:
Legal provisions and operative procedure*
Artioli A.\*, Ronca P.\*\*

\*head of the Soprintendenza per i Beni Architettonici-Milano
(Italian Ministry of Cultural Heritage)
\*\*head of Master School F.lli Pesenti, Struct.Eng.Depart.-
Politecnico di Milano

# VADEMECUM
## DELLA PROGETTAZIONE CONSAPEVOLE

Giancarlo Chiesa - Giacomo Elias
Alberto Franchi - Antonio Migliacci

# Costruire per la
# qualità della vita
Expo 2015 un'occasione concreta

FAST - Milano, 10 giugno 2009

Scuola Master
'F.lli Pesanti'
Politecnico di Milano

*Seminario tenuto dall'Arch. Botta presso la Facoltà di Architettura Civile – Bovisa*

**POLITECNICO DI MILANO**
DIPARTIMENTO DI INGEGNERIA STRUTTURALE
SCUOLA MASTER F.LLI PESENTI

**Italcementi**
Italcementi Group

*A world class local business*

*CONSORZIO PER LE*
*COSTRUZIONI DELL'INGEGNERIA STRUTTURALE IN EUROPA*

La Master School F.lli Pesenti

del Politecnico di Milano e

il Consorzio CIS-E

presentano il Seminario su:

*Architettura e territorio*

## arch. Mario Botta

Introduzione di:

- prof. ing. Antonio Migliacci, Presidente della Master School F.lli Pesenti e del Consorzio CIS-E

- prof. arch. Angelo Torricelli, Preside della Facoltà di Architettura Civile

Il seminario è a partecipazione gratuita

# Giovedì 25 giugno 2009

## Ore 16,00

Aula De Carli
Via Durando 10
Politecnico di Milano
Campus Bovisa

Segreteria Organizzativa: Consorzio CIS-E
tel. 02.2399.4252
arch. Emanuela Ghidini
consorziocise@stru.polimi.it

# Tesi e stages

Il *"co-operative system"*, cioè l'attività di stage prolungato, che ha caratterizzato l'offerta formativa della Scuola fin dal primo anno di attivazione dei Master Universitari, si è andata affermando e consolidando, come idea vincente, grazie alla continua attenzione per una <u>sempre maggiore efficienza ed efficacia del rapporto "formazione-stage lavorativo"</u> e alla determinazione e capacità di lavoro dei nostri allievi stagisti.

Di seguito alcuni esempi di tesi svolte sulla scia delle esperienze dello stage, e discusse negli esami finali per conseguire il Diploma di Master.

### Master in "Progettazione delle strutture in c.a."

**Allievo: Manunza Michele – Stage presso ARUP**
**Relatore: Prof. Ing. Pietro Crespi**

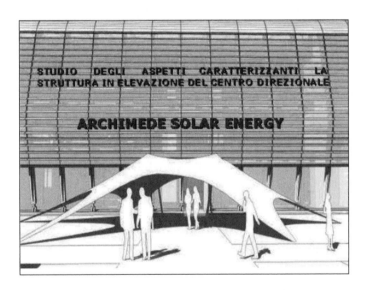

Present thesis work analyses functional and structural aspects of the Directional Centre Archimede Solar Energy, in particular vertical structures studied. This building is to be destined to offices and will be located in Massa Martana (PG), where seismic actions are considerable.

**Allievo: Sogni Mauro – Stage presso ROCKSOIL**
**Relatore: Prof. Antonio Migliacci**
**Titolo: Linea 5 metropolitana milanese – Progetto esecutivo**

This work analyzes the detailed design of the 5th line of the Milan underground, concerning the part from Bignami station to Lagosta, under the responsibility of Rocksoil S.p.A.

This project will be briefly presented from the urban point of view, thus having a quick view of the interferences with existing situations, later we will analyze the structural and geotechnical issues. We will try to underline the connection between structural and geotechnical issues and the designing solutions.

**Allievo: Carlo Morroni – Stage presso Dante O. Benini & Partners Architects**
**Relatore: Prof. Alberto Franchi**
**Titolo: Progetto di una Social Housing nell'area Bicocca di Milano: ipotesi sperimentale**

Il lavoro svolto presso lo Studio Dante O. Benini & Partners Architetcs affronta le problematiche, sia a livello tecnico, sia a livello finanziario, soprattutto rintracciabili in sede di legislazione europea, per la realizzazione di "Social Housing".

# Master in "Aspetti e tecnologie strutturali in architettura"

**Allievo: Andrea Garcia Benatti – Stage presso CIS-E**
**Relatore: Prof. Alberto Franchi**
**Titolo: Ristrutturazione della facciata della Torre Velasca**

Lo stage formativo si è svolto all'interno del Consorzio CIS-E – Costruzioni e Ingegneria Strutturale in Europa – a Milano, nell'ambito della ristrutturazione dell'intonaco e degli elementi di facciata della "Torre Velasca", avendo come tutor il Prof. Antonio Migliacci e il Prof. Alberto Franchi.

**Allievo: Gustavo Manuel Belmonte – Stage presso VITTORIO GRASSI Architetto**
**Relatore: Prof.ssa Paola Ronca, Arch. Vittorio Grassi**
**Titolo: La nuova mensa del Polo di eccellenza a Bresso**

La tesi analizza il progetto preliminare della nuova mensa del Polo di eccellenza a Bresso, con particolare riguardo alle scelte più opportune per le problematiche strutturali, di impatto ambientale e di efficienza energetica, sia anche dal punto di vista illuminotecnico naturale.

**Allievo: Farah Deeba Karimi – Stage presso Architetto Alberico Barbiano di Belgiojoso**
**Relatore: Prof. Alberto Franchi**
**Titolo: Urban quality and Design for all**

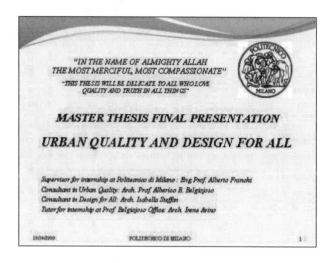

**Allievi: Maria Claudia Blanco – Leyla Ozdemir – Stage presso Renato Sarno Group**
**Relatore: Prof.ssa Paola Ronca**
**Titolo: Master Plan for the area of via Vallenary**

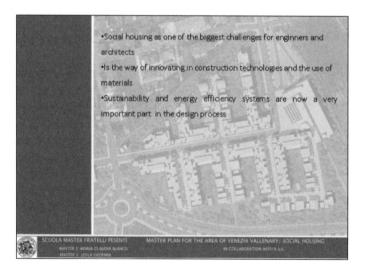

# Master in "Opere strutturali e impiantistiche per lo sviluppo sostenibile del territorio"

**Allievo: Raffaele Biasino – Stage presso Studio Prof.Ing. L. Jurina**
**Relatore: Prof.ssa Paola Ronca, Prof. Lorenzo Jurina**
**Titolo: Il Monastero di S.Monica – Interventi di consolidamento delle colonne del chiostro**

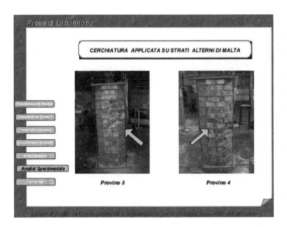

This thesis faces the problem of the crushing of the columns in bricks masonry in the monastery of S. Monica in Cremona and it proposes a new technique of intervention denominated "Cerchiatura Invisibile" (*Invisible ringing*). The static resistance of the "Cerchiatura Invisibile" has been shown from numerical analysis and experimental tests.

**Allievo: Flavio Pizzamiglio – Stage presso BEST**
**Relatore: Prof. Giancarlo Chiesa**
**Titolo: Risanamento conservativo dell'Ostello della Gioventù in Milano – controllo del comfort termico e illuminotecnico secondo il protocollo LEED**

The purpose of this study was to identify whether the indoor environmental quality design criteria: thermal comfort, indoor air quality, lighting and cleanliness and maintenance in relation to the overall workspace for LEED accreditation, could significantly affect occupants' perce-

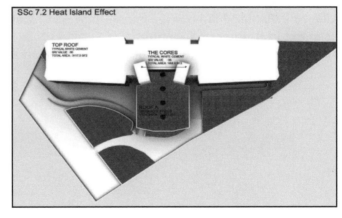

ption of their workspace satisfaction and their work performances.

# Master in "Project Management delle opere strutturali e infrastrutturali"

**Allievo: Renato Campos – Stage presso IREALP**
**Relatore: Prof.ssa Giovanna Fossa**
**Titolo: Valutazione degli investimenti per la valorizzazione del territorio della Media – Alta Valtellina**

La tesi si inserisce nell'ambito delle problematiche riguardanti il Piano Territoriale d'Area media e Alta Valtellina "Sviluppo del Territorio della Media e Alta Valtellina mediante la valorizzazione del patrimonio ambientale e il governo delle opportunità economiche, conseguenti agli eventi connessi ai Mondiali di sci 2005". L'evoluzione futura dei progetti previsti nel piano riguarderà la sistemazione dei principali interventi di sviluppo degli eventi sportivi nei prossimi cinque anni, rimasti in eredità al territorio della Valtellina.

**Allievo: Palladino John – Stage presso Impresa Cavalleri Ottavio**
**Relatore: Prof. Roberto Cigolini**
**Titolo: Tangenziale Sud di Bergamo – 1° lotto , 2° stralcio Treviolo - Stezzano**

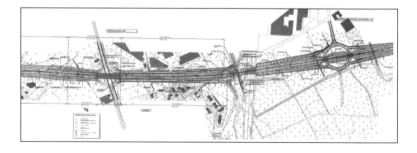

Il lavoro si inserisce all'interno del progetto di grande viabilità in programmazione e in costruzione per il sistema tangenziale attorno alla conurbazione di Bergamo.

# Master in "Design and management of structural technologies in architectural works"

**Allievo: José Teixeira – Stage presso Studio d'Ingegneria Andreotti & Partners**
**Relatori: Prof.ssa Paola Ronca, Ing. Mauro Rezzonico**
**Titolo: Aspetti procedurali e gestionali dei grandi progetti: il caso dell'Impianto Cantonale di termovalorizzazione dei rifiuti a Giubiasco (Ti/CH)**

La tesi è stata sviluppata nell'ambito del periodo di stage, presso anche l'ACR (Azienda Cantonale dei Rifiuti) e riguarda la realizzazione del termovalorizzatore di Giubiasco, di cui l'azienda è responsabile dell'organizzazione, dell'attuazione e della gestione, coi particolari criteri di efficienza, economicità e salvaguardia ambientale.

 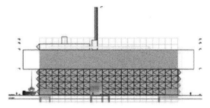

**Allievi: Basar Unsal, Selin Athmaz – Stage presso Navigli Lombardi S.C.A.R.L.**
**Relatore: Prof.ssa Paola Ronca**
**Titolo: Environmental impacts in building construction: the case of the old spining mill in Turbigo**

The thesis has been developed with the supervision of Doctor Meinardi, Director of the SCARL, Navigli Lombardi of Lombardia Region. It concerns the energy project environmental impact assessment of the upgrading and rifuntioning of old spinning mill in Turbigo, within the area of the canal Naviglio Grande.

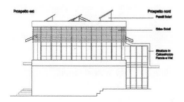 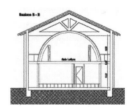

**Ringraziamenti** particolari, nella speranza di continuare le proficue collaborazioni, sono sicuramente dovuti agli Enti che collaborano con la Scuola per il completamento dei curricula dei Corsi di Master.

Favero & Milan Ingegneria

SINECO

**Mario Bellini Associati**

ARCHITECTURE
MASTERPLANNING
INTERIORS

O B R
Open Building Research

Studio di Architettura
V. Benati - A. Gallo - E.G. Tomasi

Architetti Achilli e Canella

**GDM** Costruzioni S.p.a.
Gruppo G.D.M. Holding S.p.a.

Studio di Blasi

**ODB** Architects

LDB Progetti s.r.l.

**Dante O. Benini & Partners Architects**

**VITTORIO GRASSI** architetto

CONSORZIO PER LE
COSTRUZIONI DELL'INGEGNERIA STRUTTURALE IN EUROPA

**DEC**
Società per Azioni

**MAPEI**

**Ferretti**
International

CTG
Italcementi Group

PANDINI

ATM

BOERI STUDIO

DIPARTIMENTO BEST

POLITECNICO DI MILANO

DIPARTIMENTO DI
ARCHITETTURA E
PIANIFICAZIONE

SaliniLocatelli
grandi lavori

**ALDO POLLONIO S.p.A.**

**PERI**

CNS

402

# NOTES

# NOTES